# This Ain't ER

*A Heart Surgeon's Struggle to
Keep the Faith*

by

C. Patrick Murrah, M.D.

Robert D. Reed Publishers
San Francisco

ISBN 1-885003-49-8

Library of Congress Catalog Card Number: 00-100651

Cover design by Irene Taylor, it grafx
Typesetting by Barbara Kruger

**Robert D. Reed Publishers**
**San Francisco**

# Dedication

Dedicated to Alison, the one that stands beside me and keeps me together. You are smarter than I am. I had to write this damned book just to stay sane.

Also dedicated to my children, Charles and Anna. Your dad was a good guy with good intentions. He took the hard road "because it was hard" and tried to do what was right. You can read this book when you become literate and, if nothing else, it may help to explain where I was when you were kids.

—CPM

# Foreword

You cannot remember pain. All of the books that I have read about the residency process have been written by folks that have never endured the pain that is experienced uniquely by a surgery resident, or were too far removed from the process to accurately depict it. The reality of a surgery residency is not some old fart recanting the glories of medicine and the noble missions that he has held to. The real story of the surgery resident has to portray the pain, in all of its miserable glory. If you did not do a surgery residency of five years or longer (and preferably at a university program), I don't want to hear it. With that assumption having been made, I don't want your watered down version twenty years removed from the fight. I want real time.

If you want pain you need to come to the temple, the general surgery residency. Within the temple lies a few of the "old school" programs. Take that short list of "old school" programs and add a little bit of that "good old boy" southern charm (a la "Cool Hand Luke" / "Deliverance") and you have the seven year spanking machine that was my general surgery residency.

This book has served mainly as a catharsis of the emotional baggage that I have accumulated in the course of training to become a cardiothoracic surgeon. I have progressed in many ways as a result of writing this book. I used to hate lawyers, but now they don't bother me because, in addition to screwing people, they occasionally help people that get screwed. I used to think that residency was too hard, but now understand that that is the way that it has to be (save a few fine points). I used to hate HMOs...well, I guess I have not progressed on all fronts...

I think that I may have been a little bit too sensitive for the whole thing, but I never quit. The best way that I could describe my toleration of this process is the way that I feel when I am out of shape and trying to get through a long run. I have set a clear-cut goal. It is easy to set the goal (and fun to be able to tell everybody that you run). You can feel good about the course you have set towards good physical condition (then eat a Twinkie, since you are going to run).

The run begins and you are still feeling inspired. As things progress the thinking starts. The rationalizing for quitting comes in intermittently at first (only to be beaten down by the potential shame of quitting). The pain begins and the wild thoughts charge in from all directions. The thoughts are very complex, but all lead to the same simple conclusion...quit. I start to look at my feet at this point.

"Take one step at a time. Don't look at the one hour of running that you have to go."

Footsteps...

"I'm going to quit..."

Footsteps...

"I'm going to quit..."

Then the energy required to have these thoughts becomes tiring in itself. By this time you have made it a mile or so. A blank mental condition holds you for 10 more minutes. Now your heart rate is up, and you are making progress. The rest of the time becomes a struggle to control your thoughts.

Discipline may be the key to my happiness.

The wild and complex thoughts of quitting only take away your energy. The stretch is coming. Thought control, discipline. Your only hope. There are a million reasons to stop. A million people do. Some keep going. I know that I was not the smartest guy in my medical school class. I just kept going.

Writing this book helped me to get through some of the harder times. I have spent years worrying about whether I was going to become a jerk that spoke to patients in that characteristic high volume impersonal tone that some doctors get. I have spent years worrying about my biceps becoming smaller than my forearms (like I noticed on an otherwise normal appearing urologist during my first year of residency). I have spent years worrying that Alison would get tired of this bullshit and leave. I have spent years worrying that I was going to make my kids into heavy-metal T-shirt wearing by-products of an egotistical, dynamic, self-absorbed success machine who had no time for them and was therefore no success at all.

Above all of this is the image that this must project to the reader.

"Who gives a damn. You're just going to be a rich doctor anyway." I submit that the combination of arbitrary reimbursement cutbacks by HMOs and the federal government, lawsuits from attorneys that do not even know the case but know that your name is on the chart and that a patient died, and ridiculous working conditions is weeding out some of those who went into it for the money. There are a hell of a lot easier ways to make money in America today than going to law school 4.6 times.

I want to know that I faced all of the challenges of life and tried to do the right thing. I did cardiothoracic surgery because it was hard. All of the misery that follows is indeed my fault because I signed up for it. This book is a catharsis. It details my struggle to stay idealistic in tough surroundings. It also gives you the reader unique insight into the hardest form of medical training that there is. It is unique because nobody has ever taken the time to write it down in the heat of the battle. They always wait until the pain is gone. You cannot remember pain.

# 1

# A Struggle to Maintain My Ideals

"What is this book about? What you have given me is a middle. What is the story here, Patrick? Is this just another 'report from Hell'? Yes, it sounds like you were indeed in Hell."

These were the words so carefully and politely spoken by my editor as he looked across his desk at this tired looking resident that had brought him this long-winded catharsis that he was calling a manuscript. He was almost as interested to meet this guy as he was to read the manuscript. Who in the Hell has enough time to crank out a 400-page book during the course of training to become a heart surgeon? There had to be a great deal of unbalanced something in this guy's head to do this. He seems a little fidgety, but near normal in appearance. He shaved. There are no nervous tics that I can see. Oh, well, I guess it takes all kinds.

My first try at writing all of this down resulted in what my editor called a "middle." I just sort of exploded out onto the pages with a catharsis that would rival anything that I have ever coaxed out of an impacted (stool-corked) "dried up granny lady." I had to go back and write this first chapter last to put my "middle" into perspective. I am only now stepping away from my "growth opportunities" and just beginning to realize what was going on inside of my head that motivated me to spend so many of my precious few free hours writing a book.

Most of this book was written during the course of my general surgery residency. This time was full of what Dr. Sternalpunch (one of my heroes, who you will meet later in the text) calls "growth opportunities." Growth opportunities are tough times that make you a better person and don't kill you like you think they might while they are going on. I was usually tired and sometimes miserable during my general surgery residency and some of the real-time dialogues (which are presented in italics) presented will reflect this. It is typical of a general surgery resident in training to lose perspective of the long-term benefits of being well trained due to the short-term factors such as lack of sleep, lack of money, and a wealth of folks telling you what to do. My lack of perspective may be evident in these passages.

The fact remains that I was being well trained. I was being taught that you do not clock in and clock out on patients. They remain sick when you go home. They are in total need. Everything that you do for them helps. Barry Goldwater said "moderation in the defense of freedom is no virtue..." (among other things). Barry Goldwater would have liked Bayview (the home of my surgery residency). Moderation in the defense of doing the right thing (taking care of the patient, in this instance) was not tolerated there either.

I have been in such a state over the past years. I was driven to write my experiences down by forces within me that I did not understand, nor was the process completely under my control. I became obsessed in a way (surprise, surprise). I did not write it down because I was bored and wanted to do something with my spare time. Cardiothoracic surgery fellows and general surgery residents (at least good ones) don't have any time to spare, especially when they have a wife (Alison) and two children (Charles and Anna).

I was driven to write. I realized what was driving me only last week, a full five years after the book's initiation. I was in the office of my editor, meeting with him and a literary agent. I had requested that they read my book because they were smart and not in the medical field. I knew what a tangent my life had taken. I was not confident that my reality matched up too well with that of the general public at that point in my life. I thought that they would give me some fresh perspective on my work.

We spoke for a while and I realized that this book is all about a struggle to maintain my ideals. It made me feel so much better about myself. Maybe I am not just another whiner. There is something inside of me trying to preserve the guy that went into this for all of the right reasons. I still give a damn about my patients. That is a feeling that is harder to preserve than it may seem. I sound at times in this book like I am going down, but I was going down with undaunted intensity. As of the summer of 1999, I am still afloat.

A lot of heat (what I will later term "AWs"—ass whippings; or "AAWs"—automatic ass whippings) is injected into you over the eighteen-year process of becoming a cardiothoracic surgeon. You are expected to absorb that heat with some semblance of grace (and certainly not to melt or explode—which I have watched happen a few dozen times). You are expected to emerge from this process having converted all of this heat into a light that gently projects onto your patients. You are the gentle provider of information, therapy, and comfort for patients in need of your help. The patient does not give a damn what it took for you to get to this point. He only sees a young doctor looking down at him in his bed and telling him the horrible news that he has a lung cancer stuck to his aorta. All he can do is hope that this kid can accurately diagnose his disease, treat his disease, and be normal enough to explain things along the way. This book is about my personal struggle to maintain that "normal" part while acquiring the former diagnostic and therapeutic skills.

The diagnostic and therapeutic tools have to come first. The "normal" part is a bonus, allowing for things like kids and spouses that like you and old friends that don't think that you have turned into a dickhead. "Normal" in the absence of the diagnostic and therapeutic tools is a dangerous situation. That means that you have to go to a very very small town (with no internet connections or English-speaking physicians) where they might think you are good, or that you just ought to quit altogether.

I was going for the big haul, the "bonus." To get to the bonus round, you have to go to one of the strong training programs (which happen to be occupied by some of those dickheads that you are trying not to become). That is the way it works. You have to pay your dues, like anything in life. With the help of Alison and some others that I will mention later in this book, I was willing to take on Bayview Medical Center. I do not have any regrets, and I am writing this with what is left of me, thinking that most of the callous, cynical, angry changes that may have come about are for the most part reversible. I think that I have a real shot at good and normal.

"Normal"? Was I normal at the start of this process? Have I emerged from this process as the same guy that went in? Certainly not. I have grown into an adult. Alison, Charles and Anna have joined me. I would have changed anyway. There is no way that I can extract the effect of my residency experience from the effect of my genetics and the rest of the world around me. Maybe I would have found some other form of Spartan existence had it not been for cardiothoracic surgery. "Maybe you are just misery looking for a medium" (there is a frequently self-posed question).

I am going to give myself a break. I am going to say that I was pretty normal as a kid. I was the third of four children. My dad was an engineer. My mom was a housewife that turned into a nurse to pay for all of the kids as they started going to college. We were neither poor nor rich. Nobody beat the hell out of me other than my older brother Chip. I was a nerd with athletic ability. I was shy. During trigonometry class, I used to draw a detailed map of the United States and then draw the course of huge hurricanes in the Gulf of Mexico that destroyed the Eastern seaboard. Okay, so I was in the 9th grade. Perhaps I was a little serious and detached. My grandmother said that I was too busy thinking about the world's pressing questions to think about tying my shoes. Seems more likely that I was just a nerd.

Hmmm. Maybe I was pushing the confidence limits of "normal." I memorized the square roots of the prime numbers to the 10th decimal point. I thought that my reading skills were not good enough to score well on the SAT, so I read a glossary and the book "Shogun" for a couple of years (and got a National Merit Scholarship as a result). Then there were the early attempts at man-powered flight during the (late) elementary years. Imagine the conflict within a guy that is going with the best looking girl in his sixth grade class by day and asking his older brother Chip to push him and his mattress-box cardboard airplane off the roof by evening. I guess there may have been some unrest in that cerebrum.

There has also been an ongoing frustration at having to give up things that formed an important part of my life before medicine. I was an excellent golfer in my youth and wanted to become a professional golfer into my early high school years. I was the number one player on the Titusville High School golf team. Scott Gump was the number one player on the Merritt Island golf team. We competed in high school. I went pre-med. He kept playing golf. I was accepted to medical school. He finished second in the U.S. Amateur. Last week he finished second in The Players Championship. I turned 34 and was on call with a lady's cold leg and an intraaortic balloon pump disaster. (An intraaortic balloon pump is a device that is placed through the artery in the groin and sits in the descending aorta. It assists the failing heart by inflating and deflating during certain periods of the cardiac cycle.) I am more of a long-term thinker these days, but sometimes it is hard to watch the outside world go by. It is very hard when your children are alone with mom on the weekend, the weather is beautiful, and you are stuck in the hospital again. Function as a fellow in this system that cranks out over 3,000 open-heart operations per year does not guarantee function at home or in the general public for that matter. Losing touch at home has always been a fear of mine.

I figured during high school that I could be a doctor and still play golf. I could not be a golfer and still help people like a doctor could. A golfer can win a few skins on TV and even help to build a Children's Hospital, but you never hear about a golfer directly saving somebody's life. A busy cardiothoracic surgeon (which I wanted to be from the start) can save an average of three lives per day. That is what I used to tell people. I was just talking about being a doctor, and it was very simple back then.

### Doctors save people's lives

I have not said no to any challenge since that time and have now ended up in the best cardiothoracic surgery fellowship in the country trying to decide if I want to be an academic heart surgeon or just take the easier path and be a private heart surgeon. The decision seems a little bit unimportant when you put it into perspective. It is sort of like deciding what type of astronaut you want to be, a moon-walker or a space walker. Either way, you are in pretty thick, and chances are your golf game is going to stink.

I have gotten in this deep because I am and have been very much an idealist. I wanted to do the most good possible in the least amount of time. My minister (who married Alison and me, and who I would pronounce dead on my service 8 years later) said.. "Life flashes by in an instant, why not do the right thing? Why not have the courage to do what is right?" Your life is not much of an event in the grand scheme of things. The correct principles that have and always will exist do matter. I always wanted to live my life by these rules. I have sometimes failed miserably with respect to deeds, maybe not so miserably with the effort.

I was also overly sensitive when I was a kid. I see that sensitivity in my children now, and I love that about Alison. I do not believe that there is such thing as "too nice" or "too sensitive." There may be such things as "too nice to survive" or "too sensitive to survive," but I am not sure. I was told over and over by different people not to go into surgery because "you are too nice." The nurse Jane who worked on the "killing fields" (renal medicine ward) at Bayview told me this at the end of medical school. The jury is still out, Jane, but I would still say that the whole process is for nothing if I have lost that 18-year-old golfer that knew that doctors can save lives.

I went in hard. Not just into combat (becoming a doctor), but onto the shores of Omaha Beach (becoming a cardiothoracic surgeon). Armed with an abundance mentality, I stormed ashore with the intent of capturing the bunker that held a cardiothoracic surgical fellowship. There is no such thing as "too nice to survive." I took the challenge head-on. The following pages detail my struggle to make it through my training unscathed. I have been a little hard on myself along the way. I want to be a normal person with a normal life, and I also want to be a cardiothoracic surgeon. It is very hard to do both. When my "normalcy" is failing, I sometimes remind myself that all you have to do is live through it all. It is not about how many of the enemy that you take out along the way, it is about being alive at the end. Then you can recover your normalcy. Of course, taking a few out makes the latter all the more possible.

I will end this chapter with some excerpts from a journal that I kept in my college years. I sought out some primary history source to more accurately understand what the guy that started down this long road was about.

*Friday 1/9/87*

*......If you are reading this, please understand that these scattered thoughts drift through my mind often and I enjoy writing these things down. I cannot be the only one that thinks this way. It is not that I am scatterbrained, I am simply more concerned with ideas and people that make up this world. This is why I choose medicine. Interactions, challenges, principles, and scrapping to put things right is what makes me go. I am idealistic and I do not apologize for being a person with ideas about how the world should be.*

*Anyone and everyone has ideals and they often sport an idealistic view of how things should be. Only the great person goes a step further and works, and sticks with his or her ideals when everything falls down on them.*

*Mom speaks of doctors that come into the hospital (nurses too) and make things work as they should. They want to care for all of their patients and get wrapped up in their fate. Then they get hit with malpractice (one of these patients that he worked so hard to save turns around and sues him or a fellow doctor), they get hit with depressing death and feel a sense of failure and some kind of vague association with this tragedy. Mom says that they learn to avoid such an idealistic approach. They form a protective shell. This is all going to hit me too, and I want to be ready.*

*I realize that I cannot get so involved with my work that it consumes me. This is a private fear of mine. I need to find a balance, but I must stick with my idealism or I am nothing but a moneygrubber.*

*I can't get too serious and ruin my own family life. A family that dearly loves each other and is proud of their heritage and self-worth is a primary concern of mine as well. I want my children to grow up happy and loving and to form a positive image of themselves and this world.*

*I must find a balance between my family and my work. First, there is no problem with devotion to each as long as I am an unselfish person. I need to finish growing up and mature... I say that a person's worth is graded based on how much positive input he can make into his world, how much he can do to make others' stay in this world a better experience. It starts small, and sometimes there is no favorable result at all. It is the intent to help that is the key. I am idealistic, but I'm damned right also. As long as I put forth the effort to help others and do what I feel to be right, I can fear no man nor have any regrets.*

*The key is to try. I try hard in school, not always my hardest ( I am not close to perfect), but I am carrying out a good proportion of my actions based on ideals that I believe in. In my work, I will pursue personal health for my patients to the best of my ability and take the failures with the successes with no regrets as long as I know that I gave it my best and acted out of care for my patients' dignity and respect for their place in God's world.*

(Dramatic sentence that could only end with the word "God")

*I will not carry my job home to the point where I negatively affect my family. I have a definite responsibility and obligation to my patients, but I will have this and a strong sense of love for my children and wife. My family is first with me, no exceptions. The job and everything else can go to Hell before I will sacrifice my family.*

*Well, I guess that that brings up another requirement, she has to be fertile. It is my ultimate desire (as well as my responsibility) to raise my children with a belief in themselves. A sense of self-pride. I will enjoy this world with my wife and kids.*

(You have to get a girl to like you first)

*We will have a blast. Nothing but positive. I will discipline my children when they wander around (like they will). I won't strike them, but I will be stern and uncompromising on what is bad for them. I won't simply run my mouth about good and bad but set a positive example that they will eventually learn to follow.*

(Predictable deterioration into a list occurs)

*In order to carry out such a life, there are certain things that I need to emphasize in my maturation process.*

*1) Self-confidence to the point of being a bit opinionated and a bit cocky. If I don't have strength here, I won't have the ability to carry out these ideas that right now only float around in my head and are written here. The great person takes that extra step and applies and asserts his ideas into actions.*

*2) Be able to accept failure along with success. Keep an even keel and be cool. Pretend like you are flying in a plane. Be cool at the wheel.*

*3) Do not be too selfish. I will have to take some time to do what only I want and be selfish, otherwise I will go nuts. I am not a monk, saint, priest, or anything close to near that.*

(The statement "close to near that" proves that this document is of peripubertal origin)

*4) Never grind if things do not work out (oops, that is number two)*

*5) Enjoy your life and the things that God gave to you. Enjoy the world and never take it too seriously.*

(Like making lists on your weekend off in college)

*6) As stated earlier, you are very imperfect, not a monk, priest, saint, Pope, etc. You should never come down too hard on yourself.*

It is my goal to walk out of The Big City University Cardiothoracic Surgery Program and be one hell of a heart surgeon and full of the stuff that the geek wrote in 1987.

# 2

# Work, Sleep, and Cynicism

It has been a very long journey, and it has not yet come to an end. I think that everyone places an inflated sense of importance on the experiences of their life. I am no different. Perhaps everyone has some degree of feelings of unfulfilled potential or of being misunderstood by the world. There is a loneliness to coming and going like any other species on this earth. I wrote this to document my struggle to maintain myself as I fulfill a dream. Perhaps I also wrote this to document that I was here.

The struggles that I endured during college, medical school, general surgery residency, and a cardiothoracic surgery fellowship have been experienced by others in other professions and other walks of life. I am not the only one who has had to work for it. My struggles just happen to equal the sum total of all of theirs combined (times six). A residency is one of the hardest forms of training that I am aware of. A general surgery residency is the hardest form of residency. Bayview offers the hardest version of a general surgery residency. Then I tacked on three more years for cardiothoracic surgery.

I am not the only one who has had to work for it. I have had the luxury of knowing that I was going to be some sort of doctor since I was accepted to medical school in the spring of 1986. This guarantee of sorts is a big cushion that many others never have. I consider my job to be a minimum wage privilege.

I believe that the physician should see himself more as a servant than one to be honored. The physician is honored because he acts as a servant. Servant must come first. I am indebted by the trust given to me by the patient as he places his welfare into my hands. Have you ever had the feeling of a total loss of control of your life? I am not sure that I have. Pure trust. All of this hard work and training is the price that you pay to gain this trust.

Nowhere is this trusting interaction more evident than in my chosen field, cardiothoracic surgery. A desire to make a difference is the engine that allows me to get through this eighteen-year journey. I have finished four years of college, four years of medical school, seven years of general surgery residency, and have three years to go to become a fully trained cardiothoracic surgeon. I have had to drop some "baggage" along the way (some would call that baggage a life).

It is interesting to see the effect of fatigue on the ideals expressed during the course of my training. I selected three passages written at stages where I was progressively more fatigued... Morning; Night (post-call); and Night (post-call and at the end of a Trauma rotation).

Mood descent...I am the Chief General Surgery Resident on the Trauma Service in the morning, coffee loaded, at the beginning of the rotation:
(Written October, 1997)

*Idealism comes in the morning. This is the time for the purest emotions to come out. These are the ones that I try listen to. I can reestablish true North. Sometimes I feel like I went into this with so much eagerness and diversity, and am now ready to leave with the ability to save lives but perhaps having sacrificed my own. Nevertheless, as I near the end of my journey, I am even more certain that the course that I have chosen is correct.*

Further mood descent... Chief General Surgery Resident on the Trauma Service, at night, coffee toxic, post-call, no sleep for 40 hours, having responded to sixty pages over the past day and a half and six thousand over the past seven years. We have a much less noble and more desperate being:
(Written November, 1997)

*There are the streaks of lean eating, exercise, and self discipline that I feel that I need to keep my mind and body up with the other 32 year old Jones'. That never lasts. I have always wanted to come out of my fifteenth (4 pre med, 4 med school, 7 general surgery) year of training being in shape and not mentally spent. I can say that I have made great strides in the latter department, the body leaves a little to be*

*desired. Some day someone will do a study on the effects of chronic
fatigue on the body's composition. I'll give that person a jump as a personal model. The body does not gain a tremendous amount of weight,
just a little. Your eyes go bad from reading. You lose muscle mass and
gain fat. You get softer. Your biceps get straight and smaller in diame-
ter than your forearm. This is the point (along with the presence of
breasts) where you become socially obligated to stop going without a
shirt in public.*

*It goes beyond not exercising. Hold very very still so that you can sew
that coronary artery graft in place. Hold still. Don't move a muscle (for
four hours); even stop breathing when the critical portion of the anastomosis, comes. Hold still and worry about the patient dying all the
while. Then when it is all over, and all of the blood has pooled in your
legs; run over to the cafeteria and eat some shit. Sure there is celery and
other nutritious things, but shit just seems to work better on this schedule. Don't take too long, there is another case coming.*

*That can't be good for you. Pretty soon, you are well on the way to
resident fitness, and you adopt the stairwell policy of "down one, up
none."*

*Were I to lose all of the fat now I am not sure what would be left.
Your hair falls out, but you do not care so much because it looks consistent with your body. The acne goes away because you now have kids
that are almost old enough to have acne. ... There is still hope. I can
always rally. I am starting a fellowship in 8 months. I don't have a
chance.*

*The transition or rationalizing of a quest for internal rather than
external health happens at about 28 in between external appearance
pushes... What you are saying is, "I give up, let's try the next lower level."*

Mood impact... Chief General Surgery Resident on the Trauma
Service, coffee loaded to the point of abdominal pain, on a bad day
near the end of the rotation (having endured eight weeks and one bad
night of it):
(Written November, 1998)

*I am writing this book under the probably false assumption that I
am safe from retaliation by some of my attendings at the Bayview
Medical Center Department of Surgery. I assume that if I tell the truth
that I cannot be harmed. I know that I have never read an account
of this nature. What could be wrong with telling the truth? I am sure
that I have lost perspective on what is normal given the nature of my
recent surroundings, but things that seem fucked up usually are. I*

*will continue to be 100% honest and accurate in my accounts. The strength of this work will be drawn from this honesty.*

*I have progressed in my residency to the role of Chief Resident, and the emotional state of not giving a damn what they think* (unless they are kicking your butt you mean). *I know that they can try to mess with me, but I am being honest* (what you meant to say is "get me the Hell out of here, I will pretend to be anyone or do anything, let me go play golf like when I was a kid"). *The ability to achieve the completion of this general surgery quest was paid for with a certain degree of insanity (the magnitude I am yet unable to perceive). But I made it.*

The preceding three passages demonstrate (in an albeit crude fashion) the direct relationship between fatigue and cynicism. Fatigue level appears to be an independent risk factor for cynicism in me, and perhaps in other surgeons-in-training. I will admit that the sample size is small (making the demonstration of a statistically significant effect impossible), and my experimental control is inadequate. The burning question comes, "Is the effect reversible?" ...You have to read the book to see.

All of these reflect somewhat different views, but they are all my own. They come from feelings that I have felt, mostly as a reaction to my environment. I believe that the mixed up collection of thoughts and actions that I constantly try to reign in and adjust during my life make up in fact, my life. That magical time of peace when everything is organized and accomplished never arrives for the compulsive. The endpoint is redefined and stays a few years ahead of me.

This comedy ends when the rug gets pulled out from under you in the form of some sort of health disaster. Then you scramble to close off the chapters that you started and make them make sense and try to understand who you were and what you stood for. The following may at times seem more like a mess. It represents my thoughts, often given at or very near to the time that the major events of my training took place. This mess is my life.

I think of what defines me as I complete this section. I am defined by the desire to continue to experience the love that my wife and I share. I am defined by a desire to give my kids their own life. Cardiothoracic surgery is what I want to do as my service to the world, so that I don't go out a completely selfish being.

# 3

# The Residency Process

There is a very big knowledge gap that exists between medicine and the general public. Humorist George Carlin once told an audience that "Somewhere out there is the world's worst doctor, and you know what?; somebody has an appointment to see him in the morning." It is true that referrals come mostly by word of mouth. Now things have become even tougher with the introduction of the dreaded HMO "provider list." Now the question has changed from "Do you know a good doctor?" to "Do you know a good doctor on this damned list?"

Hell, I was a doctor for seven years in Bayview City and I did not recognize anybody on the primary care provider list that my institutional HMO sent me. I made the mistake of just picking one at random in order to finish filling out the form and 6 months later ended up getting an antibiotic shot in the rear end just to get a referral to see a podiatrist for a severely ingrown toenail that precluded me from being able to walk around the hospital. Imagine the frustration among non-medical people with this system.

It is mostly word of mouth. Very smart people are able to pick out a good doctor as well as I can pick out a good jeweler. The public also wants perfect. They don't want to know that we are just guys that did well in school and are working our butts off to be perfect, but can't. Hopefully my book will provide a view into our humanity, or inhumanity, as it may be.

The United States has the world's best system for the training of surgery residents. This system represents another aspect of medicine that very smart non-medical people understand very little about. It dates back to the turn of the century when Dr. William Halsted brought the German method of Von Langenbeck to the Johns Hopkins Hospital. Dr. Halsted set up surgical services based upon the idea that residents should be trained under the close supervision of an "attending" physician in a teaching hospital. The wards were to provide a means for progress in teaching, clinical surgery, and research. Johns Hopkins was the first teaching hospital set up that way in the United States.

The process of becoming a heart surgeon takes 18 years of training after high school for many, including myself. I first complete four years of college as a pre-medical student, taking hard science classes that preclude a lot of other things (golf game killer for me). Medical school is next. It lasts four years. The first two years of medical school are spent taking more classes, and involve introduction to caffeine pills and glasses. The third and fourth years of medical school involve work in the hospital walking around with a tuning fork, starched clothes, and a confused look on your face. Then comes the surgery residency. I picked a hard one because I wanted to be well trained and finish off the destruction of my golf game. The surgery residency lasts seven years if you include a two-year research stint. The process is completed with a three-year cardiothoracic surgery fellowship. Then you are 36, in the 30th grade.

The end result of your training is good judgment. In an article published in The American Journal of Surgery, good judgment was the number one characteristic that chairmen of surgery departments around the country recognized as their goal in the training of a general surgery resident. Superman (my chairman) was certainly no different. Good judgment comes from experience (under the supervision of an attending physician), experience comes from hard work.

Dr. Halsted was a very hard worker and expected the same from his residents. In fact, I once heard from an attending at Bayview that Dr. Halsted did not even use the modality of speech to acknowledge the presence of his junior resident Harvey Cushing (the now famous "Father of Neurosurgery") for his entire first year. Talk about discipline. That is amazing. It was a much more difficult system in those days. Some of my current attendings that trained in such prestigious places have endured unbelievable hardship to reach their current position.

There was Baylor University under Dr. DeBakey, and the line in the Intensive Care Unit (ICU) that was not to be crossed for the first month of residency. You stayed on the ICU side, the food was brought to you. I suppose sex (or a lack of it) was your problem. Cross the line and you were gone.

There were the unannounced rounds that often occurred in the middle of the night under Dr. Sabiston at Duke University. You had to be ready.

There is the "pyramid system" that was practiced at The Johns Hopkins Hospital. You started with around seven superstars and one goes on to become the "Halsted Resident." The other six stars find something else to do, or somewhere else to go.

There was The Father at Bayview University. He never asked for any more than he was willing to do. The only problem being that The Father was relentless in his pursuit of perfection. The residents had a hard time keeping up. When asked as a member of the Bayview Medical School core curriculum planning committee what the medical students should know by the end of their four years; The Father responded, "everything."

These institutions were teaching the same principle, a commitment to patient care above all else. The buck stops with you. These institutions trained a generation of leaders in surgery.

Dr. Halsted was a visionary, and the system that he set up is alive and well at the country's finest surgery programs. Bayview is one of these " old school" programs. My chairman, Superman, was a clear example of the virtues of this system, but the face of surgery training in this country is changing. The Libby Zion case (a lawsuit brought against a hospital for keeping a resident awake for too long and allegedly clouding that person's judgment enough to kill the former) brought reforms in the state of New York that supposedly limited the amount of consecutive hours that a resident could work. Such reforms had the potential to impact surgery residency most dramatically (since they work the greatest number of hours), and implementation of these reforms has either been given lip service only or been abandoned all together. The fact remains that you cannot instill solid judgment and teach a sense of personal responsibility to your resident if he is allowed to walk out on his patients when he gets tired.

My experience with residents from the "kinder gentler" programs has been marked mostly by disappointment. Something is lost. There is a fine line that must be walked if we are to continue to train responsible, results-oriented surgeons with good judgment. They probably do need better working conditions, but all should be done within the framework of the principles brought to this country by Dr. Halsted. We must not lose those "growing opportunities" that Dr. Sternalpunch talks about. I am a Bayview graduate and I am proud of it. People notice when I tell them where I spent my seven years of general surgery residency. I see their reaction, and am very proud to include the fact that I even brought a family that still likes me through it all.

Yes, I am a fan of the old school. I never would have admitted it two years ago. It is a strange thing how I came full circle. Bayview and a few others are the last of the "old school" programs in this country. We are just seeing the first give at some of the "old school" programs. Sure we teach them the latest in minimally invasive techniques, and how to sew someone up in new and better ways with less hospital stay and less cost to society, but this "softening" that we are seeing across the country threatens to create a surgeon that is willing to accept average care for patients because he or she is "just cross–covering that patient." We must not accept mediocrity.

(Written February, 1997; I am a sixth year general surgery resident at Bayview Hospital)....

I was much less idealistic during my run in the trenches of the "old school."

*The working conditions in residency stink. The hours are too long, the pay sucks, and the residencies are too long (especially in surgery, coming from the, 6 years post-M.D., phone got turned off yesterday, kid). Our working conditions are in many ways an artifact of some guys that were at the cutting edge in the early 1900s and had to "pay their dues."*

In addition to this not being ER, this "ain't no reform book." There are some things that need to change in our system, and I make reference to them at the end of this book; however, improvements in the surgery resident working conditions should not be instituted if they compromise the transmission of the excellent education that I received at Bayview. I have come full circle, and I believe in extremism in the defense of excellence in patient care. Do not go into surgery, and certainly not into cardiothoracic surgery if you want rest, money, or both. Be a stockbroker.

(Written February, 1997; I am a sixth year general surgery resident at Bayview Hospital)....

*I cannot count the number of conversations that I have had with very intelligent non-medical people that have lead to the same question....*
*"Why do they make you stay up so late? Don't you get too tired to make rational decisions and to operate effectively?" They laugh and say,*

*"I sure don't want you operating on me on zero sleep!"*

*My first reaction (at least on the inside) used to be one of incredulity at people's obvious ignorance of the surgeon's world, but as of late, I have begun to question myself. Is it likely that these people, who are clearly extremely intelligent, are right everywhere else but somehow only wrong when they say that we ought to be able to sleep before doing surgery? They would not let a pilot fly 300 people to Europe after staying up all night. Why is it okay for me to take the stomach out of the mother of three young boys without adequate rest? Is surgery of the stomach easier than flying a plane? Is this one patient less important?; or is it just cheaper to have low wage workers in teaching hospitals to keep them financially afloat in the face of massive reimbursement cutbacks? Perhaps it is collective bargaining power that has enabled tan airline pilots to push buttons ten days a month and take the other twenty off. Perhaps it is a complete lack of collective bargaining power that has made residents in training sort of like those guys that got pulled into the weenie-making machines in the unsafe Chicago meat factories in the early 1900s. Our bosses (whoever the hell they are) know that we have to do it.*

*I continue to get the same questions. I recently had the question of sleep and performance posed to me by a man that sits on the Board of one of the most powerful banks in the nation. This man is smarter than I am. For the first time, I felt that the system was just flat wrong, or could at least be made better by smart guys like the one that I was talking to. Hell, he helped to invent the ATM.*

*What we need in residency programs is a system that elicits peak learning and performance from its trainees, and does not kill them in the process. I know that there must be a balance out there. I think that we ought to work the residents like hell and then let them breathe one day per week. I think that we ought to teach the residents to be the "stopper" for their patients, but at the same time avoid wearing them down to the point of having to write a fucking book.....*

*Our method of training surgeons in this country works. That is clear. We produce the finest surgeons in the world in this country. I am being trained in one of these programs by one of the, if not the, finest Chairmen in the country. However, I am not convinced that it cannot be done without the extracurricular abuses, or the long hours that bend the mind's decision-making ability. I can and have worked harder than the next guy can. I can stay up an amazing number of consecutive hours. But do I have to?*

Perhaps there is something to be said for that tired resident's comments. There are improvements in working conditions that can be made at some programs without compromising the quality of training. I suggest that programs continue the long, hard hours that give continuity of care and subsequently lead to good judgment. I also suggest that programs strictly enforce the policy of allowing one day each week when the pager is turned off and allowing a one week vacation three times per year. This has worked out well for me and my family in my cardiothoracic surgery fellowship. I am able to re-establish the things that are important to me in my life and I also find myself rededicated to becoming a better cardiothoracic surgeon.

I will leave it to the guys who are going to overhaul the way that we train surgeons. They are coming very soon. This book may serve as a document to let others know what it was like under the old system, but for me it is really all about becoming a strong heart surgeon and remembering who I was when I started (an idealistic/corny guy from Titusville). The "old school" provided me with the training, however painful it may have been. This text is about staying human.

(Written July, 1995; I am a fourth year general surgery resident working in the laboratory)
(Spot me the cynicism)

*It's funny. You start your residency thinking you are talented and smart. You spend the majority of the time in this program feeling like you are in trouble (a good resident feels like he is in trouble all of the time). You finish realizing that you are talented and smart and that they are okay guys that were just giving you a hard time.*

*They did not teach you what you needed to know about being nice to the referring doctors, or at least they did not seem too impressed with nice guys. Then you seem to forgive them when it is over and they treat you nicely, and ask you to call them by their first name. Perhaps they are nice to you because you are a product of them.*

*There is a refractory period during which you do not want them to be nice to you because a) you feel bad about yourself and do not feel like you deserve it, or b) you are still mad at them for the seven year run of slavery. I am still refractory.*

The same subject of the training system in this country was addressed by a less rested and more tired organism. This one had just finished getting an AW on a trauma case... I think that the language is jaded by the state that I was in, and I do not necessarily agree with some of the statements made, but I think that it captures a feeling that

I cannot give the reader from this comfortable chair, years removed from the battle.

(Written in early 1998; I am in my seventh and final year of general surgery training at Bayview)

*I used to dislike lawyers (save my father in law who helped me to see that there were some good guys out there), now I feel very differently. I feel very strongly that they are promoting the principles of justice and equality, principles that this country was founded on and make it so great. People probably don't like lawyers because they make so much money. These attorneys that we physicians as a group do not trust can come in pretty handy to any person that feels that they have been rendered an injustice. You can take on the whole system with just a complaint. America will not only be remembered for its great military might or wealth; more importantly, it will be remembered for its struggle to protect the freedom of people that the majority despises to speak out. Our country makes it illegal to squash them. If you have ever been on the other side of the fence, you appreciate what lawyers do. It is nice to know that they are there. I feel like this general surgery residency has placed me smack dab on the other side of that fence at times, and I have learned to appreciate the cause of those "obnoxious lawyers." Those "obnoxious lawyers" might even straighten out the HMOs some day.*

*It reminds me of the scene in the movie "Jurassic Park" where two velociraptors are chasing a kid through a building. The kid gets away because they start eating each other. Lawyer eats doctor, HMO eats doctor, lawyer eats HMO...doctor escapes? It will be the group that the public perceives to still give a shit about them that will ultimately determine the survivor in this greed game.*

*We are losing multiple residents from our program. It is the weeding process. It is the Charles Darwin Department of Surgery. Morale is at an all-time low. The beatings will continue until morale improves. Miss Kitty is going to be fired. She is dangerous. She was the sheep running behind the flock. She was one of the cavemen (cavepersons) that could not figure out exactly when the pterodactyls liked to feed in the meadow. Natural selection. I ran with the other sheep. I should have helped her more than I did. I do not disagree with letting her go. It is like the young private in the movie "A Few Good Men" at the end of the trial after he is thrown out of the Marines for following the orders of his commanding officer...*

*"What did we do wrong?."*

*His senior buddy responded... "We should have done the right thing. We should have helped Perez" (or whatever his name was). I ran with the flock, scared shitless like the rest of the crew. The program should have canned her earlier in her career, certainly much earlier than the year before she was supposed to finish. I guess that it is hard to fire a girl these days. She is 36 years old and does not need this kind of bullshit. Two interns in the program are leaving. Jeff is just sick of it, and Mike is going for a better life, radiology. We lose 2 interns every year. They don't get fired, they just quit. It's as Darwinistic as the dumb asses that drive around town drunk, wreck, and show up in our ER with their bones showing. Such powerful selection forces are convenient in that they usually preclude the necessity of firing. Funny how 120 hours per week with random, intermittent psychotorture will improve your focus.*

Then again, would you want a surgeon operating on you that was a frustrated radiologist? These firings and "assisted resignations" are a necessary part of the process. This is surgery, this is serious.

There was a time on the Trauma Service during my sixth year of residency that I was ready to give it all up. I had not matched in cardiothoracic surgery yet. I was not yet a general surgeon. All that I had was my M.D. This meant ER work, the land of the half-trained (in that state). I recall very clearly the drive that Alison, Charles and I made around the perimeter road of the city. I had a quart of Natural Lite (cheap) beer in one hand and was grabbing my aching forehead with the other.

We went around the city five or six times. Alison never batted an eye. She was totally supportive. It is a real credit to her that the question "how are we going to eat?" did not come out until the 5th loop around the city. I was not really sure about that one. I talked to Stan that night. He called to make sure that I was okay. I was not. Stan told me not to give them the satisfaction of watching you give up your dreams of cardiothoracic surgery.

"Both of these fuckers tried and failed to get into CT (cardiothoracic) programs. Don't let them do it to you. Don't give them the satisfaction."

Stan was right. I went back to work. The rest is history. I cannot describe the depth of my emotions that night. I had been awake for almost 2 days, seen nothing but death despite my best (and medically correct) efforts, and had taken a huge AW from a couple of people that I did not respect. My world was upside down.

I wrote a short passage with reference to that time. I leave it in my book because I promised myself that I would not polish over the way that things really were. I think that it was one of my Trauma attendings that said to "forgive, but never forget."

*This is an archaic system. It has been sheer hell at times. There was a time on the Trauma Service that I told my wife that I was not going in to work the next day. She said okay. We drove around the city and talked about what we would do in the future. I went into work anyway. I feel that I have been worked over by attending physicians on the Trauma Service that were less than enthusiastic about my desire to enter the field of cardiothoracic surgery. Two of the trauma attendings were, how do I say, not invited to pursue that course and have given me never ending crap about it. I truly think that their consistent insanity makes this effort possible.*

*This probably serves as more of a catharsis at this point in my life. I am just coming off of the Trauma Service. I feel like I am finally over the hump. The rest is supposedly downhill. I will probably catch cancer now, or get a brain abscess from a resistant strain of staphylococcus from handling patients without gloves then picking my nose. I just had to write this down. I know that there is no guaranteed justice in life, I just want to document how much it hurt.*

I had to leave the program to realize how good we all were. We were all initially committed to the patients because we were afraid to screw up and get an AW. Experience eventually lead to our being the best person in the hospital when the shit hit the fan and somebody is really sick. This talent leads to a sense of pride that sneaks in around the fifth year. The following is written near the end of my general surgery residency.

I was quite skeptical of the whole process near the end of my general surgery run. This can be seen in the following commentary.

*Let's talk about solutions.*

*If you stay up all night, some consideration should be given to its effects on your performance the following day. You ought to be able to go home early that day, so that you can eat, sleep, and visit your wife.*

*Your pager should be turned off for a 24-hour period each week.*

*Even if I spot you the bad hours, don't even try to tell me that it is okay to keep me in $80,000 dog debt until I am 36 to become a heart surgeon. How about spreading out the misery? Spot me the $400 per month loan payments until I finish my eternal quest. That way Alison won't have to buy that nappy generic peanut butter.*

*Where's the money? You gave it to the CEO of the HMO that you sold out to. The government is trying to balance its budget with it. We have already been factored in. Maybe somewhere there is a central screwing office run by Cathy Lee.*

*Residents should be paid as much as the nurses. They aren't. Why not? The real answer is that the old guys had to do it too, and the ever-growing legion of hospital administrators' fat asses are not getting the reimbursement that they used to get for OUR work. They continue to use us as a cheap source of labor. It is the natural history of any organization that has no representation. It is against the nature of a surgery resident to complain. It is okay to go on strike when you are an airline pilot or an automaker; people miss their flights or big car companies lose money, but nobody dies.*

*Health care organizations should approach their jobs from a mindset of "How can I support the providers, the only ones that are directly providing the service that makes health care exist?" They ought to remember that there is nothing without our skill, judgment, and compassion. They ought to think of ways to create and distribute excellence rather than sending policies down from CEO central that hold the physician-patient relationship in contempt.*

*One of the largest HMOs in the country operated in this fashion and their house fell down in the absence of a foundation. They saw the light (with the help of the FBI) and realized that principles like trust, honesty, compassion, and charity existed in this world long before these large organizations came into being and will still be around long after they are gone. Physicians are wise to stick by their patients. HMOs are wise to stick by the mission of the providers, and to learn from them.*

So this is the residency process and the ideas of one of its "processed" subjects. They break you down and build you back up. Hopefully I am something better than lunchmeat with the beef lips and pork-fanny parts. I think that I am.

# 4

# What Kind of a Person Signs Up for This?

Sometimes when I am busy complaining about something related to my job/life/hours, I am asked the question: "So why did you do it?" or "Why don't you quit?"

Good question. Harder to answer than I at first realized. I know that I am one of the type that would no nothing else than cardiothoracic surgery.

What type of person signs on the dotted line?

A masochist.

A person with discipline. This leads perhaps to a person that likes to run marathons (one of the few things that requires more mental discipline than operating on someone's beating heart).

A person that admires veterans and likes to watch war movies so that he can admire the bravery of men putting it all at risk for a cause.

A person that played competitive sports all of his life and wants to extend that experience into the OR.

A person that can stay up all night taking care of society's dukey, take a shower at 6 AM, scrape one of those dull Schick prep razors (that they use to shave the patients, and are thus designated "free" and dull enough for resident use) across his dry face, get dressed, operate (and take AWs—ass whippings) for another 12 hours, and go home in a decent mood.

A person with an the ability to achieve an overwhelming and irrational sense of calm in the presence of certain disaster (and 3 doomsayers circling like Indians on a warpath).

A person that is aggressive. There is a popular saying in surgery that it is "far better to beg forgiveness than to ask permission." The aggressive surgery resident says, "I thought it would be okay for me to take that appendix out" rather than to ask for permission to do it. I am not comfortable with that statement, and think of a "cowboy" type of attitude when I hear that statement.

Cowboys get shot at Bayview.

One thing that separates the medicine doctor from the surgeon is the necessity for the surgeon to act on sometimes incomplete information. Things happen fast in surgery, and there is often not time to vacillate. Good judgment allows the experienced surgeon to know when to hold back. The internal medicine doctor acts more deliberately after establishing a clear-cut diagnosis. It is a more slow-moving chronic situation for them. Surgeons often do not have the luxury of time.

Cardiothoracic surgeons are thought by some to be the "top dogs" in their field. I am of the belief that many of the top dogs in any field are somehow "balancing an inherent imbalance." You know the person. They never go home, or seem to have an endless drive to excel. I am sure that that is not normal. Those people are few and far between. I am not sure that these people are any more "successful" than the guy at the Zippy Mart counter. He may already have his balance. Perhaps it is just a little easier to keep intact, with less dynamic components. I used the phrase "top dog" rather than the term "successful" for that reason. I will say, however, that most cardiothoracic surgeons love to operate. The more you do it, better you get at it. The better you get at it, the more you like it.

I am the kind of person that thinks in terms of words like competition (the idea of someone being more well trained in the hospital is very hard for me to deal with), personal responsibility (perhaps martyrdom is closer to that one), and work. I am certain that I have an imbalance within me, but I have almost given up trying to understand it. This is a waste of time.

I should also throw in the fact that I have a hard time saying no to the expectations of others, though I am working on this. I achieved my current position more by endurance than intelligence. Endurance is a quality that is probably common to all heart surgeons. They may or may not be the fastest, but they endure. They are tough in a long-term sort of way.

The cardiothoracic surgeon is very much an obsessive personality type, with a special obsession for the plight of his patient. I consider every cut and move that I make in the operating room to be an effort to save my patient from the next "snake under every rock." I see a young patient like the 40-year-old man from Chicago that I performed a 6-vessel coronary artery bypass grafting (CABG) on yesterday, and I know that he has a 4-year-old daughter. I will fight to get him out of the hospital. I have a healthy sense of paranoia that everything and everyone in the hospital is trying to kill him (by the way, that mindset does not work as well in society). Cardiothoracic surgeons are general surgeons first and learn the concept of total responsibility for your patient.

Some would say that a cardiothoracic surgeon is callous and desensitized to death. I submit that going home before you really "should" when you have a sick patient and hauling ass out of the hospital early on Friday afternoon only to show up with your shining face on Monday is an order of magnitude more insensitive. The patients are sick 168 hours per week. Anything less than everything is......less than everything.

A sense of ingenuity helps, once you are locked into the chase. I have always been impressed that my friend Stan (now in the Baylor Cardiothoracic Surgery Program) still works on his car and argues technical points with his mechanic. A good friend of mine's father is a well-known heart surgeon. He describes the qualities of an attractive cardiothoracic surgery applicant as one that he would trust to take his family across the plains in a wagon train in the days of the Old West. There were times during the structured ego takedown that I did not feel very smart. I felt like I would have only made it out to the Chattahoochee River in central Georgia where I would have been accosted by men saying things like, "you're perty" and "squeal like a pig."

It is important for me to establish to you, the reader, that I am a good resident. I have always prided myself on hard work. I have a strong record. I would stack it up against most any other resident in the country. It took a strong record to match at one of the country's top cardiothoracic surgery programs. Sure, some feelings of impatience (mostly at my income to age ratio) leak out on occasion, but I manage that with the help of my wife and children. My words do not come from a slant other than fatigue and the desire to document this stuff before I forget it. I am sure that my life will become easier in the near future, and the primary history (that which is recorded as the events progress) will surely be lost. One day I will write a happier version of things, but such an account would not reflect my true feelings right now. I have worked hard to preserve the raw stuff.

Oh yes, and one more thing....It helps to have to have a rock (whatever that may be). My rock is named Alison.

# 5

# It Has Everything to Do with your Priorities

My family comes first, though I am never home to prove it to them. It hurts to be away from your family so much. They feel sorry for you at first, but that wears off, just like the great feeling of power you get from getting a pager for the first time. Then the pager goes off, and goes off again. In an unchecked state, this is the natural history of the workaholic (what is "workahol") surgeon and his wife. There is an initial pity. This is quickly replaced by waiting, and more waiting, and finally by resentment. There is resentment first of your job, and finally you as you continue to do the same thing day in and day out.

It is a constant struggle. I am losing as I write this, but I am never going to give it up. It is very hard to work so much and tell your wife and kids that they are more important. Are they really your priority? This residency process has a way of selecting marriages out and answering that for you.

Can you do both? Cardiothoracic surgery and family? Definitely yes. Is it easy? Definitely no.

Can you do both and play golf? Definitely not, at least not very well. Your golf game and family life do in fact have an inverse relationship. I have found good golf to be the dark outer cliff marking the limit of my attempts at an "abundance mentality."

I just want to stay good enough at golf to continue to take my friend Bufkin at will, and that is not very hard.

# 6

# Love and Fear: Heading off the Doomsayers

In my opinion, there are two sides to reality. There is a fear side and an abundance of love side. The abundance side says that there is enough of everything to go around (even coronary artery disease). Adopting this mentality has to be the single most important thing that I have done as a young adult. The fear side says that they will invent a wonder drug to render cardiothoracic surgeons poor and obsolete. The abundance side says that this would be a great step forward for mankind. The fear mentality is ever present, and should be ignored.

Don't let anybody tell you that you do not have the surgeon's mentality, or that you have to get a divorce, or that you have to be obsessed with surgery. You just have to like what you do, be smart, energetic, and have a strong sense of compassion for your fellow man. Two years in the dog lab also helps too. Often times, the ones that speak the loudest are the ones that are trying to rationalize their own defeat.

I was told that I was too nice and too sensitive. Well I guess that I am not so nice anymore, but I certainly seem to have retained my sensitivity (I wrote this book, didn't I?). It really would not have been worth it to make all of this effort and come out being irritated by the folks that I was supposed to help. It was my goal to get through this without sacrificing the guy that started this process 18 years before.

Some say that you have to become detached from the emotional aspects associated with the loss of the patient. I say BS. I say get into it. Try to save their life with everything that you have. It is not going to kill you. You are their only chance. Try to save them like you are the only one that can (and you frequently are in the ER), or don't do it.

The world opens up to the ones who want to serve. We need doctors that want to give more than receive. You can shoot right to the top. It is just hard work and a desire to serve. Every other field and mine are wide open.

Another small piece of advice for students with a slow Texas drawl. When the patient is waking up from anesthesia, don't say "open up your eyes." "Eyes" can sound like "ass" and it may make the patient think that he or she has died and gone to Hell and that you are the welcoming committee ready for the indoctrination ritual.

A truly "abundant" budding cardiothoracic surgeon does not drink coffee.....

## Coffee

*Don't do it. Do not start. I have been there.*
*So you want to be a heart surgeon?*
*Think about the things that are required to accomplish this....*
*A clean coat.*

*This is a good start. The giant coat that they give you covers 80% of your body. The coat can make or break you. It is the way you look. The coat needs to be white and starched. Coffee tends to leave stripes that you cannot see when you first spill it. As the coffee dries, it becomes brown (like your teeth). If you move fast, carry coffee, and wear a white coat; you will see the stripes.*

*The patient sees you with the tattered coat and wonders if you are going to take his heart out, put it on the back table, beat the shit out of it, and then put some of those brown stripes on it too.*

## Energy

*There is only so much energy in your body. You are making big withdrawals in the morning on that set energy level when you suck down that nappy brown broth. You are pulling the energy out to create a 60 cycles per second whole body vibration and the mental buzz that leads you to want to make another withdrawal from your account two hours later. You are going to feel it when the cath lab crash comes and you are stuck doing a 10 hour disaster; your fifth of the day.*

*Drink another cup.*
*Don't spill it on your coat.*
*Don't let Superman see you doing it. You shameful brown-toothed rat; cowering behind the ice machine.*

*It is all about endurance. It is about the long run. It is not about fur-*
*ther withdrawals on a bum account.*

Steady hands
   It really is hard to sew tiny grafts to the diseased coronary vessels of
a patient with atherosclerosis. Why add your own vibration to the situ-
ation? I like to do heart surgery well. I like for my patients to do well.
   Dr. Sternalpunch (my hero) and a post coronary artery bypass
grafting debriefing:
   *The obligatory shot to the chest...... "Good job, son!"*
   *Air....... "Thank you, sir."......Air*
   *"You sewed the marginal well. The case went well."*
   *"Thank you, sir."*
   *"You shake some. You drink coffee?"*
   *"Yes sir"*
   *"No more coffee.......Good job, son."*
   *"Thank you, sir."*
   Coffee is about as easy to give up as cigarettes. I am sure that Dr.
Sternalpunch's words of encouragement helped that fellow!

A calm demeanor in the face of certain disaster
   The patient is just back from the OR. A large dump of 600 ml of
blood is running into the chest tubes.
   Anesthesia: "We need to go back! (to the OR)."
   Nurse (horrified by the sight and having heard anesthesia bring the
option of departure from the ICU to the table): Get the bleeder out of here
comes in the form "I think he needs to go back!"
   No words from the calm cardiothoracic surgery fellow.
   Anesthesia: "Have you seen the chest x-ray?"
   Surgeon (Responding only because he knows that it is much more
rude to ignore two consecutive comments than only one): "It has not
come up yet."
   Nurse: "Has the chest x-ray come up yet?"
   Surgeon (Responding only with a look of flattened affect and 3 con-
sonants because he knows that it is much less rude to ignore two con-
secutive comments if the second comment was the same as the first one
that you just replied to): "mmm."
   Anesthesia: "We may need to go back! (to the OR)."
   Surgeon (Now having an out of body experience. Rage from the
pecking gives in to an overwhelming and irrational sense of calm.
Down boy. They will all go home at 5 PM): "mmm."
   Nurse: "This guy is bleeding. Does the family know?"

*Anesthesia: "So what are you going to do?"*

*Surgeon (Still out of body and calm......Play golf until I am on the Senior Tour and get laid four times a day when I get out of this place. Hmmmm. They are not going to stop. Back to the dust bowl. The stirring continues. It will not settle. I had better speak): "mmm."*

*Anesthesia: "Do we need to get the room ready?"*

*Surgeon: "Let me speak to Dr. Hakkin' Mika." (Let's inflict his 20-year perfected calming force since you cannot stop. We have no information. We only have emotion creating statements, creating further statements from others and their emotions. Much heat. No light.)*

*The chest x-ray arrives showing a large collection of undrained fluid in the left chest. Hakkin' Mika orders that a chest tube (a thin plastic tube that is inserted between the ribs to drain fluid collections in the chest) be put in the left pleural space (chest).*

*We place the chest tube. The fluid collection is drained and totals approximately one liter of serous looking fluid. The fluid was not adequately drained by the original chest tubes at operation. Inaccurate placement of the chest tube and our not having sucked out the pleural space adequately prior to closing lead to the appearance of ongoing bleeding.*

*The sun comes out. Light is shed. There is no more "bleeding."*

*The fact remains that calm lead us to look at the situation after the dust had settled. Not having to take this guy back to the OR will save this patient from being exposed to a greatly increased risk of infection and many other possible untoward events.*

*Calm is an essential part of the cardiothoracic surgeon's armamentarium.*

*Coffee is the enemy of calm.*

*Don't start.*

Don't wear those Little Dutch Boy sissy clogs on your feet either. Those are for elves. I know that they are more comfortable. So is a sun dress, but you don't wear that. Think if you all of a sudden died, would you want to have those things on?

# 7

## My Curriculum Vitae (Which my kids probably will never read)

Let me also introduce myself using the standard of worth of any academic, the dreaded Curriculum Vitae. For those entering into what I have done, remember.... Your kids will probably never read it.

Curriculum Vitae
C. Patrick Murrah, M.D.

Office Address:
Resident
Department of Surgery
Division of General Surgery
Bayview Medical Center
Bayview City, USA

Let's dissect this by the line:
"Office Address"

*Actually I do not have an office. We were offered them when we became Chief Residents at Bayview. I always thought that I should either be working, reading, or with my family. Sitting around at the hospital in an office is not one of those options.*
*A physician who is Chairman of the Department of Surgery at a major Midwestern medical center was the first person that I heard say*

*that, without exception, a resident ought to be working, reading, or with his family. This is what I have always done, and I am very proud of it. I gave up golf, fishing, being tan, and flying; but did so gladly at the price of becoming a man.*

*I frequently question such a one-dimensional existence, but resolve that there is no other way to become a heart surgeon and stay attached to your family. Maybe I am just not smart enough or do not have enough energy. Maybe I should drink supplements or make myself throw up more like the guys in L.A.*

Department of Surgery

Bayview has one of the top ten general surgery residency programs in the United States. It has a very tough history. There was terror even before the arrival of The Father in the late 1960s. The Chairman of the Department of Surgery before The Father (Dr. Lionheart) inspired such fear that sick patients would often be hid from him on rounds. It was the responsibility of the intern on the service to take the sick patient and ride him up and down on the elevator until rounds were over with. Some of the original studies of the aerodynamic characteristics of various instruments and indeed instrument trays were also tested in the operating theatres at Bayview during the early 1960s. The chairman before The Father liked to announce his presence in the OR by throwing a tray full of instruments down the hallway. Time to pucker up those sphincters boys.

The Father came down from the Mayo Clinic in the late 1960s and ran Bayview as Chairman of the Department until 1983. Superman has been king since that time. Perhaps I am biased, but I consider him to be the best chairman in the country. He is the Department of Surgery.

Superman's leadership is strong and very simple. He has the perfect combination of an outer toughness and a deep inner sensitivity. The toughness allows him to effectively lead a world class surgical department. The sensitivity allows him to care for the smallest trouble that befalls one of his many patients. His kidney transplant patient population now numbers almost 5000 (the world's largest series). He also has a very large number of patients that have undergone some form of endocrine (thyroid, parathyroid, and adrenal) surgery. I have called him many a night with a question about a patient that he may have operated on fifteen years ago. He remembers them all by name. He also does not mind being called at any time of the day or night.

Superman stands around six feet tall. His hair is thin and gray but neatly trimmed. He has a dark complexion. He has a distinctly square jaw that sort of juts into your world when you are face to face with him. He reminds me of Don Shula after the defense has fucked up. He looks directly at you through his slightly tinted wire rimmed glasses. He tends to grind his jaw and speaks often out of the side of his clinched mouth in a low nasal New York tone. He is very controlled, but appears poised to take a large chunk out of your carotid artery and spit it back out at you at any given moment. He never does, but you are like the one in the circus with your head in the lion's mouth, and you know that he could. He does not have to shout, but you hear that he has. Free weight training has given him very large biceps muscles. His hands are very large and have very prominent veins on their backside. Superman's clothes are always neatly pressed. His shoes are dark, expensive looking, and shiny.

I still remember the intimidating force of Superman's presence at the scrub sink. There are two main hallways in the non-cardiac portion of the operating suite at Bayview. The scrub sinks are two long troughs that line a corridor connecting the two hallways. The attendings and residents perform their cleaning ritual within this corridor. If Superman was already there when you came into the corridor, you found a nice corner, and remained quiet. If he came up beside you after you were already there, well, you stayed there and remained quiet. You spoke only if you were spoken to. It takes 10 minutes to scrub your hands for your first case. Cutting that interval back just a little bit was a viable option if Superman happened to come up beside you.

I remember the image of Superman at the completion of his scrub. He held his arms out in front of him with his palms rotated slightly upwards, fingers spread, water dripping down. You could see his biceps that were twice as big as yours, even though he was twice your age. His hands were disproportionately large, which of course implies that his tallywacker was twice as big as yours.

Superman was born at the Johns Hopkins Hospital sixty some-odd years ago, the son of a well-known psychiatrist. He played college football at Washington State University, and has maintained the spirit of a tough competitor. He spent his early years in New York, completing his general surgery training at Cornell University. He trained at the Brigham and Women's Medical Center in the field of transplantation. He studied under the Nobel Prize winning surgeon Joseph Murray, the man who performed the first successful kidney transplantation.

The Father (a person that I will introduce later, who is, in many people's opinion, the most important figure in the development of modern cardiothoracic surgery) recruited Superman to Bayview in the late 1960s. Superman started performing kidney transplants at the

Veteran's Hospital, and they worked. There had never been anything remotely resembling such a complex procedure performed in this facility. The amount of work and focus that he put forward to single-handedly create a successful Renal Transplantation Service in these surroundings is remarkable.

Now in his mid to late 60s, Superman continues to maintain a pace that rivals any iron man. The third year surgery resident on the Renal Transplantation Service is expected to call him at home at 5:45 AM. That is 5:45:00, not 5:45:05. He notices the difference. Perhaps it is because the residents have spoiled him over the years. Perhaps. It seems more likely that the 5:45:05ers were selected out by subtle and sometimes not so subtle 5:45:20 AWs. Anyway, it is a 5:45:00 call.

The events surrounding the 5:45:00 call go something like this...

There are around 40 patients in the hospital on the Renal Transplantation Service at any given time. The third year general surgery resident is the Chief Resident on the service. This is the first time in your residency that you function as a Chief Resident. It means that you are in charge of the service. It is sort of like the beeper phenomenon, great to wear one until it goes off, and keeps going off. Now you are truly responsible. Being in charge means that you are the one at the helm when things happen, good or bad. Being the Chief Resident also means that there is nothing between you and the attending. These are not your patients, and you are wise to remember this.

The Chief Resident has an intern (first year surgery resident), and (hopefully) a medical student at his disposal. You have to have all of the patients seen by 5:30 AM. The intern and the medical student go over the entire service until just before the 5:45:00 AM deadline. The sheets with the patient names on them and all of the lab values from the morning blood draws are all laid out at your desk in the call room. The intern stands by for emergency data transmission. The clock is on the wall to your left. The telephone number is dialed. First the first six numbers... 653-000...then the final 1 is dialed at 5:44:55.... anticipating a ring at 5:45:00 at his house. Superman answers the phone on the second ring.

"Hello."

"Good morning sir."

"God morning Pat."

We start in the ICU with Mr. Jones. The conversation is hopefully one-sided, with you doing all of the talking.

The principle that the 5:45:00 call teaches is very important. You must have everything ready, every day, regardless of external forces. Believe me, there are a lot of things that can go wrong to destroy your timing. You must make do. It is a results-oriented "I will do the job sir" approach. That is a principle that helps in all phases of life. It transfers over to the patient... "I will be there for you," regardless of what happens. That is how I want my doctor to be. No buck-passing involved.

The 5:45:00 phone call is your entire world, but it is only part of Superman's. I have no idea what time he gets up in the morning. I do know that he never sounds like he just got up when I speak to him at 5:45 AM. I also know that he gets phone calls from the Organ Center and the OR at some scheduled point in the morning. There is even a time, among resident legend that he is in the shower and is not to be called by anyone. He is a very hard working and principled man. He makes me want to be a better person and take better care of my patients. I suppose that that defines the word leadership.

Division of General Surgery
General Surgery is a Division within the Department of Surgery. Superman is the Chairman of the Department of Surgery. Superman gave The Brain the reigns to direct the Division of General Surgery when he hit 65. Bayview is one of the top ten programs in the country in Superman's, and therefore my own, opinion. Things that he said had a way of bearing out to be solid fact.

The Brain is a Johns Hopkins trained academician. He practices Surgical Oncology (cancer surgery) with a special emphasis on melanoma and breast disease. He is a thinking man with an added gift for surgical technique. He has thought everything out.

I remember when I was a third year medical student and my roommate David began his clinical rotation on the Surgical Oncology Service. I remember a conversation that we had while eating a cheeseburger at Wendy's...

"Pat, he knows everything."
"What do you mean, Dave?"
"I mean he knows...everything!"
"About surgery?"
"Surgery and everything else."
"Damn."

That conversation had a big impact on me. How could someone know everything? Was it possible? Well, The Brain comes close.

It is interesting that two educated guys could so quickly buy into the possibility that somebody other than the God that we worshipped could be all knowing. I had essentially been bought over within the course of a "single-cheese-everything." Imagine how easily a patient might be bought over on the fact that you are some kind of all-knowing swami.

Looking back over 11 years of medical training, it makes me realize that I have learned a lot. I certainly do not know everything, but I have been specializing and subspecializing all day every day for a very long time. I can see how some patients might think that I know everything. I have sort of gone off on a tangent. I know my trade pretty well. This tangent also creates a void between you and the patient. You have to breach that void every time that you communicate a problem to a patient. That takes a lot of non-scientific things like patience, insight, and compassion.

Bayview Medical Center

This is the "House that The Father built." This medical center was transformed by one individual's brains and determination like no other center ever has been. Four physicians created The Johns Hopkins Hospital. Two brothers created The Mayo Clinic. One man put Bayview on the map. Bayview was built around the ideals and efforts of one great individual. The huge medical corporations that threaten the existence of such national treasures as our academic health centers (AHCs) are very foolhardy and shortsighted if they think that our healthcare system can survive without them.

The Father's brain came first. The buildings and the money and the growth followed his ideas. They followed his quest to make more kids live after open-heart operations. His passion was to perfect the use of the heart lung machine. His passion was excellence in patient care. Twenty years of intense efforts built Bayview from the medical center of the perennial #50 state (with a good football team) to the medical center where people from all over the world go to have their heart operation, have their cancer treated, or even to get their face lift.

I was proud to be there. This is reflected in the least cynical passage that I could find from my time in the trenches.....

*Bayview Medical Center was recently ranked third in the nation by a poll that the hospital found and continues to quote. The hospital's ranking is somewhere between the best poll that they can find and the way that I feel about it when I am post call and stuck in the ER with a retarded Emergency Doc, a drunken patient, and no nurse in sight. Truly, we are quite strong in all areas. It is better to make sure that you are shot if you come to the ER, however, that way you can skip the local part-time help, traffic cop, agency ER docs and see a surgeon more quickly.*

I am very proud to be a part of this hospital......

*...a turn for the worse occurs, and I am on any of a million roads that all lead to that final common "cynical superhighway." I have led Alison down this road with such frequency that it just doesn't faze her anymore. She does not even roll her eyes anymore...*

*I am from a small town in Florida named Titusville. I grew up thinking that foreigners were the smart ones because they were the doctors in my hometown. They had very foreign sounding names, adding to their mystery. They were so mysterious and brilliant. It turns out that many of them were just winging it in the sticks with the simple folks. Their training was probably mediocre on the average, but we really did not know the difference. It really is hard to tell who is good.*

...and off we go on another anti "shitty doctor" crusade....

*As a doctor, I think about how hard it would be for me to pick out a good jeweler. I really don't know. I just count on the word of a friend. I think that the public deserves better data. The injection of free enterprise and the information age into medicine should fix that. Everything can be ranked, including doctors. I hope that the information age will provide us with that list. I am sure that some doctors would not like that, but it might help patients to make better choices. It might also allow us to shine the light on that bottom 10% that keep getting in the news, take a better look at our house, and maybe even clean it.*

Bayview City, USA

This is the home of my residency. It was a great place in many ways. The people were very friendly for the most part. Then of course there is the Death Star, and that is of course where I have to work. This city has pulled itself up from a collapse of the steel industry in the 1970s. The Father and a Senator (the "Hill" part of the Hill-Burton Act") built them a world class medical facility and took up the slack.

Provincial

Everything in Bayview was named Shelby; the county, the Senator, the men, the women, boys, girls, even a dog that lived down the street (who was a female). The young girl that died of renal failure on Steel Magnolias was named Shelby.

Was there somebody famous named Shelby that I missed in history class?

It is pronounced "Shay-ul-bee." It has three syllables.

Everything, and everybody is named Shelby.

It was almost as incredible as the mink coats worn by the elite of the region as they strolled through the Piggly Wiggly on a warm day, no doubt looking for some Fancy Feast cat food for their cat...Shelby.

It was a very segregated town. I did not like that. The years of racial tension had taken their toll on the next generation. They all live in separate (and not equal) parts of town. There is a complete lack of a black middle class. During my interviews for medical school, some old lady told me that I would become more conservative as I progressed in my career. Now she is dead and I am still waiting for the transformation. Perhaps I have not progressed. I do not know what happened to me, but seeing poor people get shot or look so pitiful sent me the other way. The social conscience of some/most liberals appeals to me in many ways. Adding in some courage would help. The sense of personal responsibility of some/most conservatives also appeals to me. Removing some arrogance would help. I try to practice both, and usually fail.

A more opinionated view of things, given very early in the heat of the fight: This may be the mother-of-all cynical passages.

*April, 1995*

*... That hosing stuff really bothers me, though I don't ever see those people around here any more. Maybe they are all in church, confessing. That would be an excellent reason why I never see them. They probably are serving their terms out in the State Capitol. Not in jail, but in the Senate, House, or Governor's Office. Perhaps they are out there at a nursing home tonight, eating creamed corn, being served to them by a black lady. Maybe one is developing abdominal distention. Maybe he is getting ready to barf, prompting an ER admission and of course a phone call from some ER gimp that could not finish his residency and has resorted to locum tenens work in the third world of a rural part of this state.*

*I am reminded of a dark part of my town's past when I see something like I saw this morning, an old black man riding his bike along Highway 82 in 25 degree weather at 5 AM. Probably going to or from work. It personally makes me very sad and ashamed. Parts of this city are very cozy places to live, but much of this lifestyle is carried out with exclusion of the less fortunate or those of color...Bad. This certainly is a generalization, there are so many great people in this town that want to make a difference; the talent and resources just have not been developed. I know what you are saying...why don't you do it and stop complaining? The answer...my butt is out of here when the bell rings June 23rd, 1998. Fix it yourself. Maybe I'll come back after I get some sleep.*

Home Address:
422 Departure Avenue
Bayview City, USA

I liked my house. It served as a refuge from the hospital. My wife, Alison, is not a nurse, and worked harder than me taking care of our two young children.

Born:
April 12, 1965; Huntsville, Alabama

I did not live there more than six months, so don't try to call me a redneck. Worse still, I am from Florida. The land of tight pants and fitted shirts.

Marital Status:   Married to wife Alison June 1991

I really wrote, "married to wife"...and still got a spot in cardiothoracic surgery. Hard to believe.

Written near the end of my trauma rotation. Pardon the post-traumatic stress disorder. This is more of the growing opportunity stuff. I would not change one thing about my residency program, save perhaps the chance to do a Trauma externship in another solar system.

*We are still married. My program was reputed among the resident applicants to have a 100% divorce rate. That aids so greatly in recruiting bright and idealistic individuals. I once again appeal for some of that politically correct stuff that is so fake, but at least protects the interests of the resident.*
*I want somebody like Anderson Consulting or Steven Covey to come in and just look. Maybe someone could put it in the newspaper. Maybe some former resident should work hard enough to record things the way that they actually were and then take time to write a book instead of*

*waiting until he got old and had forgotten the pain or wanted the young guys to have to suffer the way he did. ...Not a bad idea.*

Children:            Two: one son, Charles; one daughter, Anna

My kids are perfect, or perfectly imperfect.

Education:
Undergraduate: Florida State University; 1983-1987; BS Biochemistry

I worked very hard there. So hard that I sometimes regret it. The insecurity of not being anywhere (save perhaps a lab) if you do not get into medical school may be the worst feeling that you feel at any stage of the "I want to be a real doctor" process.

I am only now slowly getting over my regret and realizing that I should be proud of taking the hard road. This job is hard, but the hours and the training process are the price that you pay for being placed in the exalted position of being able to save someone's life. All during college, I was either too broke or too worried about exams to have fun. Then again, maybe I was just born that way.

Medical School: Bayview School of Medicine; 1987-1991; M.D.

Internship:         General Surgery; Florida Private Hospital; 1991-1992

This was a year of much personal growth for my wife and I. Still, I am glad that I left. When I think back on that year, I think of the evaluation letter that I received from a Chief Resident who said that I did not have the tools to become a general surgeon. I will remember that when I pull my first sick patient off of cardiopulmonary bypass and give his kids ten more good years with their dad.

Residency:          General Surgery; Bayview Medical Center; 1992-1998

Self-explanatory. My good friend Jerry told me that I need to keep this account locked up for a very long time; but to make sure that it does win the Pulitzer Prize if it does get out, otherwise I will surely pay for my efforts. I am aware of my touchability. I would ask those who might be upset by my book, "what part of this is not true?" Honesty in my accounts is my defense.

This is only one account of the surgical training process that I have undergone. I hope that I can provide young students with an idea of what it felt like for me. This certainly may not be the experience that others have had or will have.

Honors and Awards:

National Merit Scholarship:
Florida State University 1983-1987

I studied a glossary to get ready for the SAT when I was a kid. Most of the kids in my hometown were normal. Other kids were getting an early start learning about sex, drugs, and alcohol in my hometown. Some of them went on to become trauma patients, I was learning to stop them from dying. A sort of spinning wheel concept. Nerds and druggies cancel each other out.

Honors Degree in Biochemistry:
Florida State University 1987

I am actually quite proud of the time that I spent working hard in college. Regrets are not necessary because your life only happens once, and you do what you do in a much less random way than you think. I was supposed to be that serious... I suppose.

National Cancer Society Research Fellowship:
"Effect of Copper on Hemolysis of Red Blood Cells"
Florida State University; summer 1986

Individual Recipient: N.I.H. National Research Service Award
"Oxygen Delivery during Cardiopulmonary Bypass"
Bayview Medical Center; Division of Cardiothoracic Surgery 1994-1996

Teaching:
Instructor:
American College of Surgeons,
Advanced Trauma Life Support Course 1991-present

I was commissioned by the Trauma Service to do this, but actually liked it. You got a free lunch.

Grants:

National Cancer Society Research Fellowship:

"Effect of Copper on Hemolysis of Red Blood Cells"
Florida State University, summer 1986

N.I.H. National Research Service Award
"Oxygen Delivery during Cardiopulmonary Bypass"
Bayview Division of Cardiothoracic Surgery 1994-1996

Key here to mention the same stuff again to look really scientific.

Computer Training:

"SAS Fundamentals, a Programming Approach." SAS Institute, 1995.

How many times can I write the word nerd? Nerds taught me how to use computers. I conclude that a nerd can be recognized by the inability that he has to transmit information effectively to other humans. The information in this case is 'how to use computers'. The lack of transmittal comes both from a complete lack of ability to relate to others and a superimposed unwillingness to give up something that they are better at than others. The playground can scar.

Presentations:

Honors Program Thesis Defense: "Effect of Copper on Hemolysis of Red Blood Cells." Department of Chemistry, Florida State University 1987.

"Effect of Perfluorocabon Emulsions on Optical Densitometric Measurements"
American Society of Artificial Internal Organs:
Washington D.C., May 1996

"Complex Aortic Reconstruction after Catheter-Induced Dissection"
American College of Surgeons
Video Presentation
Orlando, Florida; October 1998

Publications:

I will not list my publications. I had 16 publications in major cardiothoracic surgical and scientific journals. Their publication date ranged from the mid to late 1990s and included 2 book chapters.

Professional Societies:

I am a member of several surgical societies, though they are not listed here.

American Board of Surgery In-Training Exam:

| YEAR | PERCENTILE SCORE |
|------|------------------|
| 1992 | 86 |
| 1993 | 90 |
| 1994 | 76 |
| 1995 | 95 |
| 1996 | 80 |
| 70 | |

Passed General Surgery Written Board Examination

Licensed to practice medicine in two states.

That concludes my Curriculum Vitae.

# 8

# Preserving the Academic Surgeon

My bosses are the so-called "attending" physicians. They have completed their training in various branches of surgery and have returned to the world of academics for different reasons. Most are very good at what they do and have chosen the high road. They want to take on the tough cases. They also want to be leaders in their field.

One of the present challenges that our country's academic health centers (AHCs) face is to provide an answer to the question: "Who is going to pay for these stars?" It costs more for teaching hospitals to train residents, conduct research, and treat the indigent. AHCs maintain these unique missions and then go on to compete on a "level playing field" with other health centers that are not pressed with such noble missions.

The part of the business community that seems to have become so interested in (the money that can be sucked out of) health care delivery has not included the academic in its plans. Perhaps research is not an economically profitable push in the early phases of hospital takeover/acquisition. HMOs say that once they have secured their turf, that they will make a place for research and development. I have only seen worsening signs from where I sit.

I am worried that AHCs are going to have to scrap some of their ideals in a desperate effort to survive. Some of the leading centers have come up with creative and proactive solutions to the challenges, such as aligning themselves with HMOs. The AHCs are gaining the HMOs large referral base in exchange for the excellent name and quality of care that an AHC can provide. This is great as long as we can maintain the excellence. We have to remember that excellence in patient care is what made these centers great, and this excellence came from the bottom up. Most of our AHCs were built around the efforts and brilliance of individual providers. All of these huge buildings are nothing without great minds to occupy them. Bayview Medical Center is a good example of this. The Father came down from the Mayo Clinic with a legion of followers. The buildings were built around him, the Senators lobbied to attract him, but The Father's brilliance came first.

AHCs need to remember the importance of supporting the provider, whose mission is to do everything in his power to save lives. The investigator who spends his life perfecting the use of the heart-lung machine in order to save children with congenital heart disease, turned down an invitation to join the prestigious Bayview Country Club, and never made more than $250,000 in one year (the average salary of up and coming middle managers of the large HMO) has aligned himself with correct principles. His mission will stand the test of time. The corporate suits are wise to follow his lead, not vice versa.

The academic surgeon survives by being the best at what he does and by keeping the patient's welfare at the center. Come HMO. Go HMO. We always need folks that want to do good, and are good. The guys that want to make money off of them may come and go. The academic surgeon deserves our respect. He or she has flown in the face of all of the financial cuts and the added pressure to publish. The academicians are the ones that taught me to operate and to take care of patients. Some of them were merely present when I learned how, most were outstanding.

It is important for the reader to understand before he reads my stories from this residency, that the attendings are here at Bayview for the purpose of training residents, promoting the specialty, and taking on the hard cases that nobody else wants. Sure there is an element of "I can hide from the 'let's get along' private practice world, be a rear-end in an insulated environment, get the residents to see my patients for me, and collect a decent salary" mentality, but you have to offer these stars credit.

I get to comment on them because I paid my dues. I would defend most of them against others' disparaging remarks... Still my overwhelming feeling remains...

*"Get me the hell out of here, I will pretend to be anyone or do anything, let me go play golf like when I was a kid."*

There are four kinds of guys in academic surgery. There are the

Self-Servers (20%), the Hiders (15%), the Middle Guys (60%), and there are Servers (5%). All have taken pay cuts by entering academics. Only the Hiders had to do it. The rest of them are keeping our surgical centers the best in the world. The academic surgeons are in need of preservation. The present economic climate has threatened their existence. The big money goes to the guys in private practice, the very guys that they are training. What's that all about? Are we planning to keep the stars in the AHCs by appealing to their sense of altruism? News flash, communism did not work.

Certainly, we must give recognition to the guy in private practice. He is putting himself out on the line. He is well removed from the protection of the big name of the place that trained him. Every wound infection or death is his and is associated with his name only. Frequently, the private practitioner is good enough to take on the guys that trained him. The academic guy does get some return on his pay cut. He gets residents to take care of his patients and he gets the name of his big teaching hospital.

As I stated, we have this mix of 4 types in the academic field, as I see it from the "being trained" seats. The Self-Servers are very functional within the system. They are motivated to some degree by the desire to be famous or powerful, or both. They love to hear themselves talk. They do well. It is not so bad to be a Self-Server, I suppose. People do that on Wall Street all day long, and they never save anybody's life.

The Hiders take the pay cut because they have to. They are the boobs of the group. They tend to be "clinically challenged," "interpersonally challenged," or both. They also tend to be very smart. They just keep training and reading, never having the courage or ability to step into the world.

The Middle Guys make up the majority of the folks. Some of these are the good guys that we may lose if we cannot pay our academic guys enough to compete with the private world.

The Servers are the ones that are quite rare. They are in it for the service. They are in it for the excellence. You know that they could be out in private practice knocking the competition dead. They will be the last ones to leave the academic ship (along with the Hiders). I have worked with a few of these in my surgical training. The Servers are the leaders in the field. They always win out over the Self-Server in the long run because they hitch themselves to correct principles.

We need all of these people. The economic climate today makes it difficult for the AHCs to survive. They are forced to compete with the private world, while training residents and treating the indigent at the same time. This is not fair. The overall goal should be to preserve excellence. The overall goal should be to keep the best surgeons (and other physicians) in the AHCs so that they may pass on their knowledge and expertise. The AHC ought to be the place where the rich people in the city want to go when they get sick. The AHC ought to be providing the highest level of clinical care in the city in which they are located. The AHCs are going to have to pay for this excellence. The academic physician's salary should be comparable to or better than that provided in private practice. There is no question about that.

The rest of the game is figuring out how to find the money to do it. I believe that the only way to secure their financial future is to aggressively recruit charitable endowments and set up strong research environments that annually win federal grants.

Aligning with HMOs and their large patient base is one strategy, though I fear that the missions of teaching and research will be seen as "leg weights" when push comes to shove and an AHC/HMO is faced with extinction. It is all too easy to cut the "chaff" just to stay alive. The centers of excellence (AHCs) in this country have been painstakingly built over the course of 100 years, beginning with Dr.s Halsted, Kelly, Welch, and Osler at the Johns Hopkins Hospital. These centers were built around the tireless efforts of great minds such as the Mayo brothers in Minnesota, and (as a more recent example) The Father at Bayview. I believe that AHCs should be designated as centers of excellence that are completely insulated, and funded by large private and federal endowments. I have seen an egress of talent from the AHCs where I have trained, and it looks like it is picking up speed. It is happening in other divisions of my program, and in many programs around the country. My division is secure; due to the presence of many of those rare Server types, but how much can they take?

# 9

## Institutionalized

I am reminded of the great movie with Tim Robbins and Morgan Freeman entitled "The Shawshank Redemption." During the movie, Freeman talks about becoming "institutionalized." It is a point where you become afraid to leave the prison. You feel a comfort within the prison walls. Your fate is secure, though it may be painful and bleak. You feel as if you are in some sad way deserving of unnecessary abuses.

As I read back through the notes that I had made in the course of my general surgery residency, this passage struck me as particularly slanted in that mode of thought. As you read it, you can sense runs of protest of my plight, immediately countered by the institutionalized mentality that helped me to deal with what were very tough times.

*I am writing this book to relieve tension, and to document what has happened to me over the past 15 years that I have donated to becoming well trained. Perhaps there is some sort of a lame quest for justice, though justice is not something that one ever can expect as a general surgery resident. You learn to accept the short end of a double standard. Slave to the patients, slave to the attorneys, slave to the attendings, slave to the hospital administrators, slave to the insurance carriers. The sooner you learn to drop expectations of justice, the better.*

*I am grateful to the faculty at the Bayview Hospital for training me. They are all exceptional in one way or another. Some of them actually in only one way, most of them in many ways. I am proud of my training program. The problem is not with any specific person; save perhaps some of the nights on call with the trauma torture squad. The problem is with the system.*

*Sometimes I may seem very angry when I write this. You will probably be able to tell that. The work will not flow for that reason. I feel ups and downs. I do not want to record only the good and pleasant feelings. That would not be honest. I will also sound like a whining fool frequently. That is because sometimes I am. Don't think of me as a wuss. Do what I did, then think of me as a wuss.*

*Yes, I am very angry. It may be an inherited thing, but I think it has more to do with what I have had to endure in the past few years, and what I have given up in order to apply for this experience that I have endured. I actually paid for the college and medical school. It was tough, but reasonable. The residency in surgery was not reasonable. Nobody promised me that it would be. Life is not fair, residency is not fair. This was a good lesson to learn; you just get a rawer version of this lesson and exposure to it a little earlier in life than the rest of your friends that went into business, etc.*

*Writing this will provide me with a catharsis, and a record of my life that my kids can read about. I must warn you that I am just coming off of the Trauma Service and frequently may lapse into a posttraumatic phase of anger, the editor will probably squeeze that out though, and I can keep the original here on my computer at home.*

*From catharsis to free association. Does a surgeon become like a surgeon (you know the personality type) because of the nature of his training, or is he attracted to the profession because of the way that he is? This latter statement seems more accurate.*

# 10

## College: The Marathon Begins

Total Years:   1-4 (1983-1987)............18-22 years old
Salary/Debt:   Merit Scholarship, no debt
Hours:        Like any other college student with a ton of hours

This may be the most insecure time of all in the training of a surgeon. It is a time when it is decided whether or not you will be a doctor. It is an all-or-none type of situation. I remember a friend asking me.... "what do they call the guy that finishes last in his medical school class?"

"Doctor."

Getting into medical school was a very intense and competitive process, but I was up to the task.

I guess that you could say that I was a little naive leaving Titusville. I had always been a very good athlete and a very intense guy with anything that I pursued. I was giving up golf and flying, two things that I had loved to do, and had worked my butt off to become adept at. I pumped gas at the airport after school and during the summers in college and put all of the money back into my flying lesson account. As a second job, I picked up range balls at the course and hung out at the golf course the rest of the day.

A characteristic that probably helps me with my job today is the ability to focus on one thing for prolonged periods of time. These can be frustrating characteristics if you are trying to be that person's parent, or wife for that matter. This single-mindedness is often needed to get you through the 15 years that I have spent in the higher education process in the pursuit of a license to do cardiothoracic surgery.

Another saving grace that kept me from being a complete nerd was that I was routinely beaten by my older brother Chip (for no good reason) and my parents (for good reason). I am also proud that I was too busy to watch Star Trek and play Dungeon's and Dragon's, and too poor to play Nintendo. Overseeing all of this were my parents, who knew the right track, and kept me on it.

*Losing the Green Hat*

*I grew up in Titusville, Florida. It was a very safe place to grow up. I spent all of my time at the golf course. I became quite good. I was a scratch golfer in my late teens and thought about playing professionally. I also wanted to be a Harlem Globetrotter as a younger man. Same odds, in retrospect.*

*Golfer before golf was cool. There was nothing else to do in Titusville.*

*I am a natural.*

*I thought that I was a natural. Playing just a little bit less than constantly took my game apart, piece by piece. Naturals keep playing well. I slowly fell apart.*

*I am not a natural.*

*I began playing golf when I was ten. My younger brother Lee followed me into the game. He was four. We had tournaments in the back yard with wiffle balls. It was the Frog Club Open every weekend. I dug holes all over the yard. The bushes that my mom tried so diligently to preserve were the hazards.*

*We were the hazards to mom.*

*Lee was very small until he was around ten years old. I was his teacher. I was his older brother.*

*He began to break away when I entered college at the Florida State University. I left him alone. I left him alone just as the folks were splitting up. These were very hard times.*

*I went away.*

*I gave him my Masters hat the day that I left for college. He was 13.*

*"I am going to come back and take this from you."*

*I did.*

*"Beat me and it is yours."*

*He could not. He was too small. I was still shooting in the low 70s.*

*He grew. He still could not take me. I was playing in the mid 70s, with slippage into the 80s with primal temper tantrums, organic chemistry, and spray-mode tee shots.*

*He was coming.*

*I was going in another direction.*

*He wanted the green hat. I wanted to spend time with him. Losing the hat was not going to happen. That was not as much of an issue.*

*We had played the back nine first that summer afternoon. I shot 39. Lee shot 39. He stood around 5 feet tall. He was 14 and ready for the transition.*

*I was one up as I stepped onto the tee at the ninth hole at Royal Oak Country Club. It was a 425-yard dogleg left. I was wearing the green hat.*

*Spending time with Lee? Leaving him alone in Titusville? Big brother buried in chemistry 300 miles away?*

*Screw him.*

*The grip...The stance.*

*This is real. Half big brother, half future heart surgeon/competitor. Now just competitor.*

*Crack.*

*Spray-mode 285. A straight drive on a hole that moves left.*

*Out of bounds. Six.*

*The hat was his.*

*Losing was a relief. I felt like a proud father.*

*I would win it back on occasion. It was fun for about a year. The matches heated up. He kept growing.*

*The matches begin to matter more to me than to him.*

*He goes to college and becomes a professional golfer. I go to medical school. Never again to take the hat.*

*I carry him with me every day, to the present moment.*

*This is what I have been doing Lee. You are your own man. You know how proud I am of you.*

*Don't throw that hat away. There is always that cush private practice job, a house on the golf course, and one hot day when you and I are "just out for a round of golf."*

I studied very hard and in an insecure, very worried fashion during college. It was my goal to get As in Organic Chemistry, and I accomplished that goal. It was my goal to get into the best medical school possible, even if it meant getting one of the out of state spots. I succeeded, to my own amazement, by being accepted to the Bayview School of Medicine. Only around seven of the class of 160 were from out of state.

Overall, this was a very good four years, although some of the things that I gave up hurt at the time. I wanted to be a heart surgeon, but there was no specific plan other than that. It sounded good, and certainly was a challenge.

I was 22, still young enough to see my abs.

# 11

## Medical School

Total Years: 5-8 (1987-1991)............22-26 years old
Salary/Debt: No salary, $80,000 debt
Hours: Like any other college student with a ton of hours x 4
Pay Rate ...........................................$0

The early years of medical school were a time to do the things that I felt that I had missed out on in high school and college. How much can you learn about life before actually getting serious about a career in cardiothoracic surgery?

My financial strategy was not the greatest. Too bad that they gave you your loans all in one lump sum. I spent a long winter staying in a basement apartment, not able to pay the rent and not having power. It really hurt when the phone went down and the hard freeze set in. It was very cold in the apartment.

I learned many ways to stay financially afloat during the more lean periods. I had a Chevron card for gas. I learned of the power of the "Chevron Food Mart." I went a month on Coke, chips, and "Ruth's" packaged sandwiches. It was my own damned fault.

### Taking my first History and Physical

*Where do you go to practice your History and Physical examinations? The Veteran's Hospital, of course.*

*The sign on the front of the hospital says "Quality Care for America's Heroes." The last two words of that phrase are correct.*

*The whole VA experience is funny, but not funny at all.*

*These guys are members of the last generation in this country that had balls.*

*You are the funny ones, you snotty nosed little play doctors. I got shot in the head by a Jap. You have to go home early to watch an episode of "Friends" with your wine tasting sissy buddies.*

*I suppose we were fighting to allow you to have such an insulated existence.*

*Go ahead and take care of me. I am poor. I do not have much of an education. I may or may not be able to tell if you are a good doctor.*

*What does it matter? I do not have a choice anyway.*

*The VA is where the residents are given more freedom. Fortunately, they are watched very closely by the attending physicians at Bayview. That is not the case everywhere.*

*The responsibility falls even harder on the resident at the VA Hospital. Freedom comes with that price. You are a resident. Do the patients in this hospital deserve resident-level care?*

*My first History and Physical Examination comes at the VA.*

*The patient is seventy years old. He is sitting in his bed with the newspaper in his lap.*

*I am very nervous. There is the patient, and there is the medical student reading the history and physical question list. Two separate entities.*

*There are so many variables: wear your new white coat, iron your new white coat, find the hospital, find the patient, buy a stethoscope, find a place to park.*

*I begin with the reading of the questions. The list and the patient still very separate.*

*"Any cough?"*

*"Yes."*

*"Have you coughed up any blood?"*

*"Yes."*

*Is he going to cough it up here while I am talking to him and start dying?*

*A third plane of existence opens up. The list, the patient, and self awareness (of your incompetence).*

*The pain of the question-reading session increases as the encounter wears on.*

*I am sick of it. He is sick and sick of it.*

*I look around the room. No one is here with us. Plan B.*

*"What's wrong with you?"*

*The first two planes fuse. Patient and list are united.*

*He begins to tell me his story.*

*I thought at the time that I was cheating. Doing it wrong. It turns out that I was doing it perfectly.*

*Just shut up doctor. Listen to the patient. Let the patient tell you what is wrong with him. He will. Every time. Just shut up.*

*The patient continued to tell of his woes. I sat there and listened.*

*List and patient together. Self-awareness present.*

*He keeps talking.*

*Is this guy lonely?*

*Have I opened Pandora's box? What time is it?*

*Is this guy lonely? What time is it?*

*Self-awareness takes charge. The out of body experience begins as he continues to talk of his dead wife and children that will not visit him.*

*Is this still a History and Physical? Maybe I am better off being some sort of a counselor.*

*No. They don't make enough money. What time is it? Is anyone watching me?*

*Hmmm. What's in the news? I begin to read the paper in his lap.*

*The list is gone. The patient is rambling on about something that I cannot hear because I am orbiting in outer space.*

*"Hey! Are you listening to me?"*

*"Yes sir"*

*Five more minutes pass and I give up.*

*"Thank you sir. I need to examine you now."*

*"Okay." He takes the gown off of his chest as some sort of conditioned reflex to the stimulus of a resident holding a stethoscope.*

*I guess I will start with his chest since he is pointing it at me.*

*The most thorough and disorganized examination in the history of medicine ensues (save the rectal exam, which was cleared for exclusion by another check-the-room head fake).*

*"Thank you sir, and good luck."*

*As if to echo the above commentary on the predicament of the veteran patient and his green helper doctors he says, "Would you like the paper son?"*

*"No thank you sir."*

I worked out instead of studying. I made a D in Correlative Pathology. I was in excellent physical condition. My parents had no idea that I was on the edge of failing out of medical school. The other students were starting their clinical rotations. I had to come home for a summer because I was ineligible to take Part 1 of the Board Exams due to the D in Correlative Pathology. I was in excellent physical condition. This was one of the low points, and also a time when I saw the status that a doctor held, and how much losing that privilege means.

I went back to Bayview after that long summer and passed my makeup exams in renal and musculoskeletal pathology. I also passed Part 1 of the boards with flying colors.

The clinical rotations started that fall, now that I was eligible.

*Learning How to scrub my Hands*

*Washing your hands is a big deal in surgery, as is infection. Infections in surgical patients cost the hospital untold amounts of money. To quote a heart surgeon-friend of mine that I recently worked with..."Bacteria are very small, so small in fact that we cannot see them."*

*Our surgical rotation begins with a lesson on how to effectively scrub our hands.*

*We receive a lecture from an older scrub nurse. She has an "AITF" (ass in the front—implying that you pull up a chair in front of her rather than behind her when you are gentleman enough to offer her a chair).*

*My mind wanders. What is an AITF? Is that fat? Is it extra intestines? Is it a spinal column abnormality?*

*Do you pull the underpants up over the AITF (grandma), or do you swing them underneath?*

*It is a pooch. A pooch and a Prince Valiant haircut.*

*That is what I recall. We must learn from her.*

*She looks weather-beaten.*

*Does she have a separate agenda in volunteering to do this? Is she trying to get to us before we become egotistical doctors? She has us for sure.*

*"Keep your hands in the air. Don't touch anything. Let the water run down to your elbows. Don't touch that. Stop. No. Scrub for ten minutes with the first scrub. Then scrub for five minutes with each ensuing scrub."*

*Am I tough enough for this?*

*"Superman wears a hood and there are never infections in his cases."*

*What time is it?*

*An atom bomb goes off in her underpants, transforming her into dust particles and ending this session.*

*"We will tell you what to do and where to go in the OR. Don't move if we tell you to stop."*

*Control trouble? Hitler in scrubs? Doctor hater? Left by doctor after he finished his residency?*

*"Don't touch the scrub nurse's Mayo stand. Stop when we say stop and you will be okay."*

*You said that. What time is it?*

*"Make sure that your hands stay in the air, high above your elbows."*

*Elbows and hands are connected. This old nurse naked in knee high Go Go boots. What time is it?*

*"That will be all. You may now report to your Chief Surgical Resident for your rotation."*

I made major academic improvements in the second half of medical school, ending my last 4 rotations with As. I had nearly completely overhauled myself in the clinics. It was very rewarding to see that I could actually be good at taking care of patients. Being good started a vicious cycle of my wanting to do the thing that I was good at. It was not golf anymore; it was saving lives (or at least taking part).

OB-GYN Expert to the Poor
We clearly have a problem in health care....

"I know you ain't gone stick your hand in my cat!!!!!"
"Uh, yes......"
Evil Aunt Esther stare...changing my frame of reference.
"Uh, no ma'am."
I know you ain't sticking your hand in my cat!!!!!

It was a reasonable place to start when you are the Ob-gyn expert for the poor. I caught the babies when and wherever they shot out (dead or alive).

My chief resident found a part of a potato and the plant that it had spawned in the vagina of a rather obese lady with non-specific complaint of "itching in my neighborhood." We seemed to be getting the first crack at what HMOs are calling primary care.

I recall the "terrarium" that came with each box of Super Sugar Crisp Cereal. You put soil in the clear plastic container, added seeds, and left it in the windowsill. The plant would grow in about seven days.

This was a comparable situation in which she was the terrarium, the seeds were the potato, but I never met the "Sugar Bear" that shoved it up there.

During my fourth and last year of medical school, I rotated on the Cardiothoracic Surgery Service with The Holy Ghost. He had been called the "best surgeon that I ever saw" by perhaps the greatest surgeon that ever lived, the man that pushed our medical center ahead...The Father.

I took a good look at the life of a cardiothoracic surgeon. The life of a cardiothoracic surgeon is not easy. Can you achieve balance? World famous heart surgeon on one side, somebody that your children recognize and do not resent for working too much on the other. To quote a Japanese heart surgeon's perception of the life of an American heart surgeon:

*American heart surgeon have very interesting rife.*
*He work very hard. Reave first wife after she support him for 15 year.*
*Then he work very hard. Make rots of money. Get new very young*
*wife and have very large house. Very interesting!*

I liked what I saw during that rotation. I jumped ship and took another spot for my cardiothoracic surgery fellowship. This was partly because I had been there so long, partly because the fellows did not get enough independent experience in Bayview's cardiothoracic OR, but mostly because The Big City University has the best cardiothoracic surgery training program in the country.

The fellows are sometimes frustrated by the amount of "watching" that they do in the OR at Bayview. A former fellow told me that the second assistant would spend time focusing his headlight (that he normally wore on his head for the purpose of providing lighting on the heart) on one spot on the attending's operating gown, hoping to catch him on fire during long cases that he has to watch. Other fellows will focus their headlight on a mole that exists on a certain attending's neck at Bayview, hoping that it will be transformed eventually into a full blown malignant melanoma.

It was a great experience to see the best perform. The Holy Ghost has the confidence to operate on his own relatives. He once said that he wanted the best for his own father's surgery, so he did the operation himself. He always has an impressive line of people that follow him around the hospital. He also has a stockpile of secretaries that feed off of the residents that screw up the patient list.

My best accomplishment during this time was meeting Alison at a random party in her hometown. I was meeting a friend in the city to go out and spend some well-deserved stress release.

It turns out that I was walking into a very new situation. My friend ended up having to go to a party on that day that I was coming to town. She asked me if I wanted to go. I said okay.

One rented tuxedo later I found myself at the most exclusive club in The Big City, at some sort of post debutante function. Rented tuxedos were in the minority. So were the shiny shoes that go along with them (that I was wearing). I was seated at a table with some group of guys that all knew each other very well. The question comes to me "who are you?" in the form "what do you want to do?"

All that came to mind was the Herzing Trucking Institute (with the cones in the parking lot). "To Hell with you" came in the form of the statement "I just want to drive the big ones."

An approximately 5 second silence was fortunately broken by an attractive girl's spontaneous laugh...she got it.

I was introduced to Alison, my future wife. It was love at first sight. She wore a beautiful green dress and had black hair with a beautiful smile.

I gained confidence as the mixed drink tickets gave out. I was bartering with the bartender to trade beer tickets for mixed drinks. That was when Alison made the decisive move and handed me her date's mixed drink tickets. There was a good chance. I asked her for her telephone number when my date was in the bathroom. She told me her name and that I would have to remember it and look up the number.

That was all that I got that night. It was worth the trip to the club after all.

Things progressed quite quickly from that point. Alison made a very brave trip to Bayview City on Martin Luther King Day. I could not leave town because I was on an internal medicine rotation. I had set her roommate up with my roommate, who proceeded to pull out of the deal. She came anyway. Thank God. This trip represents the biggest step that ever happened in my pursuit of cardiothoracic surgery, and indeed happiness.

Sleep is good

I really liked Alison, as evidenced by my rotation at a hospital in Atlanta. She lived in Athens, 80 miles away. I stayed at her place many nights, but would get up at 2 AM to get to my job in Atlanta, where I had to be running at 0430 or 5 AM.

I went out on the town in Athens, which many "mornings" left me refreshed with 1 or 2 hours of sleep. There are some levels of fatigue that even coffee cannot overcome.

At least there was not much traffic on the road during those hours.

Alison's parents are also two of the finest folks that I will ever know. They embody the word class. They know everybody in The Big City but you would never know it when they meet you.

My father in law was responsible for my first contact with Dr. Sternalpunch. Dr. Sternalpunch is a very big and bold man with an extremely strong personality that was friends with my father-in-law in college. He was a lineman and captain of the football team. He was now a Professor of Cardiothoracic Surgery at The Big City University.

My father-in-law spoke so highly of him, telling me that I should give him a call. He said that he was a very down to earth guy and that he could give me good advice about my future.

*First Contact with Dr. Sternalpunch*

*The mixed up little student sailing around with the breeze meets a Panzer tank.*

*"Your momma in law tells me that you are at the top of your class, is that right?"*

*"More towards the middle sir." ...like the low end of the middle.*

*"Son where are you applying?"*

A list of small, non-university, private hospitals followed. The list included a private hospital in The Big City Baptist Medical Center. It is a small time competitor of The Big City University and also was conveniently in my future wife's hometown.

*"Don't apply there, Baptist sucks. Don't apply to some place where you want to live, that's stupid. I thought about it, you ought to go to Parkland. Go there and bust your ass. You need to be the smartest and the most hard working resident that there ever was."*

*"Yes sir."*

*"Bye now."*

I guess that I just took that conversation in for further processing. It seemed right, but a little harsh. I was worried about that 100% divorce rate that Bayview was sporting (per the other applicants).

Dr. Sternalpunch, like Superman, had spoken the truth.

I matched into a 5-year surgery spot at a private program with the help of letters from Superman and The Holy Ghost at Bayview. I would go on to that somewhat less than stellar program, suffering perhaps from a touch of the fear mentality, but having at least heard the truth (for future reference).

Alison and I were married at the very end of medical school. Married is also an understatement. Our minister looked me in the eye and talked for about 10 minutes in front of around 1000 of The Big City's finest folks.

Yes, we were married. We had a wonderful reception at the same place where I met Alison. It was an amazing sight to see. My friends still comment on this huge ball of shrimp that was in the back room. Then I took her to that little private surgery program in the hotlands of Florida. Perhaps the most generous thing that Bobby and Del did was to let me take their daughter without a word of advice.

We revisit the two sides of reality, fear and love. Going away and pursuing an easier program to avoid divorce was a step in the fear direction. I was taking it. I will bet you that my in-laws knew that we were smarter and better than that. But they also knew that we would learn, and they never spoke until I spoke first. I know that now, and appreciate that.

Overall, medical school represented another very good four years. Mostly personal progress, professional progress came from conquering myself first. I still wanted to be a heart surgeon.

I was 26, still young enough to hope for a rally and see my abs.

# 12

# First Year of General Surgery Residency: The "July Syndrome"

Total Years:    9 (1991-1992)................27 years old
Salary/Debt:    $26,000 per year; $80,000 debt
Hours:          Every second to third night in house; 100-130 hours
                per week
Title:          "Second Assistant Wound Bitch"

        Gross Pay Rate ........................$4.35
        Net Pay Rate ...........................$3.85

Don't get sick in the early summer if you can help it. They may find you. They are the rookiest of the rookies. They are the new doctors. Only the veterans are safe. You can't kill a veteran.

There was an intern that I will never, ever identify, mostly because I do not know his or her name. I will use the male default. He came from another state. A human that I did or have worked with was one of his good friends. This has to be the best example of the "July Syndrome" that I have ever heard of or seen.

The normal value for sodium in the blood is around 142 meq/liter. A patient had a value of 122...prompting the intern to call his professor and ask for the best course of action. The educated one's response was to "give him some salt." Such prophetic words.

The less informed but eager intern, suffering from the dangerous combination of power in the absence of knowledge proceeded to dissolve a salt shaker full of "salt" in the patient's IV with the aid of a nurse. It was really hard to get it to dissolve after the first shaker full, so the nurse helped him stir it as it was infused into patient's IV. This was almost a pure saline infusion that was pushed into the patient. A lethal level of sodium in the blood is around 160 to 165. The patient's sodium was around 350 when he.....died.

My first year was spent at the Florida Private Hospital. My title was "intern," synonymous with a first year resident, in the field of general surgery. I had been accepted for a five-year position. I worked from 100 to 120 hours per week. No kidding. I wish that I were.

I want to describe my working hours in the most objective way possible. I woke up at 0600, and was at work by 0630. I was on in-house call (staying in the hospital overnight and putting out "fires") every second to third night. It seemed closer to every other night. I would spend the night in the hospital taking trauma call, which was very busy. I rarely slept on call nights. Things were just too busy. The next day I would go right into another busy day taking care of patients and doing cases. I would make it home usually around 6 or 7 PM. This meant that I was awake for 36 hours straight. This went on for one year. Couple the hours with a pay scale that works out to around $4.35 per hour and the stress of dealing with lives and not really knowing what to do much of the time and I think that you have the hardest job in the world.

The difficulty of my job took its toll at home. Alison had to deal with what was left of me when I would return home. It was a very difficult time, but we approached it as a team. No one can imagine what it feels like to go through those hours and that level of stress for a year. Even today when Alison tells me about something that we did during that year, I cannot recall it. I have literally blocked out the entire time; I was just so damned tired.

*My first Central Line*

*The central line is an IV that is placed either in the neck into the internal jugular vein or under the clavicle into the subclavian vein. Placement of these catheters is one of the first things that a first year resident (intern) is asked to do.*

*The risk of the procedure is lung puncture and subsequent collapse (we call it giving the patient a pneumothorax). It is best to avoid this complication early in your residency. It is bad for the patient, and it is bad for you. Then again, they say that you "have not done enough central lines if you have not dropped a few lungs."*

*The central line comes in a sterile box.*

*The patient is lying in his bed, head down, feet up. That makes the veins bulge. A better target.*

*You draw up the lidocaine.*

*"A little pinch, Mrs. Smith." Surgical "pinches" are more like punches, and they get worse as time goes by. We get used to pinching. The patient is getting one of his first pinches. You still have not ever been pinched.*

*"Ouch!!!!"*

*"I'm sorry."*

*Not sorry. Scared of dropping your lung. Tired. Not sorry.*

*"Lots of numbing medicine."*

*In goes the needle under the collarbone (clavicle). The patient jumps when the 3-inch needle hits the periosteum (outer layer) of the clavicle.*

*"Ouch!! Are you almost done?"*

*"I'm sorry. Here's some more numbing medicine."*

*The best "numbing medicine" is to hit the vein on the first try.*

*Another dig into the shoulder. Into the vein, through the back wall, into the artery. Blood shoots back. Way too red to be the vein.*

*"Damn."*

*"Did you get it yet?"Says the wiggling patient.*

*"Hold still please, almost there."*

*Sweat.*

*Another attempt at manhood, or punt to the Chief Resident? Risk dropping the lung?*

*Go for it.*

*The dark blood of the vein is hit on the third try. Relief.*

*The wire is fed through the needle, across the vein, into the heart. You know that it is there because you see the rhythm disturbances on the patient's monitor.*

*"Are you doing okay?"*

*She is better off than you are right now.*

*The needle comes out. The skin is nicked with a blade to make a hole for the central line.*

*"Ouch!!! Do you know what you are doing?"*

*"You are doing great, Mrs. Smith. Hold still."*

*While I practice on you.*

*The central line is pushed gently over the guide wire.*

*Success. Relief.*

*"Let's get a chest x-ray for line placement please."*

*We'll put off the term saved for later. Another one not killed.*

Most of my time was spent taking care of trauma patients. Florida Private Hospital was a Level One Trauma Center (a center that treats the worst trauma cases). We had a lot of difficult trauma cases from the city and its surrounding counties. Many interesting cases passed my way.

We were called to respond to a 20 year-old boy in his jeep that had hit a train broadside. Normally the train hits you. This guy just sort of charged a train. Physical exam revealed a full body tan and a metal ring (presumably for improved staying power) around his privates that I have to assume was already there. Somewhere there is a proud set of parents.

Perhaps the worst situation was the young father who had been drinking excessively and accidentally backed over his 1 year-old child. The child's chest was partially crushed. We lost the child's vital signs in the trauma room and had to perform an emergent thoracotomy (opening the chest) in the ER. This was all done while the father was busting into the operative site demanding to get to his son.

"Uh, yes sir, this is your run-over son's smashed heart and bleeding lungs.....any questions? Perhaps you could step outside into the waiting room rather than attacking us as we try to save your son."

The father and the entire trauma team were maced. That makes it harder to work on the heart. The child died, and would have died anyway. I know what the father did was horrible, but it could not be worse than the way he must have felt that night when he was alone.

There is always someone sticking something up their or someone else's rear end. I was awed to see a small beer can on a pelvic x-ray in a patient with the typical vague complaints and strange affect. This was my first run in with the problem of rectal foreign bodies; it would not be my last.

*Enter Leroy*

*We lived in an apartment that was on a big lake. We had a small boat that we bought with wedding/furniture money.*

*I bought Alison a Scottie. He was on sale at a strip mall pet store. We named him Leroy. He was our first child. Leroy and I would go out in the boat when I had the chance. Leroy loved to stick his nose to the wind and sit at the front of the boat. He also liked to slip into the lake for a swim. Those were very good afternoons. They allowed me to relieve the stress that accumulated during the 40 hour shifts filled with the stress of horrible clinical situations mixed with my own inexperience and fatigue.*

I spent my first year as a categorical resident (meaning that I had a five-year spot) in general surgery at the Florida Private Hospital. The program was not much in comparison to Bayview. I had made the mistake of going there because I thought that I would have a better life there with my family. Bayview's 100% divorce rate (as advertised by the guys on the interview trail) loomed large in my mind. As it turns out, there is no such thing as a good life as an intern in general surgery, and you might as well be in a respected program.

I did learn a fair amount of critical care in the intensive care unit (ICU) during that intern year. I learned some of the signs and symptoms that meant that a patient was ready to be moved out of the ICU and go to the regular patient floor. One sure sign was exhibited by the guy that somehow had the presence of mind, coordination, and social grace to direct a 14 inch stool log into the narrow mouthed bedside urinal that was hanging on his bedside. His successful aim was a 100% marker for successful transfer from the unit.

While I am throwing out these critical care "pearls," I must mention another "law" of the ICU. A definite marker for a bad outcome was the "scrotocephalic index." This was the ratio of a the size of the scrotum to the size of the patient's head. When the scrotum outgrew the head (an index of >1.0) the mortality for that patient was 100%. I never saw this universal law broken during my time at Bayview.

Perhaps the worst thing about being an intern is not knowing the limits. You do not know the worst that things can be, nor do you know what the best is. You do not know the least or the most work that you have to do to do a good job. The work seems endless. This instills a sense of insecurity and despair. When you get called to see a patient in respiratory distress on the floor, you really don't have anything to go on, and for a while early in your residency, you really don't know what to do. The most energy is expended during the first year because you are confronted with so many new variables. Variable reduction and constant production is the name of the residency game. An enormous amount of energy is required to create constants. I probably work over 100 hours per week now, but the constants are in place for the most part. The variables do still come, but on a daily basis, not by the minute. Some of the constants (like Tylenol phone calls from the nurses in the middle of the night) begin to piss you off. The transition from variables and confused to constants and pissed off is a gradual one. There is no happy median transition period where you would be hypothetically at peace.

I will review some more highlights of the intern year that stand out in my mind. This passage was written during the pain of my intern year in surgery:

*We work an average of 120 hours per week, but our pay stubs read that we were paid for 80, at the smoking rate of $4.50/hour. I would pull home $1800/month net, $2200 gross. I calculate that to be a very low rate. Is this legal? Does anyone out there give a damn? Why do I make less than the nurses or the biker girl at the Chevron Food Mart that sells me coffee on the way to work? I have had the less than minimum wage joke, or the phrase "do you ever go home?" used on me probably 100 times. Tee hee hee. It isn't funny. Doctors should take care of their own. Nobody else in the business or government world is. All of the fatigue does nothing but impede performance, and those who have written papers to the contrary are full of the stuff that they operate on. If doctors do not look after their own, then good students are not going to want to do it anymore. Hello mediocrity.*

My experience in Florida was not without some interpersonal challenges. It seems that I really did not like one of my Chief Residents. He worked me over on my role as the "Second Assistant Wound Bitch" one too many times....I again request your empathy as I list the view of a very tired intern.

*...He is probably jealous that my wife is hot and in the Junior League, and does not care much about it or even need to try; and his wife is fat, bitchy, not in the Junior League and really cares about that. I did not think that there even was a Junior League in Florida. I made 86% on the American Board of Surgery In-Training Exam (ABSITE) and he made a 10. I am a good athlete. He has thick glasses. He looks like the dentist on Rudolph's Christmas. I am in shape. He is short. I am not. I want to be an academic heart surgeon. He wants to be a general surgeon. I do not want to drink and party with him because of all of the above. He has Freddie Mercury looking mustache. He flirts with everyone, despite his wife (and two kids), I don't because my wife is hot and in the Junior League.*

This "interpersonal crisis" just sort of went away. I have a theory that if you look back at all of the seemingly impossible or unbearable challenges that you face in your life that got better, no quick fix reaction was ever responsible for making that resolution come about. I guess that this is an awkward way of saying that time heals all wounds. I believe that you have to think long term and do what is right, as much as it may hurt in the acute phase, and you will prevail.

Well, that all came to a close. My record is not perfect, but I would stack it up against any resident in the nation. This is evidenced by my matching in cardiothoracic surgery at one of the top three matches in the country in the most competitive and demanding subspecialty in all of medicine.

Looking back, this Chief Resident hurt me when he wrote on one of my evaluations that he did not believe that a career in general surgery was a reality. My Junior League, hot wife, two beautiful children, The Big City University Division of Cardiothoracic Surgery, and the American Board of Surgery beg to differ.

I think about the way that I felt when I read my evaluation from him. I think of the way a young professional or pre-professional must feel. It is for this reason that I reflect on my own motives very carefully before writing anyone a bad recommendation.

*Snook Break*

*There must be some things that God throws in now and then. I get a jolt now and again. This was one of them. I caught a 30 inch snook off of the pier at Sebastian inlet using a live shrimp, then threw him back to the dismay of about ten pathologically tanned, hard core fishermen and their fish wives, all from Ohio, no doubt. I hope that that fish is still alive. It was so beautiful that I really have had no desire to fish since then. As a child, I remember my dad and my golf teacher Van Duesen catching bait and going on an all-night fishing trip to catch snook. They returned empty handed. I was about ten, and I guess that that made a big impression on me, such that I thought that a snook was out of the question. To catch that one let alone one so beautiful, ranks as one of the greatest things that I have ever done.*

I was not very enthralled by the atmosphere at this hospital. It was more of a private hospital than a teaching hospital. The residents were teaching each other how to operate. In the spring of my intern year, the killer blow was delivered. It was the acute event on the chronic that pushed me away.

I remember a case of a patient, 30 years old, two or three weeks postpartum, who was dumped on me in the recovery room after surgery. I was a fresh intern who really did not know what to do with this sick of a patient. She had been very ill with right lower quadrant abdominal pain, delivered her child, then was found at operation later to have a severely inflamed proximal colon. I think that it was a cancer that had broken through the bowel wall and at some point had spilled stool. Nonetheless, she was as sick as hell on that fateful call night when I was told to "look at her" by one of our residents.

I remember the patient being in respiratory distress in the recovery room. She was also as dry as a chip from sepsis, in severe metabolic acidosis, and on wimpy antibiotics. Looking back, I would have assassinated any resident trying to dump something like this in someone else's lap. It is called the Hippocratic Oath. As it was then, I dutifully busted my butt all that night trying to save that young mother.

I spent the night figuring out that she needed to be intubated, how to get someone intubated, then doing it. I figured out what a Swann-Ganz catheter was for, that she needed one, then put it in. I figured out that she was hypotensive (low blood pressure), what an arterial line was for (continuous blood pressure monitoring), and then put one of those in. I figured out that her hypotension was a result of her bacteremia (bacteria in the blood), that there were certain drugs used to treat this, namely neosynephrine, levophed, and epinephrine, then started those with help mostly from the nurses. All the while, I was explaining to a young husband who had only slightly less of a clue than me that she was dying.

I had never felt so alone. The guys on call were busy in the OR with some leg. The attending was on call for all vascular emergencies in the city, and gave me emotional support via the phone. He kept reinforcing that I was doing a good job. He probably expected my upper level residents to be there if I was swamped. The lady survived the night. I had kept her alive.

"Edward Scissorhands by day, Michael DeBakey by night."

When you are the bitch in the hospital, you are extended great powers and independence in the name of keeping the guys up the chain in their beds at home. You are Michael DeBakey (the famous 97-year-old heart surgeon that helped with the operation on Boris Yeltsin). You have a temporary promotion that ends abruptly in the morning when the big dogs return, at which time you abruptly become Edward Scissorhands, killing all which you touch.

Do not try to make sense of this, or justify the transition in roles. Just understand that you are the bitch, and deal with it. You can suppress the anger, only to spit it back out years later as a gray hair, an inappropriately sarcastic remark to your son, spasm of one of your coronary arteries five years early; or you can bury it.

The lady died one day later. I still cannot describe what it is like to be in charge of a young woman as she lies dying in front of you, and not know what to do. I will never forget. I came home, and told myself that I did not want to be a part of that program anymore. I remember getting home and my wife and her mother Del asking how my night was.

"It sucked, to be honest."

In retrospect, I did everything right that night. Knowing all that I know about taking care of sick patients, she did not have a chance at the time that I came into contact with her. If there was a failure on any-one or anybody's part, the last one was me. I stepped in and took the wheel of the Titanic. Not only had I done my best, but I had done what was medically as well as ethically right. I felt so terrible at the loss of a young woman with a new child. Then the family of the one that I tried to save sued the hospital and everybody on the chart. I was on the chart. Hold on, I was the one that kept her alive. Are you sure that you meant me? That was it.

*Second contact with Dr. Sternalpunch:*

*"Where the hell are you?"*
*"Uh, Florida sir"*
*"Where the hell are you?"*
*"Uh, The Florida Private Hospital sir"*
*"You need to go to a hard program and bust your ass son. You need to work hard and be the best resident that anyone has ever seen."*
*"Yes sir."*

I think the conversation lasted around 1 minute. Dr. Sternalpunch was probably in between saving lives, but he had taken the time to set his mark on me, and he means everything that he says. I ran with it.

I wrote to the Bayview Department of Surgery under a veil of secre-cy. I told them that I had seen the light. Could I please come back?

"Well we'll just have to see about that," said Superman's secretary.

I interviewed under the agreement that if I did well, I would get a second year spot. If I did not do well, I would have to repeat my first year. I interviewed well, and came in as a second year. I pulled all of this off during a one-week vacation in the spring of my intern year. I returned to my residency program with a spot at Bayview and a bunch of pissed off residents that knew. This was a great and daring move to have made, in retrospect. I had no role models in Florida, the residen-cy was weak. I wanted to be a heart surgeon. I was out of there.

*Alter Ego Golf Dream*

*I got to spend a good deal of time with my younger brother Lee and help him through some rough times in Titusville, which was an hour away from my new job. Lee was still at home, a place that held no future for him.*

*I taught Lee to play golf at the age of 4. We used wiffle balls in the back yard and played for the coveted Frog Club Open Championship. During my surgical internship, Lee would come over hang out with Alison and me. We spent valuable time together water skiing and fishing, sometimes in less than safe weather.*

*Lee and I plotted the course of a new beginning during that time. I was not long for the smaller general surgery program that I had selected to supposedly protect my marriage. Lee was not long for the smaller Brevard Community College where he had already proven himself as an All-American golfer.*

*Lee has since pulled himself up and is on his way to making a career on the PGA Tour. Alison and I pulled ourselves up and went back to Bayview and the "100% divorce rate." There had to be many reasons for our going to Orlando, one of them was not surgical.*

Finally we had made it back to Bayview. Leroy made it as well. He would get shot in the chest by a redneck and then get finished off by a soccer mom in a van (uh ...Exit Leroy...) about a year after we moved back. Bayview had something in store for me too.

# 13

## Second Year of General Surgery Residency

Total Years:    10 (1992-1993)..............28 years old
Salary/Debt:   $29,000 per year; $80,000 debt
Hours:          Varied with service
Title:          "Assistant Wound Bitch"

**Second Year of General Surgery Residency.......Surgical Oncology**

Hours:          Every other night home call; 100 hours per week
To work:        5 AM, Monday through Saturday; 6 AM Sunday
Home:           Average 7-9 PM during week; 2 PM Saturday;
                Noon Sunday

                Gross Pay Rate ......................$5.57
                Net Pay Rate ...........................$4.21

The wait was over. It was time to start at Bayview. All of the things that the other applicants had said about the program and its killer reputation loomed large. This tough reputation appealed to me in a way. Perhaps for the same reason that cardiothoracic surgery appealed to me. It was certainly an opportunity to set myself apart from the pack. I knew going in that it would be tough because of what I had witnessed during medical school. My academic record was now good, and getting better. I was determined to get to the top. I had to give something up to get to the next level. That something was nearly everything as it turns out.

Things started fast. I recall getting that call from The Lamb (this name will fit when you read of his presentation at Morbidity and Mortality Conference in the pages to follow). He ran his patient list quickly to me over the phone. It was like he was saying, "you're screwed, and I don't have the time to hear your reaction." I had come from a trauma hospital where the patients were not nearly as complex and referred. I could not believe the problems that he was checking out to me. I must have had that deer in the headlights look that I notice when my students look at the heart nowadays. I was scared.

I did not sleep that night. We were staying with my friend who was an anesthesiology resident and a good friend from my medical school days at Bayview. I had one of those 'check the clock' nights. These are the nights when Alison comes to my aid. I am my most pitiful on these nights.

Alison gave the standard (and unbelievably supportive) "we don't have to do this." I must say that her sympathy works too. Never mind that we have no finances and I have no real skill. I really do not have a choice, but it helps anyway. Behind every good man is a better woman, case in point. In fact our marriage is such a case in point that it is sometimes embarrassing. I suppose the Irish are lucky after all.

I had to decide when to go to work. I got to the hospital around 0330. I was amazed to see other residents there too. This place was truly different. What time did these people get up? Did they get up? Do they go to bed?

I thought that I was good. I was, in Florida. I was behind here as it turns out. The hours were even worse. As if there were any more time to work, I had been doing around 110 hours per week. I forgot about the very early morning, at Bayview you had to be there around 0430 on the average, and you still had the every other to every third night call schedule. This pushed the hours up to around 120 per week and the pay rate down a little bit further.

Starting your residency can be a very intimidating experience. As I stated earlier, an intern does not know the limits when he begins. He does not know the least that he is expected to know or the maximum amount of time that he has to work. This lack of perspective can lead to wild thoughts of doom.

A good example of "getting started terror" is the first phone call that my colleague John McMahon received as the new intern on the Cardiothoracic Surgical Service of the world's greatest adult heart surgeon, The Holy Ghost.

It was midnight plus 1 minute on the 1st of July. Dr. Marley had signed out his pager to the new incoming target. The call came in from an angry nurse in the Heart Transplant ICU....... "You need to come fix this pacemaker!"

Dr. McMahon described to me the terror of not knowing 1) what building the Heart Transplant ICU was in, 2) why he was getting called at midnight, 3) how emergent a situation this was, 4) how to operate a pacemaker, or most importantly 5) how to fix a pacemaker. This lack of perspective leads to an inner terror that only the lonely surgery intern ever feels. I reiterate that it is the quality of the workload in addition to the quantity that the surgical intern faces that makes it the hardest job on the planet.

By the way, Dr. McMahon must have found the building, and somehow figured a way to fix the pacemaker. After all, he is still at Bayview.

*Mr. Kitty breaks his leg*

*Never buy a cat. You can always just start feeding one. We bought Mr. Kitty because we felt sorry for him at the mall. He broke his leg one-week later when a shelf fell on him.*

*I was at work when Alison called with the financial options. $500 orthopedic surgery for a $17 kitten or the gas chamber.*

*"Don't you kill that cat," I demanded/pleaded.*

*Alison and I shelled out the $500 (1/4 of my month's salary) for a pin that was the size of a toothpick.*

*"Gee, maybe we should have killed that cat."*

*We are softhearted suckers.*

*When you are a softhearted sucker you are supposed to surround yourself with hard people. We married each other, creating a double softhearted sucker.*

One of the first principles that I learned when I came to Oncology was that the air hitting the organs when you open a patient in the OR does not cause the tumor to immediately grow and spread all over the body. This was an unbelievably common belief held by some of the less educated patrons of our state. I probably had to refute that theory to 20 families during my time in Bayview City. Lots of "rasslin'" fans.

The following is a handout that I gave my team when I was a fourth year on the Surgical Oncology Service. The schedule was essentially the same during my second and fourth years.

*Medical Students and Surgical Assistant Students*
*1) Write progress notes in the morning for at least 2 patients and*

*have them signed before morning report.*

*2) Come to morning report at 0630 every morning in the resident lounge of the cafeteria unless otherwise notified by the Chief Resident. Present your patients to the team in the standard SOAP format. Include your plan for the patient based on your patient's progress to that point.*

Having to be at morning report at 0630 and ready meant that these guys, like I had done two years prior, were getting to the hospital around 0430. This means that they were getting out of bed by 0345 if they were quick. Everybody had to wear a tie and a clean white coat. There was none of this "come in scrubs" stuff that is so prevalent at other places and on all of the non-surgical services. It always amazed me that the surgeons were the only ones that did not wear scrubs around. They had to look presentable. This is another aspect of Bayview's surgery residency that appealed to me. Superman was never asking you to do anything that he did not do himself. The only problem was that he was perfect. It is hard to be perfect for any extended period of time.

*3) Peel off to the OR at either The Clinic or University Hospital. You will be notified of the cases that you are to cover on the previous day's afternoon rounds. You should conduct focused reading in preparation for the next day's cases and be ready to answer questions from the attending on the disease being treated surgically, not necessarily the technical aspects of the procedure (The Watching Clause).*

*Watching*

*In other words, prepare not to get to do anything in the OR. I loved the creative solutions that the cardiothoracic surgery fellows had for this non-operative dilemma. They struck back by focusing their headlights on a notorious mole on the attending's skin, in hopes of helping to convert it to a melanoma. Another great passive aggressive time filler was to shine their headlight on the attending's gown in the same spot hoping to start him on fire. This could only be done if you were second assistant or worse. First assistant was the guy who was supposed to be the really intense "watcher."*

*There were some very good watchers by the time they broke into the third year. Inspired by Paul Newman in the movie "Cool Hand Luke," we called ourselves "wound bitches."*

*"You done a mighty fine job with this one boss. The wound looks good sub. Mighty fine. You done a good operation!!...Shakin' the bush*

*boss......" This was our sarcastic protest to the individuals that made us
watch them.*

*What are the potential advantages of watching? You have to be quite
creative to think of positives here. Well, if you are allowed to hold a sucker while watching, and you pass gas, you can suck the noxious gas back
into the canister and protect the attending from any potential atmos-
pheric stress.*

*4) Be in the OR with the appropriate x-rays posted and the patholo-
gy sheet filled out by 0710.*
*5) Learn how to write postoperative orders and postoperative notes.
Follow the following format:*
*Postop order: "ADCVANDISSLN"*
*A (dmit) to The Brain's service*
*D (iagnosis): status post left mod radical mastectomy*
*C (ondition): poor/fair/good*
*V (itals): q2 hours x2 then q 4h, Is and Os, daily weights*
*A (llergies): pcn*
*N (ursing procedures): JP to closed suction, record output.*
*D (iet ): clear liquids, advance as tolerated (vs NPO vs full liquids vs reg-
ular)*
*I (V fluids): LR @ 125 cc/hour (maintenance is 75 for small pts, 100 for
average, 125 for large–have to add for ongoing losses and electrolyte
disorders (no potassium until a diuresis is established)*
*S (pecific meds): cefadyl 1 gram IV q8h x 2 doses, then d/c*
*other meds that the patient has been on*
*S (ymptomatic meds): symptomatic meds (MSO4 PCA pump) no basal
rate, 2 mg IV q 15 minutes, lockout 30mg/4 hours*
*L (abs): as appropriate*
*Notifications: call ho for temp >101.5, 60 >pulse>110, 50>DBP>100,
          100>SBP>160, 10>Resp>24,UOP<30 cc/hour, mental status
          changes, excessive wound drainage or increased pain.*
*Postop note:*

*Preop dx: Melanoma*
*Postop dx: Same*
*Procedure: WLE back melanoma*
*Surgeons: Murrah/Brain/Williams/Bagg (MSIV)*
*Complications: none*
*GETA (vs LSB vs local)*
*Estimated blood loss: 50 cc*
*Total in:        Total out:*

*Disposition: recovery room (versus ICU)*

*6) See pts in The Clinic Tuesday and Thursday: present to attending*
*7) Attend resident conference and grand rounds on Saturday and make formal presentations to attendings at 0900 on Saturday morning. These are crucial. Practice these during the week with the junior residents or the Chief Resident. Presentations should summarize admission H&P, brief hospital course, the day's progress report, and the plan of management for that day. A minimum of 2 should be presented. No reading of notes.*

This Saturday morning thing was called the Circle of Death. The crowd consisted of the General (locked and loaded with the scientific method, he always said, "in God we trust, all others bring data"), The Brain (with his stare, ready to answer your questions with a disappointed look and a question for you), and Dr. Lipshave. Dr. Lipshave was a good guy, but you knew that he was not going to bail you out when things got ugly, and they did.

*8) Be present for evening rounds unless otherwise notified by the CR.*
*9) Conferences: 0700 Tuesday (head and neck-2 WP); 0715 Thursday (Tumor Board-5 S). 0700 Saturday (resident conference); 0800 Saturday (Grand Rounds). 0900 Saturday (Formal Rounds).*

*Junior Residents:*
*1) Sign student progress notes in the morning before morning report. Get the students to write as many notes in the morning as you feel appropriate; they should always write at least 2.*
*2) Come to morning report at 0630 every morning in the resident lounge of the cafeteria unless otherwise notified by the CR. Present your patients to the team in the standard SOAP format. Include your plan for the patient based on your patient's progress to that point.*
*3) Peel off to either The Clinic or UH OR at 0700. Conduct focused reading in preparation for the next day's cases. You will be notified of the cases that you are to cover on the previous days' afternoon rounds.*
*4) Be in the OR with the appropriate x-rays posted and the pathology sheet filled out by 0710. The student should do this but you need to ensure that they make it.*
*5) Teach the students to write postoperative orders and postoperative notes. I suggested the above format. You can teach them any way you like, within reason. Cosign their orders and notes.*
*6) Write or cosign postop checks on all operative pts*

*7) See patients in The Clinic on Tuesday and Thursday: present to attending*

*8) Attend resident conference and grand rounds on Saturday and make formal presentations to attendings at 0900 on Saturday morning. Each student presents at least 2. The remainder is divided amongst the junior residents. We will discuss who is to make these presentations during the week. These are crucial. Practice these during the week with the students. Presentations should summarize the admission H&P, brief hospital course, the day's progress report, and the plan of management for that day. No reading of progress notes.*

*9) Be present for evening rounds unless otherwise notified by the CR.*

*10) Conferences: 0700 Tuesday (head and neck-2 WP); 0715 Thursday (Tumor Board-5 S). 0700 Sat (resident conference); 0800 Sat (SGR). 0900 Sat (Formal Rounds).*

*11) On Thursday morning, the intern goes to 6th floor radiology and helps Dr. Brown carry the films to tumor Board conference. Each JR presents a case at Tumor Board on Thursday morning. Read up on the radiology and chemo studies so as to embarrass the medicine doctors.*

*Chief Resident*

*1) Review the student progress notes periodically. See the sickest patients in the hospital; make sure they don't die. See the pre-op patients on the 11th floor tower and the VA patients.*

*2) Come to morning report at 0630 every morning in the resident lounge of the cafeteria. Provide team with a patient list. Decide upon a plan for the patients. Reconfirm operative assignments.*

*3) Peel off to either The Clinic or UH OR at 0700. Conduct focused reading in preparation for the next day's cases.*

*4) Be in the OR with the appropriate x-rays posted and the pathology sheet filled out by 0710. Confirm that path sheet/x-rays are ready.*

*5) Teach the students to write postoperative orders and postoperative notes. Cosign their orders and notes.*

*6) Make postoperative checks on all patients; ensure that a note is written.*

*7) See pts in The Clinic Tuesday and Thursday: present to attending; run the VA clinic on Tuesday from 1200 to the end of clinic.*

*8) Attend resident conference and grand rounds on Saturday. Ensure that formal presentations to attendings at 0900 on Saturday morning are well done. Discuss who is to make these presentations during the week.*

*9) Be present for evening rounds.*

10) *Conferences: 0700 Tuesday (head and neck-2 WP); 0715 Thursday (Tumor Board-5 S). 0700 Sat (resident conference); 0800 Sat (Grand Rounds). 0900 Sat (Formal Rounds).*

11) *Organize cases for Thursday morning conference. Ensure that radiology/pathology and surgery are coordinated. Present cases at Tumor Board on Thursday morning.*

12) *Run the VA surgical service.*

There was a separation that existed between the attendings and the residents. The attendings were not nearly as approachable as I hear that they are at other medical centers. The old school lives here. No doubt, it works, but times are changing. The quality of applicant will drop, and is dropping. Whether you agree with them or not, the applicants no longer are willing to put up with that anymore. My generation cannot afford to simply let it roll down hill again, as much as it hurt us.

## Making an Incision

*You have prepped the patient for the five hundredth time. You brought him into the room. You turned the music on the radio off. You told everyone to be quiet. You reassured the patient how excellent his surgeon is.*

*When is he going to let me cut?*

*The patient is helped as he moves from the stretcher to the OR table.*

*Anesthesia has placed the IV lines in the preoperative area. Now the patient has a mask placed over his face and is told to take a deep breath.*

*They say that the stuff is oxygen. I am sure that they do not lie to him, but at some point the other gases start to come.*

*The patient nods off.*

*"Go ahead and put the foley in."*

*I place my five hundredth foley catheter into the patient's bladder.*

*I position the patient. Arms tucked at the side. Bovie grounding pad on his buttocks.*

*I tell the circulating nurse, "I am going to go scrub."*

*She will begin prepping the patient with Betadine scrub.*

*I spend my ten minutes at the sink in the corridor that I spoke of earlier. No sign of Superman. Things are very quiet. No sign of my attending.*

*I am back in the room. The nurse hands me a towel to dry my hands.*

*Gown. Gloves.*

*I should double-glove, less risk of The Virus. I am a husband with a young son. I single glove because I cannot feel my hands when I wear two pair.*

*I drape the patient with the usual ritual moves. I wait for the attending to arrive.*

*I have a scrub nurse and a circulating nurse that are both excellent. They have seen 100 residents come and go. They can tell if you are worth your salt within the first minute of your entry into the OR. It has more to do with what mom and dad taught you than what you learned in medical school.*

*The scrub nurse is the one that hands you the instruments. The circulating nurse is the one that runs in and out of the room and gets everything to the scrub nurse.*

*In walks the attending with scrubbed hands. Banter stops. He gowns and gloves.*

*He leaves me on the surgeon's side. "Make your incision from here to here."*

*Cool!.... "Knife" (Not "scalpel." That's what they say on TV).*

*"Incision time" (word to anesthesia who marks the time)*

*Anesthesia calls out... "805"*

*"Thanks." The incision runs from just under the sternum to just above the pubic bone. The incision is a little deep. Blood spills into the field. A little more than you would like.*

*"Lap" (a laparotomy pad is used to soak up blood and clear the field).*

*I incise through the layers of the abdomen with a cautery needle.*

*Skin (epidermis and dermis).*

*Subcutaneous fat (some more than others).*

*Rectus fascia (the tough stuff).*

*Muscle.*

*Rectus fascia again.*

*Transversalis fascia (read about it, hard to see it if you are a rookie like me).*

*Preperitoneal fat (some more than others).*

*Peritoneum (shiny white layer that is the last layer before the "innards" come out).*

*Out come the innards. Let's get it on.*

This was a time that some on the surgical oncology staff thought that I would not make it. I did. Perhaps their doubts were justified, but they underestimated my capacity to work. I was at a much more difficult program. I still had to learn what sick folks looked like; not just what sick folks with a knife in their chest looked like. These cases were more subtle. These were debilitated cancer patients. They have a way of just dying. Their mouths sort of pop open (The infamous "O sign"). Their tongue may pop out of the O (the "Q sign"), and they take that long last breath. Then there is the ultimate, the deadly "fly sign." I have only heard about this, and you will not find it in any medical textbook. It occurs when a fly lands on the patient's protruding tongue of and does not disturb the patient from his obtunded state. The expected mortality of the fly sign is exceeded only by the 100% mortality of the "scrotocephalic index." Few things in nature are 100%. These are two rare examples.

The head and neck surgeon in the Section of Surgical Oncology is Dr. Lipshave. He had a great sense of humor. He has a mild manner about him which he leaves at the OR front desk. At least until recently.

Dr. Lipshave used to deal out some AWs on cases that were not going well. I could describe some of the beatings in more detail; I just don't really feel like it. Suffice it to say that crap rolls downhill, and the junior resident is generally the pooper-scooper. Anything that went wrong in the OR was your fault by proximity.

*Personal Responsibility*

*AWs in the OR and on the wards happen at all general surgery programs, the frequency certainly varies among programs. It is not that it is unfair (though it is), it is a way that they are teaching you to be a vacuum of responsibility. Never mind that the head guy's blaming the others for their problems gives the exact opposite impression. You are expected to be a vacuum of responsibility. A sense of "it has to be done no matter what the situation" is a very positive trait of the good general surgery resident. I like that in particular about our general surgery program. It is better for the patient. They can sense that you are going to stick up for them no matter what. That sense was very strong at Bayview and it came from the top, Superman.*

*"We did all that we could do."......The untold end to that statement is..... "now we give up." The well-trained surgeon never gives up, until his judgment says that it is time.*

Dr. Lipshave's true interest was in basic scientific investigation of the mechanism of carcinogenesis of leukoplakia (that white stuff that accumulates in the mouth of snuff dippers). Certainly I am not the broker of virtue, but people that dip to the point of leukoplakia usually drive drunk, fart out loud in public, hate black people, and think that Skynard is still alive. This is a great group of folks to salvage for our society.

Alison reminds me that if everyone in the world wanted to be a heart surgeon, that there would not be any money or jobs left. I respond, everyone in the world wants to be a heart surgeon, they just can't. My wife then reminds me that I am a pig and that I am lucky that she loves me. She wins.

Overall the Section of Surgical Oncology is academically strong. The Brain (the Director of the Surgical Oncology Service) lets you do the breast and melanoma work. The General (fresh out of Memorial Sloan Kettering Cancer Center) loves to cut things out. The General removes all sorts of cancer, including esophageal resections and Whipple (big resections for diseases of the pancreas or bile ducts) resections. I really admire his ability.

My Chief Resident on the Surgical Oncology Service was Woodrow. He was not around very much, but he had the key ingredients to getting by in this program. Most importantly, he had the love of Superman (Chairman of the Department of Surgery) and he did not take the AWs personally. Things literally just sort of bounced off of Woodrow.

My favorite was the day during the most quiet moment in Grand Rounds (our Saturday morning conference) that Woodrow's chair broke in a pine slashing terror-filled instant. He did not go down, but watching him keep his feet was impressive, so was the look from Superman.

The Brain is the Chief of the Section of Surgical Oncology and the director of the Division of General Surgery. He is the guy that runs the residency. He runs what the trauma crew call the "touchy-feely" half of the Division of General Surgery. Everything used to be controlled by Superman, but he relinquished the residency to The Brain in 1994. This has brought forth a "kinder, gentler" half of the program. What some have called the "dark side" of the Division has been lead by Tidy Goldberg (a former resident and truly masterful strategist that we will visit shortly) since his return to Bayview in 1992.

As I stated earlier, The Brain stares at you when you ask him a question. I waited seven years for him to convert one of those smirks to a laugh. The laugh never came. He is very reserved and methodical. I sometimes suffer from flight of ideas. I tee tee outside whenever possible. He probably does not.

I knew that things were going to be rough between us when my wife and I tried to strike up a conversation at the resident party at the beginning of my first year. I mentioned to The Brain that my wife Alison was from The Big City.

The Brain replied, "Yes, I recently attended an Indian wood-carving festival there."

The conversation froze over that devastating comment. My natural reaction was to laugh at the thought of such a sissy activity. Do people at this festival hike their pants up to their chest and prance around on their tiptoes sipping wine? Maybe I should just branch out and stop urinating outdoors long enough to appreciate fine art.

Nah.

My response, "yes."

From a night in the House at The Big City University Hospital while on cardiothoracic surgery call:

*Death*

*We saw a lot of death on the Surgical Oncology Service. Try being the father of a 21 year old girl, your daughter, that is dying in the ICU on the ventilator with overwhelming Hodgkin's Disease. The sadness of the loss of a person's life equalizes everything. It comes down to one life, be it yours or mine, or the rich guy that talks so well or the redneck with a bad drinking problem with no teeth. We are all connected. It is apparent near our death.*

*What hurts me is the loss of young people. This girl was so young. I saw her today. The music that was playing in the room reminded us that "we are born innocent".... No one is more innocent than the child that dies before she has time to live. What do you tell that mother that is weeping over her bed as the song plays? This is the feeling of overwhelming sadness that I felt today.*

*I also had watched the redneck up on the floor that is a drunk, has liver failure, and a brother that asks me stupid questions daily, all the while wearing his combat boots. Boot guy's brother is DNR (do not resuscitate). He is dying tonight. I feel the same feeling again tonight. Nothing matters (like the song says). I am connected. I see his death and it reminds me of my mortality. It reminds me of our common "biologicness." It is harder to see the young ones die. That is for sure.*

**Second Year of General Surgery Residency.......Children's Hospital**

Hours:          Every other to every third night in-house call;
                125 hours per week
To work:        5 AM, Monday through Saturday; 6 AM Sunday
Home:           Average 8 PM during week; 2 PM Saturday;
                Noon Sunday

                Gross Pay Rate ............................$4.45
                Net Pay Rate ...............................$3.37

Lots of screaming babies. Protective nurses. Snippy pediatric residents that used to be your medical student. A medical student named Carl that casually told me that he had seen the movie "Ex Caliber" 146 times.

Continuous work.

I do not like screaming babies.

The ER. Sewing up screaming baby heads in the presence of yuppie parents asking for a plastic surgeon and getting me.

The ICU. Dying kids. Breaking my heart.

The outside calls. "Yes, good evening, doctor. My son has a seizure disorder, and he ran out of medication."

"What does he need?"

"Dilantin, give me 500 of those. Uh, Tegret...."

"Tegretol?"

"Yes, thank you doctor. Thank you so much. 500 of those."

"Would you like me to renew your son's LSD prescription too?"

"My goodness doctor, you don't think that this is for me?"

*Who shot Leroy?*

*Code Blue......*

*Some redneck shot Leroy in the chest. Alison's friend found Leroy in the front yard in shock. He was rushed to the "dog ER."*

*There's a "dog ER?" I'll bet there is a "dog ER" bill collector.*

*"Your dog has been shot in the chest sir."*

*"With what type of gun?," I asked in between my own little pediatric traumas.*

*"Looks like a 22-caliber," said the vet.*

*"Is he going to live?"*

*"Maybe."*

*He lived. They gave him donor doggie blood. They sucked some more of my own. Is this redneck land or what?*

I'll be back in my fourth year.

"Uh, one last thing before you go. Cody vomited all over himself. Is that bad?."

"I gotta go."

## Second Year of General Surgery Residency.......Dustfart Private Hospital

Hours:          Every other to every third night in-house call;
                100 hours per week
To work:        6 AM, Monday through Saturday; 7 AM Sunday
Home:           average 4 PM during week; Noon Saturday;
                Noon Sunday
Perk:           Every third weekend off, no beeper.

                Gross Pay Rate ...........................$5.57
                Net Pay Rate ...............................$4.22

I had made it through my first rotation at Bayview. Some of the surgical oncology guys had been okay. I felt like I was a bit behind as far as experience with really sick non-trauma patients, but I was a hard worker and would catch up quickly. Superman, whose constant belief in me made my career, had said that he knew that it would be this way. He stood beside me all the while. His support not only helped me in the way that I was perceived in the program, but it also helped me to believe in myself.

Now I was off to the Dustfart Hospital. It was the medical facility for the steelworkers during the city's industrial years. It was located in the old steel town of Dustfart. The patients tended to be very old, since those industrial days were about thirty years gone.

The cases were not the most exciting, but things had a way of popping up.

*ER Thoracotomy*

*During my first week on the service we had an unexpected treat in the form of a gunshot wound to the lower chest that arrived unannounced to our ER.*

*It was an unfortunate 23 year old male. He had been rushed up the hill to our ER, which was the closest facility available. The man lost his vital signs on arrival to the ER.. It was just me, a fresh second year resident, and a bunch of young nurses from Beaver State Community College with these little demeaning cheesecake looking hats on their heads.*

*I had done this before.*

*My approach to the patient was surprisingly cool, given the situation. I walked over to the patient and slit his left chest open.*

*Fifth intercostal space, just under the left nipple.*

*The student nurses could not believe what they were seeing. A couple of them left the room. I don't think that any of them fainted. They all wanted to see the heart after he died, which happened in the next few minutes...at least officially. He was already dead when he came in, I suppose. Another life is wasted.*

*I do not like it when people die. It bothers me. I am not detached like some say you are supposed to be. I want to save them all.*

I was assigned to work with Dr. Wire. He is a very good man. He is a little high strung, leading to his nickname "Barney Fife with a knife." He did a great job in the OR, somehow you just felt like the case was always on the brink of disaster. He kept it that way. He did a very good job, and apathy was not his problem.

In order to succeed on his service, you had to know the meaning of the terms: "up, down, in, over, under, to the side, nearer, closer, superior, inferior, lateral, anterior, posterior, slower, and faster" as they were simultaneously fired at you during any given moment of a case. It could be a little frustrating if greater than three positional terms were fired simultaneously.

One resident stopped in the middle of a laparoscopic cholecystectomy and said "that's it, I'm just not fucking doing it any more." That may have been the best move that he ever made. Dr. Wire is just playing a game, or is just trying to deal with the pressures of living, and has always had the interests of the residents at heart.

One of my first consultations was to see an old fat lady from the nursing home whose backside had essentially rotted off (the medical term is a "sacral decubitus"). She was too fat to get an IV in. So the consult comes down...

"Surgery clinic"

"This is Dr. Murrah"

"Yes, Dr. Murrah, we have a consult"

"Uh, what is the consult?"

"It is for surgery.... Let me read it...uh, sacral decubitus and needs central line placement."

Private God Dammit moment........

Those consults irritated the living dukey out of me. For one, I am sick of chipping dead stuff off of a granny's caboose. Second, it is as hard as Hell to get an IV in these typically round individuals. I was also sick of the fact that the medicine docs would call the clinic and the clinic would call us. I know that that was the system, but it sure made it easier to bestow these shameful consults if they did not have to face us.

Well, by the tenth "surgery clinic" consult of that nature, I had had enough. So I kicked a big wooden door. All that I accomplished was a left big toe that was broken into the joint and made it harder for me to get to granny assrot's bedside. The toe healed after a few weeks. The stupid consults continued.

*Getting sued because you were on the chart when someone died. Having to deal with the baseless accusations. Having the accusations dropped because they were...well, baseless. And moving on. Something is lost.......*

*The third week that I was on call I responded to a patient that arrested in the hospital. He was in for management of an abdominal abscess (pus pockets in the belly) that occurred after a laparoscopic cholecystectomy (gallbladder surgery). He was slated for surgery the next day. He died that night despite IV fluids and antibiotics. I was there to see him die. I had actually seen him earlier that night and had talked about his baseball days in this area. He had played ball with the likes of Willie Mays. We had a good feeling when I left to go to my call room that night.*

*Then he sat up and died. I assume that it was a heart attack. I felt so bad for the family and spent time consoling them. I assured them that there was nothing else that we could have done to save him. It was just a heart attack. They appreciated it all.*

*Then they sued me After all, I was on the chart.*

*I got the letter on the last day of the statute of limitations. Supposedly they do that so that the facts have been lost by that time, and they can reconstruct them in a more favorable way to the client. I may be wrong, but it was the last day possible.*

*The feeling of betrayal is large. The feeling of self-preservation is put off, and maybe that is not smart to not be defensive, but that is how I am. I do not like it when people die. I am here to serve, not to declare my righteousness. Perhaps this will kill me on the stand one day. But I believe that the doctor is a servant to the patient. Arrogance has no place in his work. It is very hard for me to defend myself, though the facts say that I should. Indeed, I did not even operate or take care of this man postoperatively. I was just in the wrong place at the wrong time. That wrong place being the chart where I wrote a progress note.*

*I always look to see how I could have done a better job, and maybe saved his life. There was no way here. Perhaps suing me was a way to help the wife deal with the loss. I have a hard time "playing hardball" and shutting down an old lady in grief. I suppose the lawyers that Bayview provide for me can handle that. I have a harder time dealing with the accusations that they lay on me simply because I am insured by the university and represent a deep pocket.*

*There is something fundamentally wrong with suing a guy in training, unless he is grossly out of bounds and away from the training program's mission. I am by definition, in training. How can I be held to a standard of care if I am not recognized as having mastered it? The demoralization that these suits incur is never recorded. There is no one person to sit over the lawyers that take advantage of these people in grief. There does not seem to be any accountability for their reckless accusations against trainees.*

*The trust that occurs between a physician and patient is severely hampered by the threat of an adverse outcome. I will say now that even if this suit is settled for a minuscule amount out of court, which is likely because I understand that they do not have a case, my name will go down on the National Practitioner's Data Bank as having settled in a lawsuit. My name gets trashed at the whim of some dipstick in BOHICA City (Bohica is a popular term that stands for... "bend over, here it comes again").*

*I have heard stories from the lawyers that defend Bayview's doctors that they receive phone calls from other firms saying "your residents killed our client's husband, we want X amount of money." They say that they know that the attorney has frequently not even opened the chart and is trying to see how much money that he can get for his efforts. A local attorney once told me that one of these lawyers had settled for as little as ten thousand dollars in a case. Settling for such a small amount is hard evidence that they knew that they had no case. They wanted to milk the system for all that it could get. The problem with this "give and take" is that it does nothing but take from me. It takes away from my name. I also have to apply for a job.*

On a lighter note, I was party to a softball being pulled out of someone's rear end while present at Dustfart. It was a good moment for both patient and doctor. I guarantee that there will be no lawsuit from that boy. He might just let this one slide.

**Second Year of General Surgery Residency.......VA Cardiothoracic Surgery**

| | |
|---|---|
| Hours: | Every night home call; 90 hours per week |
| To work: | 6 AM, Monday through Saturday; 6 AM Sunday |
| Home: | average 5 PM during week; 2 PM Saturday; Noon Sunday |

Gross Pay Rate ...........................$6.18
Net Pay Rate ...............................$4.68

Next came the VA Cardiothoracic Surgical Service. The attending was Dr. Neatcoat. He was my mentor during my research years. He is the consummate surgical investigator. He is gifted both in the OR and the laboratory. This is a rare combination.

I had my first operative exposure to cardiothoracic surgery during this time. I love the specialty for the reasons given earlier. Dr. Neatcoat reinforced these feelings for me. He was a gentleman and an excellent clinician.

*Escape from the ICU: I thought that I had seen it all*

*The bypass pump can give you something called "pump head." People act a little differently after being on the pump. Strokes occur, although infrequently. A gentleman/pump head decided to get up and out of bed on his first night in the Cardiothoracic Surgical ICU. He had the breathing tube out, but still had about twenty devices in him, including chest tubes. He broke free with his pump head leading the charge. He was able to drag himself into the next room, foley catheter in the bladder, chest tubes dangling blood; oxygen ripped off of the wall. He was very belligerent and holed himself up in the supply room where the nurses were able to corner him. He was eventually calmed and apprehended. He did fine after that. It was just a surreal sight. He looked sort of like a bleeding alien.*

Other than, no, in addition to, that night, I had a very good time on the service.

I was introduced to the rapidity with which people die in this business.

*Killing People (Sniping the Sniper)*

*Cardiothoracic surgery is very interesting. It is generally done on an elective basis. The patients look pretty good before surgery. They have gotten through their cardiac catheterization. They were found to have three-vessel coronary disease. It is big stuff, but they are ready for it and upbeat.*

*Cardiothoracic surgery is different though. It is sort of like flying a fast airplane. Everything is great until it isn't. There are innumerable steps that can get you. "There is a snake under every rock," says my young professor of cardiothoracic surgery from the Texas Heart Institute.*

*Snakebite. We did a 38 year old former Viet Nam sniper. He was a father of three. He had no targets (none of his coronary arteries were graftable). The arteries were chock full of what looked like old cheese. He was already on the heart-lung machine. His heart would not come off without new bypass grafts.*

*Sorry folks.*

*Neatcoat told the family that dad was not going to make it. I was there to see mom explain it to the kids.*

*Badness. Big surgery, big problems.*

*I have not lived that one down yet.*

*His disease was so bad that he would not have lived very long at all. We just brought things to a head by trying to save him that day. We were the reason that he died that day.*

## Second Year of General Surgery Residency.......The County Hospital

Hours:          Every third night in-house call; 105 hours per week
To work:       6 AM, Monday through Saturday; 6 AM Sunday
Home:          Average 6 PM during week; 2 PM Saturday;
                    Noon Sunday

                    Gross Pay Rate ...........................$5.30
                    Net Pay Rate ...............................$4.01

Down to the County Hospital I went. There was the smell of the place, and then there was the smell of the stinky places. It even smelled worse at times than the 4th floor of the VA by the stairs where the janitor stacks bags of urine and other waste for eventual (I use that word loosely) dumping.

The County Hospital is a good place to take a crack at some

routine and not so routine stuff. It is different from the big University Hospital because the cases are not as referred (they are better described as "dumped"). It is also different from Bayview University Hospital because the patients come in at a more advanced phase. They have not had any previous care. We call this the "natural history" of the disease—what would happen if nobody did anything to something like a tumor for a long time. Natural history cases come when there is poor patient education and/or lack of medical intervention.

I always tried to look at my time at the VA and the County Hospital as a chance to give disadvantaged people excellent health care. The residents work more independently at both the VA and the County Hospital. There is however, excellent supervision at both places. This is actually quite unusual for indigent care at large teaching hospitals in this country. Close supervision by the attendings is one of the things that attracted me to Bayview in the first place.

When you hear about programs where the residents are learning from the residents, you think more in terms of mediocrity. Residents are residents because they are residents. The mediocre teach the student to be mediocre. I had bigger designs for my career. This is independent of the fact that no patient deserves mediocrity.

One of the finer teaching techniques that was used against me by one of my senior residents was the comment that I was guaranteed to receive when I did something dumb.... "Just like a goldfish, every trip around the bowl is a new experience."

Chicken Thursday was a big day in this hospital. There was a good feeling at The County Hospital because the staff all interacted for the common cause of the hospital. The nurses were friends with the doctors, who were friends with the janitors. The cafeteria buzzed with a real excitement when the yardbird hit the serving containers.

The BK Lounge (Burger King) was the only alternative to the cafeteria (which slumped on non-chicken days). You had to fight for the food there. A prostitute once propositioned me at the BK Lounge. She was a stripper at some dance club in town by night. She served Whoppers by day. The proposal made us sick. She was really nasty.

The ER docs were hired guns. Real stinkers. They came from some doctor company, which must have recruited "FMGs" (foreign medical graduates). I once got a consult for a sore toe in a guy that had worn a hole through his shoe. I am a surgeon. That is not normal. Then they would not call for the bad trauma cases. Frequently people would not get a cervical collar after high-speed collisions or ejections from their vehicles. I became disgusted with the system. The ER docs of whom I speak were in sort of collusion with the x-ray technologists to not order many films on patients. When I ordered x-rays of the neck on a drunken high-speed wreck victim (that had been ejected), I was given a great deal of resistance and passive aggression. I had to be the bad guy and get the films. In the morning, they will be gone and I will be the one treating a patient with a broken neck. Many lives were put at risk by some pretty poorly trained guys.

The surgery and medical staffs at The County Hospital were quite excellent. It was those hired guys in the ER that scared me. There were also some good ER docs that were trying to make a difference. I still do not understand why the ER doctors get such a hotshot reputation. They do the shortest residency, and have no patients in the hospital that they follow so that they can learn the natural history of the disease processes that they are treating. These guys usually only work three or four days per week. They are not ultimately responsible for any of the patients that are sick enough to be admitted. They come and go, and as a surgery resident, you stay. You never can seem to nail them down to their stupid decisions. They have already gone home to pursue one of their million hobbies.

I still say that the hard workers win in the end, and you have to be good at something. ER docs tend to be fair at a lot of things, and they never see patients in the hospital or follow up with them in clinic. They just "turf" them. Fair does not cut it when it comes to your son or your wife's care, why should it be any different for someone else's loved one.

I say that these guys need to be regulated. They ought to have to be board certified in ER or another branch of medicine, and not on the run from some place or country. I think that my experience at Bayview was skewed. Hiding doctors tend to gravitate to the # 50 states. They hide in companies that staff the Emergency Rooms.

Dr. Holley was the senior partner at The County Hospital. He used to clear his throat a lot. He was not afraid to do it all in the OR. He says that he would have started doing cardiac pump cases had they not started doing it up the street at Bayview. That's the characteristic confidence that he exuded.

Dr. Holley drove a big Cadillac and was the top dog at The County Hospital. He operated on large ladies and anything else that would move. He used all sorts of things on his wounds like alcohol, tincture of zephyrin, and scarlet red. He always told the incoming resident that he had the best wound healing record in the country, and the wound infection on the case that you scrubbed with him was the first one that he had seen in years.

There was no doubt that he was very strong. I liked him for many reasons. He was confident. He was helping the indigent. He drove a big Caddie. He was not pretty in the OR or anywhere else. He was the real deal, and his patients loved him. He was giving an entire county top-notch care on the limited resources that the county provided for him in their budget.

He recently retired. There is a place for anyone that wants to do some good in this world. You do not have to go out of the country. Just go to The County Hospital and treat them like VIPs. The world will be your oyster.

There were other more junior attendings that I worked with at The County Hospital. Dr. Bubba, as the front of his F-150 truck espouses, is a fine man. He does the job, and has it all in perspective. He always talks about his daughter and son's exploits in the world of little league. He is a proud dad and a very adept surgeon.

Dr. Bubba was trained at Bayview. This was in an earlier era, when you were every other night call in-house for five years, no questions asked. 100% divorce rate. That era was truly harsh. I am a wimp compared to those guys. Bubba was famous for supposedly cutting The Father's finger during a teaching video on cholecystectomy, to which The Father responded "camera off."

Dr. Bubba helped Dr. Holley keep order at The County Hospital in the 1980s and early 1990s, until relief showed up in the form of Supermom.

It is hard to be a guy and do this surgery thing. Try being a woman at one of the nation's toughest places in the 1970s and 1980s. There is a big double standard against women. They are either "girls" if they don't take charge, or they are "too pushy" if they take charge. Well, Supermom has done it very well. She is a mom, a fantastic surgeon, and a wife, that happens to be very nice, and very aggressive. I do not know how she does it. She does it.

You will read about my not having a place to stay near the end of my residency. Supermom offered me her recently passed mother's house to stay in, free of charge.

I will end the second year with a tale of a bizarre feeling that I got that involved a lecture from a former Marine who was chairman of the surgery department at a Midwestern medical center.

We will him call him Dr. Patton. He came to us and told us that there was no evidence that the long hours of our residency impaired our performance when performing critical tasks. It was ironic that half of the people there to see the lecture were bobbing their heads or asleep from being on call. Superman was there in the front row.

The feeling was similar to one you would get if Massa Patton came and spoke to Massa Man and his slaves and told them that he had scientific proof that they were not being treated inappropriately. You could feel the sense of despair and disbelief among the awake "wound bitches" in the audience. "Shakin' the bush boss!!!"

# 14

# Third Year of General Surgery Residency

Total Years:    11 (1993-1994) ...................29 years old
Salary/Debt:   $30,000 per year; $75,000 debt
Hours:          Varied with service
Title:          "Wound Bitch"

**Third Year of General Surgery Residency.........Thoracic Surgery**

Hours:       Every other night home call; 120 hours per week
To work:    5 AM, Monday through Saturday; 6 AM Sunday
Home:       Average 9 PM during week; 2 PM Saturday;
              Noon Sunday

              Gross Pay Rate ...........................$4.80
              Net Pay Rate ...............................$3.63

We were very busy on the Thoracic Surgery Service. There was a new cardiothoracic surgery fellow that was starting his first rotation on thoracic. He was from a much less malignant program and was quite amazed with the whole thing. Dr. Large is head of the Thoracic Surgery Service. He was feared by many (One of my fellow residents gave him the nickname "The Devil," or "La Chupacabra" to the Hispanics), but respected by all. His 6 foot 4 large frame can be quite imposing. He is a man of few words. He trained under The Father, and is a terrific teacher.

Morning Report

The morning report that the new fellow gave to Dr. Large was not going well. There were a lot of "yes sirs" spoken in the ten minutes that it took to run the patient list. Then Dr. Large just hung up on him in the middle of it all. The fellow says, "What the hell do I do now? Should I call him back?"

"No, just wait for about 15 minutes, if he does not page you, call him back at home. I think that someone did that to him when he was a resident."

The beatings continued for 8 weeks. I looked like the golden child in comparison. There is nothing that you can do to get away in this program. You cannot run in the high grass, they have dogs that can get down in there and find you.

*Loneliness and Solo Chest Incisions*

*We got one that I can operate on.*

*It is a trauma patient. He comes from an outside institution with an undrained hemothorax (blood collection in the chest).*

*"Go ahead and open the chest and see what you find."*

*Green light.*

*Wow. Just one room down from The Holy Ghost.*

*Prep. Incision. Blood.*

*Quick check to the nurse and physician's assistant at those moments of indecision.*

*Do it right. Do it wrong. Just do something.*

*I did it.*

*Make a truly independent decision, within the supervision of an experienced attending. This is the best form of training. This was the great thing about Bayview.*

*Make a truly independent decision, no attending in sight, only more residents. Residents teach residents to perform at the level of a resident. Mediocre training. Disservice to the patient. This is the reason I left Florida Private Hospital.*

I had a very good experience on the thoracic surgery service. Things were occasionally tense in the OR. I had a medical student that was the male version of an airhead. Sometimes he would spout out in the middle of a very difficult case....

"Sir, do you think he's going to make it?"

That's the whole point of us being here, stinker.

Silence...

Finally.....a look from the attending that suggested a better prognosis for the critically ill patient when compared with the individual that just threw that one up.

"Yes."

I made it through the rotation. I suspect and hope that the medical student went on to a specialty that involved 1) a stethoscope around the neck ("flea collar," plus or minus little beanie babies hanging off of it); 2) wearing one of those little "waist packs" (full of tuning forks and calipers); and 3) staying a safe distance from sick patients or any other challenges that involved the use of common sense.

## Third Year of General Surgery Residency.........Renal Transplant Surgery

Hours:      Every other night in-house call; 125 hours per week
To work:    4 AM, Monday through Saturday; 6 AM Sunday
Home:       average 8 PM during week; 2 PM Saturday;
            Noon Sunday

Gross Pay Rate ...........................$4.61
Net Pay Rate ...............................$3.49

Superman runs this service. He is Chairman of the Department of Surgery. He followed The Father as chairman. Superman was trained in Boston under Dr. Joseph Murray, the man who performed the first Kidney Transplantation and won the Nobel Prize as a result. Superman was recruited by The Father and has continued to build a tradition of excellence in surgery. He has long been known as perhaps the toughest guy that ever put on surgical scrubs.

Superman is probably the only guy who has the strength to effectively follow The Father. Thanks to these two there is a great medical center at Bayview, and a streak of excellence that is 30 years long.

Superman was born at the Johns Hopkins Hospital in the early 1930s, the son of a prominent physician. He played football in college, and was actually quite good. He is still playing ball with the people and things around him. He is a very good man. He is tough. He is hard as a rock on the outside, soft on the inside. I have seen him rip a coworker to shreds. I have seen him get choked up while introducing an old friend. I have watched him kick a resident's rear end over a mistake made in the trauma room. I have heard of how a loss in the family changed him forever.

He has the rare quality of being tough on the outside and soft on the inside. He is a very able and great role model for me. I am proud to have made it under his time at Bayview.

Superman came to Bayview in the late 1960s and built it into the world's number one center for kidney transplantation. He became chairman of the Department of Surgery and director of the residency program in 1982.

He has a spotless reputation and his integrity is without question. All of the surgery residents are terrified by his presence. He has a real presence about him, a jutting square jaw, along the lines of a Don Shula. He has been known to sport a temper from time to time. But his intimidating presence and the power that he wields in the hospital make tirades rarely necessary.

There are famous AWs (an action that is the result of "opening a can of whoop ass"). Some say that he represents one of the last figures holding up the old school. I say that he represents the best of what a physician and leader should be. If that is the old school, take me back.

Certainly Superman is very tough. He never asked anyone to do anything that he would not do himself, the problem is that he did so much that it was hard to keep up.

Things that you did not do at Bayview, and ever in the presence of Superman:

1) wear scrubs outside of the hospital...ever

2) carry coffee or food anywhere near a patient...ever

3) wear your scrubs in the hospital without a clean coat that was buttoned to the top...ever

4) not shave

5) lie or even hint that you were not on the up and up....death sentence

6) eat or wear scrubs to Saturday morning grand rounds. I don't even know what would happen with that one.

There were certainly many things that any resident that wished to survive would abide by. But these are all things that hold up a higher standard in terms of the patient's perception of the guy working to save his or her life. The rules personally made me proud.

Twice per year, Superman held a formal meeting with the residents that they affectionately termed "steak and chew." The phrase was coined by the residents that served an earlier era at Bayview in

Superman's less diplomatic reign. They give you steak, and chew your ass (when indicated). I do not recall this being a very malignant conference during my seven years of General Surgery. Everybody was glad not to get whooped on, and to get some free food. The threat was there. We would sit and laugh and then Superman would arrive.... silence.

He would go over the issues that were facing the program. He spoke quite slowly and with a clinched mouth. There is a nasal tone to his voice that all of the residents love to imitate.

Then the question would come, "Are there any problems or complaints?"

Silence.

"No problems?...Good."

There was the occasional dork that would say something. Those guys did not do well. It is not that he did not like them for asking a question. It was just that asking a question is a marker for being a dumb ass.

Woodrow once sent out an APB on a patient that he had mistakenly discharged before Superman had seen him on rounds. The State Police found the patient and Superman was able to give him a brand new kidney. That level of commitment impressed Superman. Woodrow reaped the benefit of this action for the rest of his residency.

He loved Woodrow, though he was not necessarily the star resident. Not many understood why he liked Woodrow. I did. It was because he was loyal. He also played ball in high school and had bad knees. That did not hurt.

*Woodrow and the Atomic Clock*

*As the Chief Resident on the Renal Transplantation Service, we had to call him at 0545 every morning except Sunday (God's day of rest). The phone number is 653-0001, appropriately. He always answers on the second ring. My resident friend Woodrow called Colorado and calibrated the clock in the call room to the atomic clock.*

*Superman caught on to the precise second of the phone call and investigated one morning during surgery by saying, "Woodrow, you called late this morning."*

*The junior resident blurted out; "No, we did not, sir. That is not possible." This confirmed Superman's suspicion that something was up, and he made Woodrow explain the whole story about the atomic clock. This reverence pleased Superman.*

As stated previously, we were required to call Superman at 0545. This required our getting to the hospital around 0330. This required us to get out of bed at 0245, if you were fast.

There was no getting around the time of that telephone call. No excuses. No mercy. A good lesson in "getting the job done" mentality. You will be exposed to the "thank you for shopping K-Mart" mentality later in this text; then you can decide how you want your doctor to be trained.

I had the data on an average of 40 patients laid out in front of me at 0540. The labs were all drawn at 0200 so that they would be ready for the "morning" ("nighttime" is more appropriate) report. Tensions ran high on those mornings when things were close on time.

I would call the number of his home 653-0001 (ironically). He would answer on the second ring.

"Hello"

"Good morning, Sir"

"Good morning, Patrick"

"We will start in the ICU. Mr. Jones continues to improve..."

On it went until around 6:00 AM. I would then call the other three attendings and give them the morning report. These were much less intense. All of the phone calls were made from a small call room and a telephone that was next to a clock. The clock was set by my predecessors to atomic time. It was not that Superman demanded such "atomic" precision as much as he did not like his Chief Resident to be late when he was told to call at 5:45.

My call was not the only one that Superman received. It was the first in a series of timed calls from the organ center, tissue bank, and the OR front desk. I am amazed by his work capacity. To this day I have seen no one that can rival him.

Pete was one of the Chiefs that finished with me. When he was a second year, he developed phlebitis (swelling and inflammation of the veins and other surrounding tissue) in his legs from standing too much. It got to be so bad that he was admitted to the hospital while on his own Renal Transplantation Service.

Superman was very supportive of Pete's condition. He even went to the length of providing Pete with his late medical record dictations to give him an activity while he was receiving his treatment. Superman made rounds on Pete daily. Needless to say, he was back on the floor within a few days.

Superman was a stickler for keeping food to a minimum. He once happened upon a physician in the Division of Neurosurgery who was sneaking a muffin just outside of the OR. He stated, "Bill, why do you have to make me be such an asshole?"

There was a junior attending that worked on the Liver Transplantation Service. One of his responsibilities was to procure organs for transplantation from all over the area, day or night. One night he just gave out of gas after a second donor run and refused to do another one. Superman found him the next day and laid it on the line the way that he always does.... "You're gone."

That was his last organ run. You don't compromise patient care because you are tired. Not at Bayview.

Another member of the Liver Transplantation Service once walked into a room where an organ procurement was in progress, looked in, and said in a manner that was obviously too casual for Superman (who was present removing a kidney), "No good."

Out into the hallway went the former running back. He grabbed some tail and started shaking it back and fourth. Sort of like a kill on the Serengeti. It was ugly, but it was right. It was acute on chronic. He wanted a more aggressive transplant surgeon. It would happen in the next six months.

Don't let anything get in the way of patient care. Here it was, laid out for us in very plain fashion. I knew that I was seeing the right thing done, though perhaps only one of the right ways. A resident spent a portion of an in-house call night at a local establishment. The nurses called Superman when they could not get him to come and see a patient in the ICU. In came Superman. He called the wayward resident and asked him, "Where are you right now?"

The stupid answer was "The ICU, sir."

"No, I am in the ICU, ...meet me in my office."

Gone.

Maybe it seems harsh, but do you want your doctor to lie? Do you want your doctor to be lazy and then lie? Those guys did not finish at Bayview.

There were always the AW stories that circulated around the medical center. Few understood the sensitivity of our Chairman.

He would walk down to the Children's Hospital to visit the crippled son of a former resident. He walked through snow to perform multiple transplants on a day when the city was on a virtual shutdown.

He helped a good friend of mine named Don. The relationship began when Don was a disadvantaged African American youth struggling to get through high school. Superman lifted him up and helped him to achieve a degree at the local university, then hired him on as his full-time lab director. He transformed Don's life, just as he has countless others. Hard on the outside, soft on the inside, those are the best men.

There are other stories. Suffice it to say that he was very tough on the outside. This soft thing that I mention is still my belief. I never expected much of it while he was training me to be a surgeon.

One of his all time nonfavorite residents was Dr. Chiapet. He once made Chiapet pass out from an AW passed out during a thyroidectomy. Nothing that he did was right. All that he had to do was hold things out of the way and cut suture. Chiapet really was bad and could not even do this. He was a tender lad with just enough foreign accent to be difficult to understand and to not relate to the moods of a very demanding man.

Chiapet started, "Sir, I am feeling somewhat lightheaded."

Superman threatened, "If you pass out, Chiapet, you are fired." The AWs continued, "Don't you move an inch!"

The reply came approximately 10 minutes later, "Sir, I am feeling faint." The nurses matted his brow with cold towels. Chiapet finally had to be escorted out.

Angered by a ridiculous consult for dialysis access from a nephrologist who was notorious for not taking good care of his patients, Superman climbed 13 or so flights of stairs to his eventual destination, the dreaded nephrology ward (the killing fields). His faithful junior residents followed close behind, wondering what spectacle they were about to witness. His anger continued to swell as he climbed the stairs. Perhaps there was some frothing from our beloved chairman. His feeling of dismay with the poor nephrologist progressed to the point where he said, "Why, I ought to come over this table and beat ..." I'll leave it there.

His faithful junior residents, including the one that related this story to me, followed him back down the stairs. He stopped on the fifth floor all of a sudden and, appearing to have popped out of a trance, said, "Don't you ever let me hear of you acting that way."

"Oh yes, sir!" was the appropriate response.

Superman continues to be a role model to others and myself. I will never be as imposing a figure as him, but I may be as tough. It is his work ethic and integrity that impress me the most. He gets phone calls at 0530 from the Organ Center, 0545 from the transplant resident, 0600 from the Tissue Center, showers until 0615 (the dreaded no-call interval), and is at work at 0630 every day except Sunday, when he comes in around 0700. He always stays past 7 PM.

He sometimes peeks in the OR, and will frequently come up behind you and say, "what are you doing, Patrick?" to which I will respond "Operating, sir." I was liked by the nurses enough that they would give some sort of signal when he had popped into the room.

Other residents might not be so privileged and the nurses would delight as the surprise of Superman's presence would unfold.

One attending was able to get rid of him by saying, "Operating on a Goddamned mess, sir." He says that it worked every time.

Superman also had a propensity to say GD in the OR. The quality of a resident's performance was inversely related to this value (which was religiously counted by the circulating nurse, and compared with the total counted by the scrub nurse).

He once told my buddy Stan that he was "just standing there like a Goddamned wooden Indian," and was no help at all. He also told another Chief that it was "like you are from Mars or something." These quotes were treasured pieces of history for the residents to enjoy.

When another colleague was not sucking enough, he stated "It's like I'm burning leaves down here" as he tried to cauterize a bleeder deep down in a hole full of blood that was not adequately suctioned. You don't want to be the one running the suction when there is a lot of blood coming out. You may hear a new record level of volume for the word "SUCK!!"

Superman is a man beyond reproach in my opinion. Sure there are other ways to train a surgeon, but his way works, and he has been doing it longer than I have been alive.

*A Promise to Myself*

*Promise that you will never forget how tough the third year was...*

Okay, I remembered.

## Third Year of General Surgery Residency.........Trauma

Hours:      Every other night in-house call; 120 hours per week
To work:    5 AM, Monday through Saturday; 6 AM Sunday
Home:       average 6 PM during week; 2 PM Saturday;
            2 PM Sunday

            Gross Pay Rate ...........................$4.80
            Net Pay Rate ..............................$3.63

I will never forget one of my first trauma cases early in my third year rotation.

"Gunshot to the head....unstable...in the ER now."

You never know what to expect. My Chief Resident and I opened the doors to the ER.....

"Get your asses back!!!! Hellllllllp me!!!" came the cries of a 6 foot 4 man in his blood stained briefs. He was running towards us at full speed and screaming primally with the cops in close pursuit. I assumed that this was the one that was shot in the head as he had a huge bandage wrapped around his head and draped over one eye. There was blood all over his body and squirting off of his head.

He was running to look for a place to hide his load of illegal contraband.

He almost ran us over.

My Chief Resident was amused, but not very much shaken by the whole scene. I knew that I was in for fun.

"I guess we don't have to admit that guy unless they catch him, huh?"

## The Maximizer

*He was not even the old school. He was some sort of torture devil to some, a principled man who either had no PR skills or was stubborn enough to believe that they were not necessary if you did the right thing (the latter seems more likely). He was so rough that the old school was even leery of him. The old school is an institution; The Maximizer was his own separate institution. Institutions perform within their own set of values. Two institutions often have trouble coexisting in a tight space. He was a very principled man. He was an honest man. His PR skills were his principles, not much softening involved. He deserves credit for that too.*

*He stayed up all night. He drank lots of Diet Pepsi. He had a neatly trimmed beard and tinted glasses. He was very thin and hyperactive. He spoke in a nasal tone and used dramatic gesticulations to get his points across.*

*Academia allowed something like The Maximizer to grow, and of course, we hired him.*

*He came armed with a new theory for the ICU. It was Shoemaker's principle.*

*Pump the patient up with blood, fluid, epinephrine (adrenaline), everything; and they will do better after their injury. It was a theory that had started up north. It is a sort of hyperdynamic therapy that was in vogue in the late 1980s and early 1990s. It was supercharging of the body with the theory that the charge would help the patients get over traumatic injury more readily. God is a smart guy. The body is more*

*complex than that. You have to respect it. To every complex problem that
the body presents, there is a solution that is simple, clear, ...and wrong.*

*Shoemaker's theory would later be disproved with the help of the
experience gained at our hospital under the reign of The Maximizer.
That is a nice way of saying that we knocked some people off. His competitors were instrumental in pointing this out.*

The Maximizer took Shoemaker to heart. Let's apply the theory in
a pure sense. Let's throw out common sense. Let's play the numbers.
Let's get the wound bitches to do the work.

It would take a dictatorial system and a lot of patients to see if this
worked. He was the man to do it. Bayview was the place to let it be
done to the residents.

In the midst of the Maximizer's system, a fresh new, scared recruit
appears. His name is Mr. Coffee. He came from the Midwest and was
a little nervous about starting on the Trauma Service with the
Maximizer, so he showed up at 9:00 PM the night before his first day
and started seeing patients for 6:00 AM the following morning.

The nine-hour preparation was carried out with great pain. You
could see Mr. Coffee's lack of sleep in his face as he presented the first
patient the next morning to The Maximizer.

Five o'clock shadow does not look good when it is only 0700 AM.

The Maximizer did not speak a word or look at the pitiful intern..........
Then he looked up and stated plainly and clearly (to the next man up the
ladder) that Mr. Coffee was no longer to present patients. He then turned
to the second year resident and started torching him.

Mr. Coffee was to spend the next 2 months getting one large continuous AW from the Maximizer. They would typically sit down after
rounds and go over the errors in his progress notes. The Maximizer
would tear the morning notes out of the chart and throw them away.
Mr. Coffee would write another one and the Maximizer would throw
that one away too. It got so bad that Mr. Coffee was sleeping with a
full pot of coffee by his head and his beeper on his chest so that he
would not oversleep due to his near incapacitating level of exhaustion.
The progress notes were rejected well into the evening by the
Maximizer and the Trauma work/gunshot action began to come in
before he could finish the morning notes.

Ass deep in trauma dogs, I make the 1100 PM call to Mr. Coffee.
"Mr. Coffee, where are you? We have two gunshot wounds that need
to go to the OR and another drunk driver down here."

"I have a ways to go, but the night is young......," replied a determined Mr. Coffee.

I liked Mr. Coffee because he was tough. I knew that he would learn how to write progress notes, and everything else that it takes to get through this God-forsaken place. I also knew that The Maximizer's reign of terror could not last forever. It just was not natural. It seemed much more natural to bring a locally trained guy in to torture us. You will meet him later.

Read the following case in point. This case lead to what was in my mind the worst beating of all time at a Morbidity and Mortality conference.

### Shot, Cut, Drowned, Disemboweled

*No, it's not a scene from Braveheart. It's the Bayview Trauma Service.*

*Shot...*

*A patient arrives in the Emergency Department with a gunshot wound to the chest, entering the left chest just to the left of the breastbone. He is unstable, with a blood pressure of 70 over 40. The Lamb was the lucky resident on call. He was in the wrong place at the wrong time.*

*The Lamb made his move, to the phone. He called the cardiac surgeons on call. This was reasonable since the patient was in shock and had been shot in a path that could involve the heart or a great vessel.*

*Cut......*

*The cardiac surgeons came and wisked the patient to the OR. The left internal mammary artery was found to be bleeding at operation. This was easily ligated. The patient stabilized after the bleeding was stopped.*

*The patient was parked in the Surgical ICU that night. This was the home of the Trauma Service, and guess who was on call, The Maximizer.*

*"You're in my world now, son." The postoperative course was uneventful during the early portion of the night. There was nothing to mess with. Then, around midnight, the patient's blood pressure began to drop. Of course, being in the realm of The Maximizer, this patient was hooked up to every monitoring device in the Western World. All sorts of hemodynamic indices were being continuously monitored. Some of these indices were derived from numbers that were derived from derived*

*numbers. The result was sort of a dual reality. There was the patient and his clinical situation (common sense) and the sea of indices that the Lamb was under orders to react to..*

*When this guy's blood pressure dropped, so did his "EDVI"...a juicy third order (highly derived) number that was supposed to reflect the volume status of the patient. If this number were low, it was supposed to mean that the patient had a low blood volume, and might need fluid. If the number is high, then that means that the patient either has a higher than necessary blood volume, or is in cardiogenic shock (heart failure). Some of the other, as it turns out, more direct numbers were indicating that the patient was in cardiogenic shock and perhaps in cardiac trouble again. The clinical situation (having been shot in the chest) would also seem to direct common sense towards the diagnosis of cardiogenic shock.*

*Drowned..........*

*The worst thing to do for a patient in cardiogenic shock (characterized by high numbers) is to administer fluid. The Lamb was bound by the phone call to The Maximizer and his will. The Maximizer ordered fluid for the low EDVI. He continued to do this through the night as the young kid continued to sink. He was being literally drowned (maximized). The blood pressure would not come up. The EDVI stayed low...*

*Disemboweled.......*

*The Maximizer was fixed on the EDVI. There must be blood loss from somewhere. How about the abdomen? Never mind that he was not shot in the abdomen, that would make sense.*

*So The Lamb had to take the guy to the OR with The Maximizer for an emergent abdominal exploration based on that number. Surprise, surprise, no blood in the abdomen, just drowned organs. The patient died on the way back to the ICU.*

*The cardiac surgeon came in the following morning to see his patient, not knowing anything of what had gone on the night before. He was shocked to say the least that his save had been transformed into a "clean kill."*

This was only the beginning. There was Morbidity and Mortality Conference to pay. It was a chance for the heart surgeons to retaliate at The Maximizer's efforts. This is traditionally an excellent forum for AWs. When Superman hosts the show, they become AAWs. These

"M&M" conferences occur on a Saturday morning. Their timing effectively eliminates the possibility of a sanctioned weekend off. M&M Conference can be a malignant experience. The magnitude of malignancy is related to the attending that chairs the conference. M&M is a necessary exercise of internal quality assurance. It can also be a positive educational experience. We were mostly horrified of it when Superman was there.

My friend, The Lamb was slated to present all of this mess to Superman and the major players in the Division of Cardiothoracic Surgery (who otherwise rarely come) were there. It was a show that was not to be missed. Attendance was perfect.

The Lamb began, "This was the case of a 34 year old male who sustained a gunshot wound to the left chest..."

Superman interrupted, "Did you put in a chest tube?" having reviewed the chart and knowing full well that he had not.

"No sir"

"Why not?"

"Well, uh...Baaaaaaaaaaaahhhh"

An AAW proceeded and deteriorated into phrases such as "his biggest problem wasn't the gunshot, his biggest problem was that you were his goddamned doctor!"

The Lamb's waist was loaded down with a rack of beepers for the various call responsibilities that he had that day. Each went off at the most inopportune of times.

"Turn off that beeper!" said Superman.

Another page to another beeper about a minute later... "How many goddamned beepers do you have. Turn them all off.... No, give them to me!" Snickers abound in the audience.

Superman had bloodied the waters. The cardiac surgeons went in for the kill. They pointed out that a normal wedge pressure (a more direct measure of the heart's volume) is around 16, and that this patient's was 58 at the peak of the drowning.

More snickers.

The Lamb said....Baaaaaaaaaahhhhhhhhh.

There was only silence from The Maximizer, whose job was at risk before the drowning. Before The Maximizer was able to respond, he was called away to a trauma (that his detractors stated was a stable trauma that did not require his attention, though none of this was confirmed). This situation had occurred previously when a fire alarm went off during another kill presentation on one of The Maximizer's patients with Superman presiding. Nobody ever could prove that that was set up. But some names were thrown around.

All that the Lamb could say was "Baaaahhhhhhh......," and that was the best response.

*I saved a dead guy*

*I tried to be a hero with a chronic patient that we were supporting, and had been supporting for six months.*

*I wanted to show that I am an ACLS certified winner.*

*Loser.*

*Dead Guy happened to have an arrhythmia when I was standing in front of him.*

*So I saved him. A huge AW (2 cans opened; no, shaken, then opened) followed from the whole staff. The overall theme being, "you should have let him die."*

*Dead Guy hung in there well after I went off of the service. The staff guys frequently called me to let me know about his progress and how much they appreciated my saving his corpse. You just cannot win.*

*Zipper Girl*

*Down, down, down in the darkest bowels of the medical ICU there is a patient. She is very sick. She has developed horrible respiratory failure. The "fleas" (the last thing off of a dead dog...a nickname for an internal medicine doctor) have surrounded her. She is near death. Her ventilator is set to a very high pressure to push air into her thick, stiff, sick lungs.*

*Way down deep in the flea garden a hole springs forth. A hole in her gut.....somewhere.*

*"Call the surgeons."*

*The Maximizer appears. "She is too ill to move to the OR.."*

*Let's do the dramatic. Let's make her the zipper girl.*

*We'll do the operation at the bedside, with 46 arthropods looking on at the ghoulish exercise. When we are done, we'll put a zipper on so that it will be easier to go back in for the washouts that she will be receiving.*

*Yes, it is the Zipper Girl. We were the talk of the Medical ICU. The flea's fears had been confirmed. We are so aggressive that we do ghoulish things to kill people.*

*I recall opening her abdomen with The Dalai Lama (hairshirt perfect resident). We were surrounded by a crowd of mystified residents and students. The bowel was so matted down that we could not find the hole. We irrigated her on a daily basis to prevent an abscess I suppose.*

*They did not care. They just wanted to see the guts and the zipper.*

There was nothing wrong with what we did, given the extraordinary circumstances. It was a last ditch effort in a patient that would surely die in transport to the OR. The Maximizer was such a dramatic, non schmoozer. It always opened him up to criticism when he hosted one of those "look what I am doing" events. He was perceived as a "cowboy" because he had new ideas, which he believed in very strongly and was unable to "ease" onto the old school. He was also not one of the locals. Cowboys did not last at Bayview. They got shot.

The Maximizer struck again. It was the bedside tracheostomy. Once again, he was right. He was ahead of his time. However, his ability to integrate his new ideas into the "old school" left much to be desired. He needed to introduce these new concepts in a gradual, deferential manner. He just never did.

*"Fire tracheostomy."*

*The Maximizer was a proponent of placing tracheostomies (done on patients that required prolonged ventilator treatment) at the bedside in the ICU. This particular procedure is going well. He has the usual crowd around the unit.*

*The skin incision is made two finger-breadths above the top of the sternum (breast bone) across the base of the neck. The incision is about 3 inches long.*

*The skin and subcutaneous fat are divided.*

*The platysma muscle is divided. A retractor is placed to pull the tissues away from the midline. The cutting is turned from a horizontal to a vertical plane.*

*The Maximizer stays in the midline. Moving the least bit off to the side means bleeding. Bleeding may be harder to control in this makeshift ICU "OR."*

*The cautery instrument is used until he is directly onto the trachea. The balloon of the old tracheal tube is deflated. The trachea is incised.*

*The pure oxygen that was being given to the patient ignited (from the cautery instrument). The Maximizer was quick to pull the old breathing tube out, flames shooting from the tip of the tube.*

*The Maximizer boldly pressed on. He placed the tracheostomy with no further event. It was a good save for a potentially disastrous problem. It was a windfall for the residents.*

*Fire in the ICU.*

*This solidified the in many ways unfair "grim reaper" image that The Maximizer had obtained by this point. Imagine one of those Nazi propaganda posters that pictures The Maximizer with his trimmed beard and a flaming tracheal tube..... "Come, brothers....We will build an evil empire." That image was further advanced by those on the Trauma staff that were ready to see him go.*

Amazingly, an unnamed person helped to make things uncomfortable for him by intermittently urinating behind a file cabinet in his office. The Maximizer's office was such a mess that the urine did not seem to have very much impact other than a persistent "strange odor." The Maximizer's only mild irritation at the stench was sort of like the grandma on the movie "Vacation." Knowing that the dog had urinated on the tuna sandwich in the picnic basket, she just sort of shook her head and ate it anyway.

That was a tough rotation. We had been on call every other night for 10 weeks. It was 36 hours awake, 12 hours off. Woodrow and I were exhausted. It was not just 36 hours of work, I can do that easily. I do it now as a cardiothoracic surgery fellow, no problem. It was 36 hours of hard work and AWs galore.

Times were tough. Perhaps it was all embodied by Woodrow's request that I come to his house and start an IV on him as he lay exhausted and sick in his bed...pager going off.

# 15

# Fourth and Fifth Years of General Surgery Residency: The Lab

Total Years:    12-13 (1994-1996)........30-31 years old
Salary/Debt:   2 year NIH Grant $33,000 per year; $70,000 debt
Hours:          No call; 40 hours per week
To work:        9 AM, Monday through Friday
Home:           Average 4 PM during week

Gross Pay Rate...........................$15.85
Net Pay Rate ...............................$12.00

Dr. Neatcoat was the man that instructed me in the lab. He inspired me as much as a lab can inspire me. He was very patient. He was a heart surgeon with patience. Outstanding.

*Pigs on Bypass*

*We were pig surgeons for two years.*
*We had to go get them in the cage. They had a grunt that intimidated me.*
*I grab the pig by the ear. I inject him with ketamine. He falls over.*
*I put him on the cart and take him down the hall, covered so that nobody will happen to see that I am transporting a pig and pass out.*
*I place the tracheal tube. I drape out the pig and place him on cardiopulmonary bypass with the help of my friend Stan. We had Ron on*

*the pump, The Deacon as a circulator, and Russell as our computer genius.*

*We did a total of 60 pig cases. Stan and I managed to knock off only 5. A few limped to the finish line.*

*Much manhood was gained by the surgical misadventures that we created and had to fix on our own due to the lack of an attending in our immediate vicinity.*

*We managed. I have now published 14 scientific and clinical papers, most of which stemmed from that lab experience. This time allowed me to learn about the process of scientific investigation of surgical problems. It also allowed me to get a great spot in cardiothoracic surgery.*

Bayview was a terrific place for sure, but The Big City was better. I was not ready to endure that "shine the light on the attending's mole and help to nurture the melanoma" thing that I was telling you about.

While in the lab, I had a chance to be around The Father on a very limited basis.

The Father performed the first series of operations using the Mayo-Gibbon heart lung machine in the mid 1950s at the Mayo Clinic in Rochester, Minnesota. He is probably the most important figure in the development of cardiothoracic surgery over the past 45 years.

The Father was a tough guy. He had his son do 2 fellowships in cardiothoracic surgery. The one he finished at Harvard was not enough. That might tell you a little about his standards. The Father used to comb his hair straight down in a Nero fashion, but that hairstyle looks good to you if he had saved your 2-month-old when no one else in the world would have even tried.

The Father was single-handedly responsible for building the Bayview Department of Surgery into the clinical powerhouse that it is today. He had a very strong personality. Few here at Bayview understood that the reason that he left the Mayo Clinic. There were two surgeons in the late 1960s at the Mayo Clinic who could do the operations. Sure they were both team players; it is just that one of them wanted to be the owner, general manager, coach, quarterback that threw the pass, wide receiver that caught the pass, and the fan that cheered the team on. One was fairly easy to work with; being in the OR with the other was described as like being in a shoebox with a crab. So, the blue crab came down to Bayview where people would let him run the roost.

"Gawlee, he sure is smart" said the Bayview Search Committee in 1967, "but you know, Goober, he sure combs his hair funny, you reckon that's what smart people are supposed to look like?"

"I reckon so, daddy, I reckon that's it."

Brilliant guys can do dysfunctional things and have star-fits and that is okay. They are brilliant. The problem comes when he gets old and leaves a legacy of this behavior to people that are not as smart as him and are still rear ends.

The Father planted the seed. It was a beautiful plant that sprung forth and gave recognition to the post industrial; post racial mess demoralized garden that was Bayview City. But then from this beautiful flower from Minnesota came these little buds at the very tip of the branches.

"What are those? Why they look like little hands. How cute."

"No, Bubba, those are cages like Daddy sets out back to get the Bobcats. By cracky, those are claws and he is a Venus flytrap." But it was too late, and the first was spawned of the blue crab, and his name was Superman.

My buddy Stan once tried to present a paper to an audience that included The Father. Stan made the mistake of introducing the term African-American in his second slide.

"Did you check their country of origin? asked The Father.

"No sir," confessed a demoralized Stan, knowing that the gates of Hell had been opened.

"Did you identify the other people in the study by their origin?"

On it went. I think you get the idea. I can say that we were exposed to excellence by the presence of The Father here at Bayview. It was just so Goddamned painful.

As I said, The Father transformed this city, and indeed, the entire field of cardiothoracic surgery. When he arrived from Minnesota, he immediately placed all of the indigent patients (previously cared for only by the residents) on his service. They all were given a nametag with his name on it. That is the way that things would be. They went from "one light bulb and a ward of patients" to receiving the finest care that the world had ever seen. He led by example.

The Father put an end to private practice by attendings that worked at the University. It was to be an academic-only environment. Some were forced to leave. He turned the place on its ear like no center ever has been.

The Father was performing the most difficult operations in the world at Bayview, yet he still managed to keep an active General Surgery Service across the street at the VA Hospital. This required unbelievable energy.

Many of his early congenital cardiothoracic surgery patients have become amazingly successful adults. One was my intern last year. He had surgery for a condition called transposition of the great vessels at a very young age. This resident came to Bayview (26 years later) to be like his surgeon.

The Father always said that the enemy of good is perfect. Well, he was the closest thing to perfect that I have ever seen. I value the time that Superman spent during my residency reminding us of the things that The Father not only said, but also did.

The Father has a son that operates at Bayview. He is also a star. A "triple threat," able to perform adult, congenital, and transplant surgery on the heart. They call the CV surgery department the Father, The Son, The Holy Ghost. The Son has endured the shadow of his father with what I think is incredible toughness. Two fellowships in CV surgery are more than most men could, or ever have, taken. I have a great deal of respect for this man.

*Then the House Caught on Fire*

*We made the mistake of letting our guard down. Things were going pretty well during my time in the lab. We went to a friend's house to watch the Alabama-Tennessee football game. We came home to a smoked out domicile. Our telephone was sitting on my copy of the textbook Cardiopulmonary Bypass. The phone had apparently shorted out and caught fire. The fire spread to the lamp that it was sitting under. The entire house was smoked out.*

*We were out of the house for a month. I truly enjoyed the accommodations provided by the University Inn (the local discount motel that we sought out with the noble...stupid... intention of saving the insurance company money). I still remember the Kenny G soundtrack that played every (every) morning in the breakfast lounge. I thought that we had been captured by the VC and were being asked to confess.*

*Alison has always stood by my side. I am amazed by her dedication. She left the greatest life that I have ever seen. She was raised so well that she actually had no trouble leaving all of this for the sake of love (or pity). Hell, I would have left myself at this point.*

Two folks that I must mention that I worked with in the lab were Don and the Deacon.

Don came to Bayview as a disadvantaged, uneducated, black teenager with a willingness to work. He ended up being a lab assistant for Superman, who took him under his wing. Don ran the heart-lung machine in the lab for us. As of last week, he had moved on to Baylor to be closer to his family. I miss Don's honesty very much. If there was ever any question about the compassion of Superman, ask Don.

*Exit Leroy*

*Remember that cute little Scottie that we had as our first child? He got hit by a van. We were all on a walk. Leroy came out from behind a dirt pile. The van never stopped. He flipped around the way armadillos do when you shoot them in grandma's yard. Soccer mom one....Leroy zero.*

*I picked up Leroy and caught a ride home from a passerby. I wanted to get the dog away from Alison and our son Charles. I held Leroy as we headed towards home. I felt his heart fibrillate, then stop.*

*It may sound corny to care so much about a dog, but he was a part of our family. He was a source of joy for us during my intern year in Florida.*

*Enter Mr. Sexy*

*Leroy was dead, so we got another Scottie. This one came from the pound and had an extra couple of Y-chromosomes. We brought "Fred McGriff" home. He immediately proceeded to get a huge and uncommon erection.*

*He went after the bunny on the floor. He began to mount it. He was having terrible pelvic thrusts as his sword grew even larger. My wife screamed out and threw a quilt onto the floor to cover up what was sure to be a mess.*

*His tallywacker got so large that it reached his shoulder, curving off to the right after the first 9 inches. It was the stuff of legends in the neighborhood, prompting the nickname "Mr. Sexy." My next door neighbor Jimmy always wanted to know what Mr. Sexy was up to.*

*We had purchased the antisocial dog. He had given "the pound" a whole new meaning. Another great move for the family.*

The Deacon was one of my best friends while I struggled through the residency. The Deacon was okay because he knew himself. He grew up in Bayview City under all of its racial tension. Being black was not very kosher then. He walked to work for years, yet he never was an angry man. He raised a family that is not angry. He helped The Father to build up the first automated intensive care at Bayview. I value his friendship to this day. Whenever I feel like this was a struggle, I look at the Deacon. I still call him now and then......he always answers the phone the same way.... "4709." He eliminated his anger.

*Double Eagle and a Dream Fills in with mud*

It took a lot of sacrifice to become a cardiothoracic surgeon. I gave up a lot of things that used to be important to me. I went in as a kid, and came out as a man. I left some things behind, but gained so much more, in the form of a family.

I used to be a scratch golfer as a kid and wanted to play the PGA Tour. I came close, but made a conscious decision to pursue cardiothoracic surgery. Not medicine, cardiothoracic surgery.

I still have this weakness, I want to be a professional golfer. I often place some unrealistic expectations on myself. I have not let the golf one go. Granted, most professional golfers don't have an 18 year detour on their way to golf stardom. Having a brother that is a professional golfer, and following his career practically hole by hole does not make it any easier to let go.

It was a Saturday morning.

My friend Rusty says, "Let's go play some golf."

I was supposed to go to Surgical Grand Rounds that morning. I went golfing. I had not played in a very long time. It was frustrating to play poorly. I did not have many good opportunities to play during my surgery residency. Too much time and money.

We started off the back nine, after getting permission from the guy in the pro shop.

We forgot to tell the starter (Deputy Fife, chasing kids down is my life) on the first tee..

The round began in the usual fashion. Snap hook into the woods. Chip out across the fairway, into the woods on the right side. Snap hook back to the left side again. Triple bogey. Fuck it. I am not going into another one of those 12 swing corrections mental torture fests today. I am just going to swing today.

Number 11....Push to the right, out of bounds...triple bogey. Six over par.

The twelfth hole was a 530-yard par 5. I nailed a driver and had another 275 yards to the green.

Here comes that starter that we did not consult before going off the back nine. These starters are usually guys that are retired and have made their weekend job their life cause. This one was Barney Fife. He gave us grief all the way down the fairway. I had a 275-yard shot to the green. The group in front of us was on the green with the flag out.

"Go ahead and hit son, you can't reach them."

I was going lay up with a 3-iron. The challenge was set. I asked

*Rusty if I could borrow his Yonex 3-wood.*

*I nailed it. I yelled "fore" as the ball approached the green.*

*It bounced up onto the green. It went into the hole, right in front of the foursome.*

*Double eagle.*

*No flag. Just an amazed foursome, a silenced starter, and a budding surgeon that now was going to be a pro golfer and a heart surgeon.*

*The pledge was only slightly altered that day......... I should be working, with my family, reading, or competing in a Senior Tour golf tournament.*

*"Honey, you are not going to believe this. I..."*

*"Where are you?"*

*"I'm...at the golf course."*

*"Where?"*

*"You don't understand honey. The most incredible shot...."*

*"What happened to Grand Rounds?"*

*"No, you don't understand..."*

*The usual extremism followed. I tried to take up golf again. I was going to finish my training and rehab my golf game so that I could play the Senior Tour by the age of fifty. I was not going to be able to play or practice during daylight hours, and I could not afford it. Other than that, it was a solid plan.*

*I dug a huge sand trap in my back yard. It took me a week of constant work effort (sometimes at night). I was going to practice out of the sand trap and hit balls into a net that I had ordered. The plan was to practice in the mornings and in the evenings, in the dark. This seemed to be the only way to compensate for not being able to be outside during daylight hours.*

*Time and reality set in. The sand trap turned out to be in a low part of the yard. It was huge. It became a huge bog when the rain came and filled it in. First came the water, then slid the mud. How symbolic.*

*I will compete in a Senior Tour event, and I will make the cut.*

# 16

# Sixth Year of General Surgery Residency

Total Years:  14 (1996-1997) ..................32 years old
Salary/Debt:  $31,000 per year; $70,000 debt
Hours:  Varied with service
Title:  "Opening and Closing Bitch; Assistant Maker of Wounds"

**Sixth Year of General Surgery Residency......Surgical Oncology**

Hours:  Every night home call; 80 hours per week
To work:  6 AM, Monday through Saturday; 6 AM Sunday
Home:  Average 8 PM during week; 2 PM Saturday; Noon Sunday
Note:  Chief call (protected by a junior resident, but on every night)

Gross Pay Rate ...........................$7.45
Net Pay Rate ...............................$5.64

Now I was really moving up the ladder. I was no longer a "wound bitch." I was now going to be inflicting some of the wounds myself. They really provide a strong foundation at Bayview. You only begin the building process after you feel like you have been a "wound bitch" for two years too long.

Surgical Oncology was more of the same. Circle of Death. The Brain and his cancer friends. I was better by the time I came back.

Before I was a mere transfer from a private hospital. Now I was the hotshot pre-academic guy with the best board scores in the program.

Things went well.

*Dead in Bed*

*I spent some time at the Veteran's Hospital doing cases with Dr. Lipshave during this rotation. For some mysterious reason, lots of patients are found "dead in the bed." I had one. The 'dead in bed' have pre-recorded vital signs that are of course unchanged by the act of dying. The respirations are 20 per minute. The temperature is 98.6. The blood pressure is 120/60.*

*The patient is found by someone eventually. The reaction is variable.*

*1) (most common) Call the resident and say "Mr. Jones is dead. You gonna come see him?"*

*2) "Call the Code, Mr. Jones is dead." That is a favorite. I have seen a code where the guy is so dead that they cannot get his mouth open to put the tube in, and he is shaped like the chair in which he died. Rigor Mortis usually takes a few hours.*

*3) Chart some more vital signs. Maybe he will come back from the dead if we chart some really good ones.*

*A physician's assistant told me the tale of a patient that was found dead at another VA some years back. The faithful "nurse sitter" was asleep in the chair next to his bed. I am sure that it was a beautiful sight for the resident presenting the patient to his attending. The astute attending went back to the desk and called into the room. The phone rang for a good while and then was answered by the groggy helper..."Mr. Jones' room."*

*"Yes, this is Dr. Brown, can you tell me how Mr. Jones is doing today?"*

*"He's doing all right sir."*

*"LLLLLLLLOOOOK AGAIN BITCH!!!!!!" was the phrase that was chosen by the unsettled attending.*

*All of this can best be described by the image of a former Bayview resident running down the hall and stopping briefly to ask a quick question to a nurse. She is large and seated at the desk, huddled over a chart, and quite removed from it all.*

*"Where's the code?," asked the panting resident.*

*As if to say, "I'm on eternal break, charting, eating, or any and all of the above, and there is nothing that you can do about it."......her hand, holding a large greasy drumstick, arose from the mass huddled over the chart, and casually pointed the drumstick in the direction of the code. No eye contact. No face.*

*If I have to draw the positive from this, there is a certain honesty here. The VA is like a big elephant. Waste all of your energy trying to get around it or get on and enjoy the slow ride.*

You certainly are not going to be able to change it. It is sort of like being in a hurry to go to an operation, turning the corner, and coming up behind two wide load VA health care workers walking side by side in their slow insulin-induced comatose state and making their grim march back to the nurses station after a lumberjack-style lunch. Do anything you want. Stop and have a pack of crackers. Call your parents to tell them that you love them. Do anything......Smile.... You are not going to get by.

It is true that you lose your patience as you progress in the field of cardiothoracic surgery. Sometimes the world seems like it is made up only of those two big mamas walking in the hallway. The trick is to remember that it isn't that the world is getting fatter, you are just turning into a freak.

Something else that I learned at the VA:

Pooling all of my oncologic knowledge has lead me to the conclusion that the best treatment for a Stage 4 solid organ epithelial tumor (advanced cancer) may be "6PFP."......a 6 Pack and a Fishing Pole.

### Sixth Year of General Surgery Residency......The Children's Hospital

Hours:          22 of 48 nights of in-house call; 120-140 hours
                per week
To work:        5 AM, Monday through Saturday; 6 AM Sunday
Home:           Average 9 PM during week; 2 PM Saturday;
                2 PM Sunday

Gross Pay Rate ...........................$4.59
Net Pay Rate ...............................$3.47

It is time for another primary history break. That unpolished "what it is was really like" politically incorrect kind of thing...

These accounts sound so awful. My mind was much more troubled and fatigued. The comments that I make do not represent the way that I feel now. The opinions expressed are given by a man wearing stool-colored glasses. However, I must include them because they capture my mood at the time. Also, you have to figure that if I was motivated enough to write something down given how completely exhausted I was during that rotation, something must have been up.

*I am writing this in order to document the nature of my pediatric surgery experience. I would summarize the experience as a large scale "tea bagging" (tea bag—verb—to disrespect another by dipping one's scrotum into their drink when he is not present). The "tea baggers" (noun—one who "tea bags") being the ones that make the schedule around here. I will emphasize what I feel to be the more difficult aspects of my rotation. I have given nothing but 100 % effort towards the care of my patients. I have supported my junior residents. Both of these are at the core of my philosophy as a surgical resident. My first focus was to do a good job, no matter what was handed to me.*

*Weeks one and two: When I arrived, the residents were in utter despair over the working conditions. One of my junior residents (Anderson—the guy that will take a punch to the chest shortly) had actually quit and had to be called back in by a faculty member, who I might add, has been quite supportive of changing the present organization of the Pediatric Surgery Service. This junior faculty member's pull is probably low due to his newcomer status. The Chief General Surgery Resident that preceded me thought that his junior residents were lazy and "needed to be beaten on" more. This was also the feeling of the senior faculty members (attendings).*

*A new system has just been implemented July 1, 1996. The faculty feel that it is a sound one, and that there was just a weak crop of junior residents.*

*The junior residents held a different opinion. It was immediately apparent to me that they were suffering more from a lack of leadership in the form of "mega-delegation." There are usually 40-50 patients (kids) on the service and 15 critically ill patients in the Neonatal ICU. Most of the patients are on TPN (IV nutrition). The junior residents were responsible for all of the notes and orders on these patients.*

*This army of patients must be seen by 0600. Rounds are at 0600, rain or shine. That means getting up at 0330 AM and getting to the hospital at around 0400 AM. Good morning sunshine! What day is it?*

Rounds went something like this...

"Oh yes, sir what an interesting case!"

How many more days?

"Yessuh, you done some mighty fine surgery sir. I done looked at the wound and it looks mighty fine suh, mighty fine suh; You done a good operatin' suh.....I don't know nuthin' 'bout cuttin' on no babies, but I seen the wound and took good care of it suh, and it looks mighty fine...mighty fine indeed!!!

"Yes, wound bitch, .....very well. Uh....good work, you keep this up and maybe I'll have a hernia for you some day. Now run along..."

"Yes suh. Thank you suh. You make me so happy. I'll be a good wound bitch. Yes suh."

The pediatric surgery fellows mainly operate. Who the hell can blame them? I'd hide too if I could...... I can't.....The fellows stay in the OR and let all of the dukey on the floor and in the trauma bays settle out. There is so much shit to do that going to the OR to watch only seems to cut into your time to get the scutwork on the floor done. Then after everybody has finished operating, it's late night rounds....or what I call "find the babies." There are so goddamned many of them.

How many more days?

The former Chief General Surgery Resident (my contemporary) was dumping all of the work on his juniors. Leadership means being willing to do everything that you ask your junior residents to do. Leadership means never leaving the hospital until the work was done. The junior guys were getting no leadership. This was immediately apparent from conversations with the nurses and junior residents. The former Chief had a minimal presence in the ER, Pediatric ICU, on rounds, and especially when the new interns were in a jam. He even found the time to do a great deal of Critical Care Transport (flying on the University jet to make extra cash) while on the service. I have not found the time to put gas in my car in the first two weeks. It's just sitting out there on the road, and Alison comes and picks me up. I don't have a problem with working the interns hard as long as you can show that you are willing to put out the same effort. I do have a problem with dumping and laziness, especially when one is dealing with the lives of children.

The final blow to the morale of the junior residents came from an apparent willingness of the Chief of the Division to allow this structure to exist. The junior residents (and myself) were left completely unprotected. It is the classic structure of any organization that lacks leadership... There are a shitload of screaming babies in this state and a ton of work to do at this hospital... The Chief of Surgery operates on the kids and delegates the floor work ("scut") to the troops under him. The *problem is that the delegation is continuing way down into the realm of the interns. The usual explanation for the delegation-style "leadership" that some people exhibit is the claim that "I had to do it too," though I have found it to be the case that people who shit on their help now probably found somebody to shit on 5 years ago (when they were interns).*

*The big shit boulder continues to roll downhill...*

*One junior resident says to the other... "What's that rumbling sound, and who farted?"*

*The Chief General Surgery Resident sees the boulder and says "I want to be a fellow too," and steps out of the way.*

*The big shit boulder, wrapped in the progress notes of 1,000 screaming babies, continues to roll down hill....*

*One junior resident says to the other... "Hmmmm, there's that smell again...Oh my God daddy!!!!....It's a giant ball of shit!!!! We're all going to die!!!!"*

*9/2/96......As to the complaints of the previous Chief General Surgery Residents that there are not enough cases or enough to do in the OR. I have not found this to be that case at all. You just have to work hard enough to get through the work on the floor to get to the OR. I am living well on the pediatric surgery fellows' scraps....but losing weight.*

*There are different stages of work. They can be measured by the weight change of the surgery resident.*

| | |
|---|---|
| *Lazy as shit/easy rotation* | *gain weight* |
| *Stay disciplined/easy rotation* | *get in better shape, lose weight (never happens)* |
| *Hard rotation* | *gain weight (eat Doritos and run to OR)* |
| *Ass whip rotation (rare)* | *Lose weight (this is one of those rare ones where you lose weight no matter how much you eat)* |

*9/6/96.....I have just arrived home from another run of call. One of the fellows went out of town starting Friday, 8/30. It was just the other fellow and myself as the chiefs until he returned next week. I was placed on call Sat/Sun/Tues/Thurs/Sat/Sun. My workweek was probably 140 hours this week.....*

*I did not complain. I lose my self-respect when I complain. I just do my job well. My wife will deliver our second child next week....I have entered a very strange mode, sort of like "fuck it, I'll do everything....." I have slept about 18 hours this week. My yard is a foot long, my car has a flat and a dead battery, I got 2 parking tickets at Bayview last week in a rush to a pediatric emergency last week and I have not had time to pay them, so I will get penalized. The service is running well, and the interns say that things are 1 million percent better now that I have arrived, mainly because I get off of my ass. I am drinking coffee all day every day. I have lost 12 lbs. in two weeks. I have athlete's foot and Tinea Versicolor on my skin. I have acne. I feel like quitting every hour of the day. I can honestly say that I have put in about 140 hours this week, and I feel like I am doing just enough. I do not know how long I can last.*

*The pediatric residents (the ones with the teddy bears on their stethoscopes and small phallus syndrome) hold a double standard towards the surgery residents, they are often quite confrontational in the Pediatric ICU, yet you are complained about to your attending by all facets of the staff and residents if you step out of line or assert yourself. I guess it's for the best to shut up and not subject the hospital to "Godzilla versus Tender-Touch/Pediatric Poopy pants."*

*Oh yes ma'am, I'll stay away from your baby. You are tall, dominant, and in charge.*

*It is like it is their house and the surgery residents are the red-headed stepchildren. There remains no one to stick up for the surgery residents, save possibly, Dr. Ding. I don't know if I can handle the stress of watching children die in the midst of the worst fatigue that I have ever felt in my life (bar none), and enduring the physical and psychological bullshit of this rotation. I am considering not going to work in the morning.*

*There is not much more that I can say about this other than the fact that I barely made it to my daughter's birth. I was standing there at the bedside as Alison was pushing Anna out and in comes an "unstable trauma" call. "Little girl run over by a truck........" etc. Having developed a bad case of the "It's my fault, it's my responsibility, thank you sir, may I have another?" mentality that characterizes a solid surgery resident; I bolted out of the delivery room in front of Alison, God, and my in-laws, headed for the fire. It was my own Goddamned fault. This is a good example of my creating my own misery; after all, the fellow had given me a few hours to attend my daughter's birth. I knew that the fellows had been busy in the OR when I left for Alison's delivery. I was afraid that that there might not be anyone down in the Trauma Room but a Pediatrician to help the girl.*

*I crossed Bayview City at around 100 mph, and made it there in time to see one of the fellows intubating (putting the breathing tube in) her. The little girl was stabilized for the moment. We carted her off to the Cat scanner. I was able to get back to Alison's bedside, but not before helping one of my attending's fix a 3-year-old girl's smashed liver.*

*Anna was coming out. I knew that I was really fucking up when the voice of my wife's OB-GYN rang over the speaker phone in Room 12 of The Children's Hospital....*

*"Pat, I can't hold this back much longer, how is your case going?"*

*"I'll be right there...uh....Thanks." I was thinking all along that I had become mentally ill. Something inside of me (pathologic) would not let me stand down. It was as if I had adopted a "fuck it, I can do anything" mentality as a protection against the rigors of the service. A great job was all that I had to put up.*

*This is not noble, this is fucked up. I had crossed the line. The attending working with me on the liver case finally said, "Get the Hell out of here Pat."*

*I left. Another 100 mph blow through the city allowed me to make it to Alison's bedside.*

In the midst of all of the stink, I plant a seed. My cardiothoracic surgery application goes out. The following is a copy of the personal statement that I wrote for my application for a cardiothoracic surgery fellowship. I put a lot of thought into this application, and it probably defines who I was, or thought that I was at that point in my life.

*Thoracic Surgery has appealed to me since my high school days in Titusville, Florida. My mother was prompted at that time to pursue a career in nursing by the financial prospects of a third child entering college. Her career served as my first exposure to medicine.*

*I was an accomplished golfer throughout my youth. I continue to hold the record for the lowest 4-year stroke average in East Central Florida, and was set on pursuing a career in golf. I still believe that I had the physical and mental tools to make the PGA Tour. Many of the people that I competed successfully against (including Scott Gump, and Steve Lamontagne) are doing well. I would be dishonest to deny occasional feelings of jealousy towards my former competitors. I remember recently being exhausted after a long call night on the Pediatric Surgery Service and seeing a telecast of the Hawaiian Open in which my friend Steve Lamontagne collected approximately $20,000 for playing 72 holes on a course that I probably would not have been allowed to play.*

*I mention my teen years because they represent the period of my life when I decided to pursue a career in thoracic surgery. I lost interest in golf as my interest in medicine grew. It was never a career in medicine that I wanted. It was a career in thoracic surgery. I wanted to use my athletic ability as well as my intellect. I was also attracted by what some described as the "overwhelming" challenges that a career in thoracic surgery promised.*

*I attended the Florida State University and was accepted as an out of state student at the Bayview School of Medicine. Bayview's reputation in the medical community was built around the energy of a relatively few individuals. Some very prominent thoracic surgeons played a vital role in the medical center's growth. My motivation for pursuing a career in thoracic surgery was greatly enhanced by the strong presence of these individuals at the Bayview Hospital. I was very fortunate to complete a rotation on The Holy Ghost's service as a senior medical student. I recall being very impressed by the level of intensity that existed in the operating suite, as well as the attention to detail and dexterity that were required to do the job well.*

*My surgical career progressed greatly under the guidance of Superman. I would describe Superman as a very tough and very fair individual. He demands a great deal from his residents, but has been consistently supportive of other residents' individual career aspirations and mine. It is my choice to pursue a career in academic thoracic surgery. Superman provided me with a strong clinical background as well as an environment in which I was free of all clinical duties for two years. These two years enabled me to focus on my research interests and to secure a National Research Service Award. Most importantly, however, Superman embodies the principles of hard work and integrity. I believe that hard work and integrity are central to success in academic thoracic surgery. Superman has been a model of the daily application of these principles, and I will always carry these principles with me.*

*I entered the laboratory after completing my third clinical year of surgery. Dr. Ted L. Neatcoat served as my mentor during this period. Dr. Neatcoat continues his work as a surgical investigator in the field of thoracic surgery. He has been very approachable and patient at all times. I believe that basic scientific research requires a different mindset than that required in the clinical world. Patience is an essential quality in the laboratory. Action, sometimes recognizing that there is incomplete data, is an essential quality on the clinical wards. I also feel that an effective transition from the clinical to the laboratory world requires the guidance of an experienced individual. Dr. Neatcoat provided me with this guidance.*

*Dr. Neatcoat introduced me to a broad spectrum of methods in basic scientific research, pointed me in the right direction, and allowed me to run. I was provided with constant supervision and feedback with*

*my work (often in the form of a deadly red pen and impromptu pre-
sentations), but at the same time I was able to come to understand and
develop my own unique talents. I gained a great deal of confidence during my time in the laboratory. I received an individual National
Research Service Award for investigating the use of perfluorocarbon
emulsions in the setting of cardiopulmonary bypass. This grant completely funded my two years in the lab. Most importantly, I left the laboratory knowing exactly where I wanted to be and what I wanted do in
the field of thoracic surgery. I am committed to pursuing a career as a
surgical investigator. In fifteen years, I would like to have created an
environment where problems in the clinical world are investigated in
the laboratory, and discoveries in the laboratory are translated into
improvements in the quality of patient care. Dr. Neatcoat is the individual that has been responsible for starting me on this course, and it is to
him that I am most indebted.*

*Lastly, I would like to put my aspirations into perspective, I am fore-
most a husband and a father. All that my wife Alison ever asked of me
is to do what makes me happy. The rest will take care of itself. I guess
that that is the reason that I am sending this application."*

So there you have it, a reasonably well-intentioned guy. A reasonable academic record. I hope that this will convince, or at least suggest
to the reader that I am a guy that wants to save lives and contribute to
his profession's future.

We had some strong attendings. Strong can be good. Strong can
also describe the smell of doody left on the dashboard in the Florida
sun for a day, or the smell of a dead cat.......

I made it through the Children's Hospital. It was as many hours as
I have ever worked. I was nearly a broken man at the end of that service. I had done a great job and had not complained once, something
that the other Chiefs were never able to accomplish. I had lost 25
pounds, I had athlete's foot, I had a new daughter, and I had applied
for cardiothoracic surgery.

I got sick on my last day and had to scrub out of a burn case that
I was doing with Dr. Ding. This had never happened to me. It was very
hot in the room and I was afraid that I would pass out and land on the
patient. So I went out with a whimper of sorts, but proud that I had
held up a high standard of care for those children. After all of the crap,
that was what it was all about.

Taking a beating is okay. Taking a beating and being a husband
and a dad is a little different. The buck must stop with you. I had to

write this book to get it off my chest. Your family does not deserve to catch the Hell that you get. They are just sitting at home, waiting for you.

**Sixth Year of General Surgery Residency........Trauma Service**

Hours:        Every third night in-house call; 110 hours per week
To work:     5 AM, Monday through Saturday; 6 AM Sunday
Home:        Average 6 PM during week; 2 PM Saturday;
                   2 PM Sunday

Gross Pay Rate ...........................$5.41
Net Pay Rate ..............................$4.09

I was evolving as a resident. I was pressing forward during the hard rotations. Things were definitely getting better. I was also living off of the pride that having done a good job and not complained at the Children's Hospital brought me. Some of the residents thought that I should have boycotted the service, and that I should have spoken my mind on the unfair surroundings. I chose to keep my head down and focus on doing a good job; not to be distracted and possibly compromise patient care. I relieved stress by writing about it. I did not want to look like a complainer. I just wanted to do a good job and finish. They just whined and looked like (pardon the expression) pussies...in my opinion.

From the frying pan to the fire. It was gunshot, paranoid-attending city. Trauma.

The Maximizer was gone. He knew all along that he was just a "filler" until one of the local breed was ready to step in. Tidy Goldberg was just the person for the job.

"Ladies and Gentlemen: I'm in Charge Here." Boy, this is going to be much better. Alexander Haig. Martial law. Tidy Goldberg is the Thirsten and Duncan Teabag Endowed Chief of the Trauma/Burns/Critical Care/Wound Management/Injury Control/Lots Of Other Technical Sounding Things We Do Because Everything In Trauma Is Managed Nonoperatively/Ass Whipping and Flogging Service. He is a native of Virginia. Isn't it funny how it takes about 3 minutes in a closed room with someone before you hear that they were either from Virginia, went to school at Duke, or were somehow associated with the Massachusetts General Hospital ("The MGH," also proclaimed by its graduates as Man's Greatest Hospital).

Tidy Goldberg completed his general surgery training at Bayview.

He had a brief run at private practice general surgery, but joined the Army to complete his bedside manner and burn therapy training. He returned to Bayview in the early 1990s and essentially unseated The Maximizer. Tidy Goldberg was local. He was Bayview trained. The Maximizer started feeling much more like a "filler" shortly thereafter. The Maximizer was a good doctor in many ways, but he was also driven solely by doing what he thought was right. He walked his own path rather than the one that Bayview provides for you. Some saw him as a cowboy at times, possessing the PR skills of Idi Amin. Tidy Goldberg was a little more crafty, but equally sadistic. Pick your poison.

Tidy Goldberg is a very intelligent man and a masterful clinician. He is dark-haired, approximately five feet eight inches tall, and very neat in appearance. His hair is always slightly wet looking, very neatly parted, and beginning to show a very small gray at its periphery. Each gray hair denotes a sleepless night spent resuscitating or operating on a drunken redneck. He is of Northern Virginia "blue blood" descent. He also reminded some of us of his direct lineage to George Washington. I have never spent any time in Virginia; it must be a neat, little, place.

It was quite amusing to watch the interaction between the Virginia aristocrat and the Bayview redneck trauma patient. Tidy Goldberg did everything right. He was good, and also somehow managed not to get dirty. The combination of his neatness and the dirtiness of the trauma patients was a source of much humor. Masterpiece Theatre meets stinky.

They would meet on morning rounds, in the Emergency Department, or in the OR.

Some of these folks were the dregs of society. Some of them had been shot the evening before, usually for a reason. Some of them were injured while driving drunk. The drunks had a hangover and often smelled of vomit by morning rounds. The mix of blood from the cuts and beer vomit formed tasty little pancakes that lived in the beards of our beloved patients.

The gunshot wound patients were either dead, in the ICU on the blower (ventilator), or limping in the halls asking to go home (and get revenge).

The patients were ripe by the time morning rounds arrived. They were sometimes caked with dried blood if the nurse had not gotten to them. Some of the more violent drunks were tied up and wanting to kick some ass. There was often a total of five or six teeth in the entire family that had come to visit their fallen Cody. Frequently Cody would get messages from the TV inquiring if they had been "...injured in an accident? You may be eligible for significant recoveries." These commercials played while Alistair Cooke (Tidy Goldberg) stood at about a six foot (safe) distance and talked to the patients.

They usually were not as interested in "significant recoveries" as much as they just wanted to kick some ass.

Tidy Goldberg arrives in the room. He is most clean, with freshly parted, slightly damp hair. "Good Morning, I am your host, Tidy Goldberg, and welcome to Stinky Theatre..."

Tidy Goldberg would look to the resident for data and to the patient for evidence of things that might have been missed the night before. A sense of entitlement (fostered perhaps by being provided with neatly pressed custom plaid play pants as a child) helps the attending to function well in this situation. Kiss the ring, feed me the data. A sense of entitlement helps you to ignore the fact that this tired resident presenting to you has just fought a 24-hour war that few can appreciate. A sense of entitlement makes you just want the data.

I enjoyed watching the dynamics of these encounters...."There, there sir, you are quite hurt, quite injured indeed!.... My, my, imagine the force of that truck against your face. Quite phenomenal!"

The resident would present the events, or mishaps of the evening that had brought our poor citizen to his present state. Tidy Goldberg would ensure that the correct things had been done.

"Nurse... clean him up. Very well, sir, good day." As the music plays, you know the tune.

Rounds often left the patient with the question (posed to his visiting friend and co-drunk driver Bubba Bobcat who was not injured and ran away from the scene)... "Who was that? Was that the doctor?"

A conscientious one in the rounding throng might hang back and say, "We'll be back to talk to you (slower) after rounds."

Within a couple of years, Tidy Goldberg had made his first hire during his tenure as Thirsten and Duncan Teabag Endowed Chariman of the Trauma Service. I am sure that he was looking for a world class ass whipper when he chose this one. His name was Stone Cold. Stone Cold is an ex-mercenary, ex-HBO Comedy Hour comedian, ex-black belt karate champion, six foot six gun collector that drove a camouflaged Chevy Blazer (often containing a dead animal from one of his "weekends in the woods"—not to be confused with "On Walden Pond"). I am sure that Superman was very proud to have Stone Cold's camouflaged blazer, complete with an ad on the door for his newly designed deer stand, parked next to his immaculate BMW in the faculty parking lot.

Now there were two. Now they could play "tag team ass whipping." It speaks well for Tidy Goldberg that I considered Stone Cold to be the lesser of two evils. I was soon endeared by Stone Cold with the name "Dickcheese." There are some that drive a hard bargain and it is okay for them to unleash the AWs on you as long as you respect them as a person. It was different with these two guys. You could tell that they got some sort of sadistic pleasure out of it. Boy, those were the days....

When I speak of the virtues of the "Old School," I am speaking of hard working, honorable individuals. I am talking about The Father. I am talking about Superman. I am talking about The Mighty. This was two insecure guys running amuck in their GI Joe uniforms.

*AW*

*You are the fall guy and this is the Friday Night Smackdown. You are the unnamed wrestler that gets the shit beaten out of him, and they are the ones that deal it out; releasing for a moment not only their immediate frustrations, but all in their life that remains unbalanced and troubles them. The worst of the ass whippings from these guys starts with a bad situation. It helps to have a guy that they know is sensitive enough to be upset by their childish rantings.*

*The steaming red smoking head in the white coat that hangs down near to the ground and makes him look like a 5 year-old playing doctor that was recently told that he can't have another pudding.*

*There is an angry comment from the smacker. The negative comments elevate as the smacker begins to roar and you sense that a new chamber of unresolved conflicts has been opened. The ass whipping becomes a purge run for a bilge pump, attempting to empty a sinking boat full of the shit that life has dealt him. It becomes almost as if he is not talking to you any more. It begins to feel more like some sort of necessary mating ritual that a bug has to do before it dies.*

*Goldberg had this vertical vein that would show up in the middle of his forehead at this point. Stone Cold just got red all over.*

*You nasty southern men.*

*Yuck.*

*Tag Team Ass Whipping*

*Tidy Goldberg has delegated an effective system of resident humiliation and torture that has served as the basis for some anger (as I have come to notice as I write this).*

*I have completed 7 rotations on the Trauma Service. I am now done with the last as of one week ago.*

*As I write this, my anger may wane and perhaps I will be able to be more objective.*

*Tidy Goldberg selects out a resident for torture on each rotation. I was "it" two rotations ago. I will never forget it. I came extremely close to quitting, but decided to not give them the satisfaction. Both Stone Cold and Tidy Goldberg were denied positions in cardiothoracic surgery. I believe that they hold this against me still. I have a family; they (Tidy Goldberg and Stone Cold) do not. I feel like I paid the price for that.*

*The following will give you an idea of the nature of the environment that the residents and I endured:*

*I was held personally accountable for the mistakes made by anyone or even problems that arose with patients in the Surgical ICU. An intern, who we will call Mona, was covering for another intern for a night of Trauma call. In the midst of 15 admissions through the ER that night, she failed to fill out the time of accident box on the first page of one History and Physical Exam sheet. Tidy Goldberg discovered the error the next day. I was forced to fill out every blank in every sheet of the charts of every patient or I would "wish Hitler was running the Trauma Service."*

*I was sort of used to the treatment. Dr. Hewes, who was doing a clinical year for recertification in general surgery, was also forced to help me. This was a guy who was 43 and had been out in practice and had returned to improve his clinical abilities. Joe could not believe that he was made to do this, especially by someone who was his age and had previously failed in private practice. When I say that some guys pursue academics to hide from the world of people and human interaction, this is the type that I am talking about.*

*It was Tidy Goldberg's contention was that he "was not going to go to jail for Medicaid fraud because of you!" The scary thing is that he was actually serious. Can you say paranoid?*

*As I stated earlier, I was told that if I did not get the Trauma Service under control that I was going to wish Hitler was the head of the Trauma Service. By the way, he is a weekend warrior (National Guard) who studies military tactics, and keeps a CIA folder on his desk to make it look like he is somehow being briefed by the government.*

*He said that he did not subscribe to the "touchy-feely" style of the new residency programs (which the American Board of Surgery mandated by the way, to protect against past flagrant resident abuses). He often humiliated me and others in front of the staff and nurses, especially when I was post call and rather numb.*

Stone Cold was the first guy hired by Tidy Goldberg for the Trauma Service. He is a very interesting guy. He is a past stand up comedian that appeared on the HBO Comedy Hour. He is a black belt karate expert. He brags to me about trips to Africa where he kills people as a mercenary. I do not even care if he was telling me the truth at this point.

He cracks me up when he tells Stan and me in a voice meant to imitate Darth Vader, "Tidy Goldberg has taught you well my son, now come over to the dark side of the Trauma Service." There is so much surreal crap that goes on around here. I don't even pay attention to any of the bullshit anymore. There are some medical students that rotate on this service. I am sure that we are scaring them off as they watch from the sidelines. Treating them nice while treating us like shit will not fool them. They know that it will be them one day.

How do I describe life in Stone Cold's world?

Where do I start?

I get the Gomer Pyle/Sergeant Carter routine in the OR seemingly independent of my performance. I am just in the wrong place at the wrong time. I sense that this behavior had been going on before I arrived and will continue after I leave. I try not to take it personally, or get into a spin where I am trying ever harder to please the fucker. He wants me to feel stupid, but I have a hard time doing so for two reasons: 1) the American Board of Surgery has told me otherwise (I annually make above 90% on the American Board of Surgery In-Training Exam); and 2) My evaluations have been consistently excellent on all other services. I will be gracious and not detail his experience.

There is always the continuous line of psycho-bullshit that leads to claims such as having climbed the tower behind the trauma office and put The Maximizer's head in his rifle sights as he came in one morning. I have no idea or interest whether this is true or just another example of the psycho-bullshit world that I am being forced to pass through to get where I want to be.

He talks about how much he hates the residents.

He accidentally kicked me in the gonads during a surgery case last year. I know that it was an accident, but if I had to predict a person that would accidentally do that, it would be Stone Cold.

My friend Anderson was closing a trauma case with Stone Cold and cut the wrong end of the fascial stitch at the very end of the closure. The suture unraveled under a great deal of pressure. Stone Cold proceeded to punch Anderson in the chest with such force that it knocked the wind out of him and caused him to back away and gag for his breath. That's *okay on the football field, not during an operation.*

*Stone Cold is very tall, very loud, and extremely temperamental. I always seem to be the one that provides him with the that final push that sends him into his latest promise that he is going to quit. "That's it. Thank you. Thank you very much. You have just given me reason to finally quit this fucking job."*

*These humiliating comments in the OR were a great source of amusement for some of the nurses and anesthesia folks. Some of them loved to see a surgeon get beat up. Given Stone Cold's history of comedy, why should the OR be any different? What the fuck, it's just people's lives (the patient's and the resident's). Let's have fun.*

*I recall a case when he said to the scrub nurse before the case that he had become "so good at it." It being the passing out of AWs. I suppose they were AAWs in his case.*

*He had some great one-liners that I was on the receiving end of:*

*"Did your parents have any children that lived?"*

*"You operate like old people fuck. Slow, ugly, and no one wants to watch."*

*Stone Cold also frequently made reference to the condition of his prostate. Long operations (or what he perceived to be slow operating by you) lead to a continuum of changes from the prostate "hardening" (as in a man getting old) to the prostate becoming so hard and enlarged that it actually falls out of his body the way an old lady's rectum can do with a good strain.*

*"Hurry up, Dickcheese, I swear my fucking prostate is going to fall out of my body!!!"*

*"If I had a knife I would stab you in the head until you were dead."*

*One of Stone Cold's favorite stunts was to hold a pair of forceps in the front of my chest and tell me that he was going to "stab you in the heart" if I screwed up. It made for great comedy in the OR. I did not enjoy it.*

*I would like to qualify this by saying that my treatment was not an exception. I am generally regarded as one of the top residents in the program as noted on my evaluations by the faculty. I made the mistake of being sensitive, honest, hard working, available, and going into cardiothoracic surgery. I was the perfect outlet for his own unhappiness. I took it like no person I have ever directly been associated with. I made it through and I dedicate every moment of happiness that I have from the time that I leave Bayview to your total failure to break my spirit.*

*I want to contribute. I want to train young surgeons that have sensitivity for their patients and a strong desire to contribute. The world opens up for those who want to help out for unselfish reasons. Some of these guys are in this for a sadistic pleasure of handing out AWs, getting their butts kissed, and getting paid for it. They are a joke to the private practice world.*

By the way, Mr. Coffee (the guy that just kept on writing notes) was airborne and moving forward. He had conquered the progress note, and The Maximizer was gone. Times were good for Mr. Coffee. The only major setback that he had suffered to this point was his fiancée's winning a raffle for a party of sixty at a local 1970s retro pick-up bar and giving the name and office address of Superman as the winner. Superman's army of secretaries investigated and I am sure that they marked one notch for Mr. Coffee.

Another interesting character was a Chief Resident who rotated with me on the Trauma Service. He had been given the name "Fingers" due to his uncanny ability to stock the call room with luxury items (such as a television with a cable hook-up) that were previously located in other parts of the hospital. He had a history of cathartic obsession (which we all had to different degrees). One of his most impressive acts was to consume a bottle of magnesium citrate (the green stuff that could make even the most "dried up granny lady" express herself) and to bet his junior resident that he could make it through rounds with the attending without having to excuse himself. Such totally unprovoked daring impressed me.

Fingers and the Trauma Service were a good mix.....

The pager reads the message of doom for the fifteenth time....... "Stable Trauma alert, five minutes.".

Fingers strides downstairs with a characteristic casual pace. He has in his right hand "The Divining Rod" that has served him so well to this point. The Rod is an empty chest tube container measuring about 2 feet in length and with a sturdy plastic framework. It is used for the textbook/intense physical exam that is to follow in the event that this man on the trauma table is a drunken driver asshole who has already endangered his family by driving around the city and now comes to his place of work ready to launch tainted body fluids in his direction (80% of our patient population).

Into the trauma bay strides a well dressed Fingers to the greeting.... "Let my Goddamned hands a-loose!!!!" ("a-loose" being a term that was ingrained into his vocabulary by the greatest influence of his life, Gomer Pyle).

Yep. It's time for The Rod. Fingers draws his examining wand and begins with a gentle poke to the abdomen (allowing maximum doctor-to-patient separation distance).

"You tender???"

"Hey, God Damnit!!"

"You tender???"

"Hey, God Damnit!!"

Hmmm, hard to tell. The neuro exam is indicated to test the reliability of the Divining Rod's findings. The exam is carried out with the precision that only Fingers can deliver at this critical juncture......

A firm kick to a wheel of the stretcher, sending a precise vibratory impulse through Wild Turkey's latest victim. Are the vibrations sensed?

"Hey God Damnit!!"

Yes, we have sensory function. Let's repeat the abdominal exam and correlate the findings......

Poke to the liver.

"You tender???"

"Hey, God Damnit!!"

All of the activity, all of the confusion that surrounds Fingers. They spin in ever tightening gyrations. There is such noise. So many secretions. Speak to us Master. Which way do we travel from here?

Hmmm. Definite tenderness, marginal neuro response, stable vital signs....

"CAT scan."

With a wave to the crowd he ascends to his remodeled loft. Another soul potentially salvaged. "Call me if this guy needs to go to the OR."

I should mention the "scenarios" while on the subject of Fingers. The intern had the job on rounds to present a concise, organized, update on each patient. A logical plan of action was then presented to the attending, who generally looked directly at the intern and offered few, if any, softening gestures.

Feed the attending the data.

The intern on Fingers' service had the added task of trying to keep a straight face after having a few scenarios whispered into his ear between presentations to the attending.

"Scenario, ........ Melatine (a large, verbal, oily person on the janitorial staff), in Environmental Services, jogs around the entire medical center 15 times in the dead heat of summer in plastic underwear. You are given the choice to wear her underwear over your head every night or repeat your intern year. If you say 'neither,' you will be shot..."

I recall Cliff's efforts to keep a straight face while presenting to the attending. Thoughts of being fired for giggling during a presentation of a critically ill patient made clamming up much easier. The scenarios flowed out of Fingers, much like the response obtained from one of his cathartic challenges.

Some pursue academic surgery as an escape. Some like to hear themselves talk. Some truly are idealistic and want to contribute. Academic surgery is only occasionally blessed by the latter. We have a few of the latter here. They are not trauma attendings.

*I am through with all of this. I made it out. I have always considered it my wife and kids against the Trauma Service. I will make it my life's quest not to pass the angry nasty buck that was given to me.*

*Cutting into The Virus*

*Unstable trauma......3 minutes.*
*A 50-year old male comes into the ER with a gunshot wound to the left thigh. The patient was known to be HIV positive (by patient history).*
*He arrived on time. He was thrashing around on the stretcher. There was blood spraying throughout the trauma room. It was a surreal sight.*
*Where are your ER doctors now?.........Watching.*
*Pete (a Chief Resident) and I took this guy directly to the OR after applying effective pressure to his wildly bleeding wounds. No mind that the guy is literally spraying HIV-riddled blood all over me. I have to save him. I also know that when I save him, he will go right back and do the same thing that got him shot in the first place.*
*We got to the OR. Stone Cold is the guy on call.*
*It was the same old crap. I thought that things might be altered just a bit given the situation.*
*Hell no. He yelled at us at the very top of his lungs. He used his forceps to the chest stunt to get attention from the watchers.*
*"Don't fuck up or I will stab you in the heart." The risk of exposure on this case was tremendous. It was an emergency, and it was a vascular injury. There was a need for calm so that we could get on with the*

*real business of the case. Saving the patient. Remember?*

*Stone Cold continued to yell at us despite all of this. It may be okay for basic training on Paris Island, but not when I am a father and have young children at home that are counting on me to come home and be there for them as they grow. I thought about that during the entire case. If I stuck myself or exposed myself to this patient's blood, it would all be over with. I made it through the case okay. Stone Cold ended up sticking himself during the case. He did not seroconvert that I know of. I would not wish that on even my greatest enemies.*

I found a piece of paper today in an old chest that sits in our living room. The chest is full of letters and papers that I accumulated during my time in Bayview City.

There is a memo from the Cleveland Clinic. It is dated February 10, 1997 and gives miscellaneous information about what was an upcoming visit. I was interviewing for a cardiothoracic surgery fellowship at that time.

The interesting thing about this document is what is on the back. There is a list scribbled in pencil on the upper left-hand corner. The document is folded in thirds, so I was probably carrying it around in my coat. The list looks as if it were written in a hurried fashion, though my handwriting is bad even when I write slowly. I probably wrote it during a boring part of rounds, or in a desperate moment of self-awareness.

Below are the plans for yet another overhaul of what sounds like a stressed guy. Listed to the right is the two year follow up results.

| | |
|---|---|
| Diet—low fat, high carbohydrate | I still eat horribly |
| Exercise q day (daily) | I do not exercise, I work hard |
| Meditate q day | I drink alcohol |
| No Reading | Done okay with that one |
| Speak your mind | Done okay there too |
| Reduce coffee intake | Down to one pot per day |
| Prepare for conferences | Too busy operating |
| To work early (1 hour early) | Work is early |
| Two beers after work | Near drinking before work |
| Don't beat yourself up, coast | Have not killed myself yet. |

Does anyone wish to lay down some money on the success odds of this latest overhaul plan of escape?

*A Refuge is Discovered*

*Woody's Barber Shop. It is the stuff of legends. I do not know if any-one has ever published an account of this place. It gives the Bayview Hospital an added sense of character.*

*The shop is located on the first floor of Cumberland Tower. Cumberland Tower was built as part of the New Deal/Reconstruction effort. It was erected in 1938. The shop is the size of a large patient room. It is near the waiting room for the intensive care units.*

*There is one of those rotating cylinders with the red spiral on the outside. I always marveled at those as a child. The progression of the stripe up the cylinder and its eventual disappearance troubled me. I look back at my confusion and realize that I have not made much progress in understanding the stripe. My confusion persists, and now I am a heart surgeon. That also troubles me. Can I make it in the absence of such spatial orientation? I proceed with the assumption that I can. I guess we will see.*

*To the readers: I promise that I will not operate if I am one of those licensed killers. I'll write stupid books.*

*The shop has two barber chairs. There is only one barber, Woody Woodall. Woody has worked in the shop for about thirty years. He is a heavy-set gentleman from the Deep South. He speaks slowly. He stares at you over his low set reading glasses. He speaks his mind, and his hon-esty is refreshing. He knows about almost everyone in the hospital. He is sort of the talk show host for the shop. Any topic is game.*

*Woody occasionally gives haircuts that are not symmetrical. I have heard people complain about the quality of his haircuts. They missed the point of the shop. They were in the wrong place by definition. They wanted to look good. Do not go to his shop if you are looking to be pret-ty. You go to get your hair cut so that you don't look like a hippie.*

*Function.*

*How old is that stuff in the barbicide jar?*

*What is in the barbicide jar?*

*Woody does not care who or what you are; though he loves to meet new female customers. He is honest. Egos are leveled here. It is the real world. Leave your big doctor stuff at the door. The heart surgeon talks to the cafeteria guy. Even the resident talks to the attending. Nobody is spe-cial. Everybody (man) likes sports and sex, so they have Playboy and Sports Illustrated issues lining the windowsills.*

*Woody's shop provided me with a refuge. Where else could you go*

*and get a bad haircut and talk about how fucked up your job is? It was
a great refuge from "political correctness."*

*A Second Refuge......The Porch*

*This is the place where I would be on equal grounds with Stone Cold.
We smoked cigarettes together. It was the side of him that I liked. We
could go there and be antisocial together. After all of the mercenary,
high-powered rifle, AW, dead bobcats in the truck, stab you in the head,
psycho fatigue torture was over, he was not such a bad guy. He really
did not think so highly of the majority of the people in the world either.*
*I'm sick too.*
*One of my favorite themes that was discussed on The Porch was
"Good touch, Bad touch."*
*You know the difference.*
*There's the slap on the back for a job well done....good touch.*
*There is the bilateral shoulder squeeze that lasts over 1.0 seconds
and is from behind...bad touch.*
*There is the punch on the chest after a great job with a distal coro-
nary bypass.....good touch.*
*There is the hand on the arm and a look into the eye.....bad touch.*
*There is the stare into the eye from a man with a neatly trimmed
beard...bad touch without touch.*
*I came away from the porch a newly inspired man. I felt like Stone
Cold and I were okay. Then another disaster trauma case would come
in. The topic of conversation would inevitably deteriorate into comments about old people's sexual practices ("you operate like old people
fuck.....slow, ugly, and nobody wants to watch...), and sharp objects
going into my head until I stopped moving. Oh well. Only a few more
years. Too late to quit now. We had to have the most pathologic friendship of all time.*
*The abuser and the abusee that feels like he has done something to
deserve it; or allows himself to be abused to keep the abuser satisfied.*

I interviewed for a spot in cardiothoracic surgery at The Big City
while on the Trauma Service. These letters serve as a good set of primary history to let you know what I was thinking at the time. You can
guess that I was more than a little motivated to do well and take my
family and myself away from the preceding.

The interview went well. I felt like I had a chance. It was definitely the best residency spot in the nation for cardiothoracic surgery. The

hospital was great. The surgeons were at the peak of their careers, and the residents looked like they worked hard but were treated like human beings.

I wrote away to The Chairman of Cardiothoracic Surgery:

*May 8, 1997*

*Chief, Cardiothoracic Surgery*
*Director, Residency Training*
*The Big City School of Medicine*

*Dear Sir,*

*I want to thank you for the opportunity to interview at The Big City University for a position in cardiothoracic surgery.*

*I was impressed by the large volume and complexity of cases that are available in every area of cardiothoracic surgery. Two additional outstanding features of your program are the facilities available for basic scientific research and the obvious commitment of your faculty to resident education.*

*I have thought long and hard about where I would like to complete my surgical training. I intend to rank your program highly.*

*I am very proud of what I have accomplished in Bayview City. I have approached my education from the frame of mind that I owe it to my patients to spare no measure in becoming the best physician possible. I have always sought the more difficult task when given the choice, and have dedicated my life to one of service rather than personal gain. It is this frame of reference that I believe will make me an asset to your residency program. I hope that these three years will serve as a springboard to a lifetime of leadership and service in cardiothoracic surgery.*

*Please understand how much that I want to come to The Big City. I thank you for your consideration.*

*Sincerely,*


*C. Patrick Murrah, M.D.*

My role model was and is Dr. Sternalpunch:

*May 8, 1997*

*Dr. Sternalpunch*
*Professor of Surgery*
*The Big City University School of Medicine*

*Dear Dr. Sternalpunch,*

*I want to thank you for the opportunity to interview at The Big City for a position in cardiothoracic surgery. I was impressed by the large volume and complexity of cases that are available in every area of cardiothoracic surgery. Two additional outstanding features of your program are the facilities available for basic scientific research and the obvious commitment of your faculty to resident education.*

*I have thought long and hard about where I would like to complete my surgical training. I intend to rank your program highly.*

*I am very proud of what I have accomplished in Bayview City. I have approached my education from the frame of mind that I owe it to my patients to spare no measure in becoming the best physician possible. I have always sought the more difficult task when given the choice, and have dedicated my life to one of service rather than personal gain. It is this frame of reference that I believe will make me an asset to your residency program. I hope that these three years will serve as a springboard to a lifetime of leadership and service in cardiothoracic surgery.*

*Please understand how much that I want to come to The Big City. I hope that I will be favorably ranked by your program; however, I will continue to practice by your example and give 110% regardless of the outcome of the match.*

*Thank you for your consideration.*

*Sincerely,*

*C. Patrick Murrah, M.D.*

On the morning of June 13th; I received the piece of mail that I had been waiting for. It was Match Day. The day that you find out where you would be living for the next three years. I had ranked The Big City University at the top of my list. I had put everything into making this match. It all came down to this one moment. I was very nervous. I knew enough about the ugly side of the world and how bad things can happen in a random way (the house fire, the soccer mom that ran Leroy over with her van).

I sat in the tub and opened the letter. My wife went into the kitchen; to stay away from me in case of disaster and mental decompensation.

*Thoracic Surgery Specialty Match—1998 Appointments*

*Match Results*
*June 13, 1997*

*Congratulations! You have been matched to the following program:*

*The Big City University Hospitals*

I matched baby!!!!!!!!!!! I got my first choice. Life was good.

*Chairman, Division of Cardiothoracic Surgery*
*The Big City University Hospital*

*C. Patrick Murrah, M.D.*
*Resident, Division of General Surgery*
*Bayview Department of Surgery*

*Dear Sir,*

*I was very pleased to learn that I matched in cardiothoracic surgery at The Big City University. I look forward to a great three years with you.*

*This year I will focus on seeking out and managing complex clinical problems in general surgery in hopes of making my year one that I, and more importantly, Superman will be very pleased with.*

*Thank you again for your consideration.*

*Sincerely,*

*C. Patrick Murrah, M.D.*

I felt like this was an appropriate note on which to end this part of my journey. Nothing else mattered. I was done. They could not touch me.

**Sixth Year of General Surgery Residency........VA Surgery**

Hours:          Every night home call; 80 hours per week
To work:        6 AM, Monday through Saturday; 6 AM Sunday
Home:           Average 5 PM during week; 2 PM Saturday;
                Noon Sunday
Note:           Chief call (protected by a junior resident, but on
                every night)

Gross Pay Rate ............................$7.45
Net Pay Rate ...............................$5.63

This consisted of gallbladders, hernias, colon cancers, and an occasional perforated ulcer. I was given more freedom at the VA. Dr. Simmons was a wise and able professor. I learned from his technique as well as his sensitivity.

He had it all together. I always respected him because he was a nice guy that was smart enough to succeed in a sometimes ugly and competitive environment.

Taking care of Bill

This was a time when I was called on to help a distant cousin who was ill. His name was Bill. Bill threw up blood at the Shoney's in Brunswick, Georgia. An extensive workup in Brunswick revealed that he had an advanced cancer of the esophagus.

Save your cousin.

I remember the day that he arrived in Bayview with his wife Kim. Bill had PTSD (post traumatic stress disorder)/alcohol/depression/mania/lithium and Kim had some sort of a fat/innocent/little girl/retard thing going on. It had been love at first sight when they met in the Chattahoochee State Mental Hospital in north Florida. They were such honest people. They helped each other take their lithium pills.

They really thought that I was going to save them.

Alison had married me for love. Taking care of these two for a year while I was at the hospital was one of those small clauses in the corner of the contract.

Esophageal cancer is a terrible disease. The 5-year survival is around 20% with surgery. The 5-year survival is closer to 0% without surgery.

We put them up at our small home for the entire process of workup, vomiting, chemotherapy, vomiting, radiation therapy, vomiting, and surgery. That was a period of about 12 months.

The process began with the diagnosis. The doctors in Brunswick put a scope in his throat and told him that he had an advanced cancer of the esophagus. Then they put what is called a PEG tube (feeding tube) in his stomach.

He then was given a six-week course of chemo and radiation therapy. He was able to go back to St. Simon's Island between some of the sessions, but he spent most of his time with us. I think back to us watching college football on the couch and him hacking up chicken noodle soup like a cat with a giant fur ball in his stomach.

"That's okay, Bill. We'll just use a pair of your skid marked briefs sitting next to the couch to clean that up."

It was a long and sometimes very painful quest. Remember that Alison had two babies (not children) in tow. I was always at work and was not the one that had to circle the Cancer Center with a car full of screaming kids, waiting to pick Bill up from his therapy. It was Alison's own private BOHICA, compliments of Patrick's good will.

Bill was a good man. He did however occasionally leave those dirty underwear around the house. My wife Alison, with two babies in tow, cleaned them faithfully.

It's okay, he's got cancer.

We're going to save him. Even if.........

My Last remaining Dog and my only Son are Poisoned

I did become more attached to the whole saga the day that Bill's wife Kim left her lithium out for my son to eat and share with the dog. Alison, with one non-poisoned baby in tow, faithfully had both the dog and my son's stomachs pumped. There was the great message that I was given in between cases...

"Dr. Murrah, please have a seat. Your dog is doing great. He was poisoned today and had his stomach pumped at the vet. Your son is at the Children's Hospital having his stomach pumped."

I ran the four blocks to Children's Hospital. I arrived just in time to see my son with the charcoal thing going on. He survived. The dog survived. I kicked Kim out of the house. As much as I loved her, I was afraid that I might murder her and mess up all of this work and career thing that I had going on.

Bill made it to operation.
Alison and I made it to Bill's operation.
My son made it to Bill's operation.
The dog made it to Bill's operation.

Kim was "invited" to go back home by "mean old daddy" who kicked her out of the house..

It was a big moment. Bill had an esophagectomy (trans-hiatal–where they cut your esophagus off and pull the stomach up into the neck and sew it to the stump of the throat). All of the family was there. We (Alison) were exhausted from taking care of Bill and Kim.

We're going to save him....

We had no life before all of this "save your cousin" fun, now we had no life minus one.

The General operated on Bill. The General was a new hotshot from Cornell and the Memorial Sloan Kettering Cancer Center. He was an excellent surgeon.

Bill made it home without any trouble, to our relief. Then came the slow downhill course of what can best be termed "the dwindles." He was so weak after surgery that he never really could get his feet back. There were the panicked phone calls to me that he was sick again. There were readmissions to the hospital in Brunswick. Then he was gone. He died at home. Hospice finished him off with a home morphine kit. It was the best thing that could have happened to him. It was clear that he had had a local recurrence of his cancer, and he was having severe back pain in addition to swallowing difficulties.

Bill was a simple man that had had to deal with great losses in his life. Spending time in Viet Nam probably was not helpful in the overall scheme of things. He lost his first wife after a bad divorce. His only daughter never came to see him, even on his deathbed. He had found love at the institution where he was treated for depression. Bill and Kim (the one that poisoned my son) shared and helped each other through a new life. He had worked hard at the Ace Hardware on Saint Simons Island. He had an honesty about him that I probably never will have.

If I were honest for more than one hour, I would be arrested.

Bill was a pain in the butt to take care of (I speak for Alison), but we did the right thing. He got a shot at the best of medical care and he was given some time to think about his life before passing.

I gave my Grand Rounds presentation on the operation that Bill received. I told the faculty how much that I appreciated their help. I also emphasized the suffering that is involved in receiving radiation and chemotherapy. I watched him try to eat, and shoot it back up. He sort of withered away. I will always remember the way that the disease took him. Life is short.

I am coming right behind you Bill.

**Sixth Year of General Surgery Residency.......Blue Surgery**

| | |
|---|---|
| Hours: | Every other night home call; 100 hours per week |
| To work: | 6 AM, Monday through Saturday; 6 AM Sunday |
| Home: | Average 8 PM during week; 2 PM Saturday; Noon Sunday |
| Note: | Chief call (protected by a junior resident, but on every night) |

Gross Pay Rate ............................$5.96
Net Pay Rate ...............................$4.51

Now I would finally be acting as a Chief Resident. I began on the General Surgery Service run by Dr. Young. He was a tough man. He reminds me of a bulldog. He does not do anything halfway. He supposedly rides a Harley. I also know that he loves the space program.

His technical ability is amazing. He has nailed down the procedures to individual moves. Nothing is wasted. I once wrote up a seven-page paper on how he does a laparoscopic cholecystectomy. He will probably edit it and add to the detail.

He taught me the methodical approach to general surgery. All of the steps can be duplicated. If you keep everything constant, you can test the effect of changing one thing.

He is the only guy that I know who has a twenty-step routine for placement of a Hickman catheter (chemotherapy catheter). His always work.

# 17

# Seventh Year of General Surgery Residency

Total Years:    15 (1997-1998) .................33 years old
Salary/Debt:    $32,000 per year; $65,000 debt
Hours:    Varied with service
Title:    "Bitch: Maker of Wounds"

**Seventh Year of General Surgery Residency......Gold Surgery**

Hours:    Every night home call; 80 hours per week
To work:    6 AM, Monday through Saturday; 6 AM Sunday
Home:    Average 7 PM during week; 2 PM Saturday;
    Noon Sunday
Note:    Chief call (protected by a junior resident, but on
    every night)

    Gross Pay Rate ...........................$7.68
    Net Pay Rate ..............................$5.81

I began my seventh year on the Gold Service. The Chief Resident on the Gold Service does endocrine (thyroid, parathyroid, and adrenal gland) surgery with Superman. He also does vascular (abdominal aortic aneurysm repair, carotid endarterectomy, leg bypass) surgery with Superman's lifelong friend, The Mighty Hoss.

The Mighty Hoss is a tremendously experienced vascular surgeon. He is a product of Bayview City. He was born in Easley, a suburb of Bayview City that prospered during the early industrial days. The

Mighty's father was the Sheriff of Cumberland County during the difficult years of racial unrest. The Mighty's father was an honorable and
tough man. This job was not fit for the faint of heart. As a boy, one of
The Mighty's family chores was to go into the old mines around the
county and take out illegal stills. He was only a young man at the time.
This experience in his youth minimized the fear incurred by, say, a ruptured abdominal aortic aneurysm. Perhaps even the sight of watching
a bad resident try to fix it.

The Mighty stayed in town and completed his medical school and
residency in general and vascular surgery. He trained during the pre-
Boss era at Bayview. Dr. Lionheart was in charge. This was a time when
the residents had absolutely no rights. All that they did was work, and
they were glad to have a job. Dr. Lionheart supposedly had an active
temper. The residents lived in fear of him. If a patient was doing poorly, it became the responsibility of the intern on the surgical service to
hide that patient from Dr. Lionheart for the duration of rounds. A common strategy was to ride that patient up and down on the elevator until
he was gone.

The Mighty used to operate all day and then into the night during
his early years as an attending physician. The residents gave him the
name Captain Midnight.

The Mighty is a solidly built, white-haired man with a Bayview
drawl. He has a very quick wit. He commands the respect of those
around him without saying much. His drawl can worsen in the OR to
the point where words fuse into a grunt of sorts that only his dedicated scrub nurse can understand. The word "forceps" becomes
"fawsu." "Bovie" (electrocautery used to coagulate bleeders) becomes
"buh."

Oh, but do not rest at ease in the OR. This is a man that can take
you out in the flip of a switch. The calcium channels empty. A white-
headed man in the evening of a celebrated career generally mellows
with age. This man maintains his charge. It begins with a look up from
the depths of the wound where, perhaps, stool has floated into a previously sterile field. The look up is followed by a high frequency total
body shake, and an extension of the word "God" with the addition of
a "w."

"Gawwwwwwwwwwwd daaaaaaaaaaaaamit!!!!!" The shaking worsens
and tightens as the word is completed. The Mighty holds his instruments in his balled up fists. His face begins to turn red.

His lifelong scrub nurse knows that it is coming and remains calm
knowing that the cat is out of the bag.

It is the man that should be playing golf somewhere. He is in room

16 with a team of nurses trying to fix a mess, teaching a bunch of green residents how to do things right.

He has seen it, and he has mastered it. He has seen every possible complication, resident and non-resident induced. He has seen so many of the even the rarest of complications that they only annoy him, and certainly do not scare him.

"Away you frickin bootlegging sissies!!!! The Mighty has arrived. Stand down!!"

This is a good man. He usually only throttles the circulating nurse. The circulator immediately summons an emergency "keep the peace crash team" of circulators. This crew begins to turn about in furious circles producing the sound of suture wrappers opening. They are searching for that suture that he has used in the previous 345,789 cases, but today was somehow excluded from the setup for the first time in his 37-year tenure at Bayview.

"You aren't ready and when the shit hits the fan the elbows start flying in the air and here we go with the wrappers."

The resident freezes. The resident shuts up, secretly thanking God that the pointer isn't on him.

"I HATE the Goddamned sound of those wrappers coming open!"

The flow signals in the patients are checked at the end of each case. It is a ritual that The Mighty performs before leaving the room. The experienced staff jumps to turn down the volume on the Doppler machine as it is being moved across the patient's foot. The experienced nurses turn the Doppler volume all of the way up when it is in the proper place. That awful scuffing sound that the Doppler probe makes when it travels along the skin irritates The Mighty Hoss.

Let him be. He has earned his peace. We are graced by his presence in the operating room. We learn from his experience. He teaches the residents what to avoid. It is the mark of an experienced surgeon to know how to stay out of trouble more than how to get out of trouble.

He leaves Room 16. The room collectively exhales. He is the greatest, and he has shown you again how to operate with courage and intensity. You leave the room wanting to be Mighty too.

He is deeply loved by the residents and the nurses. His tirades are large, but they are consistent. They are not random. He does not hold a grudge. He tells it like it is. The most important words are consistency, honesty, and respect.

The Mighty once told my friend Stan that "you have to have a resident's respect before you can teach him anything."

Some of the guys that I worked with tried to imitate The Mighty.

Some of them do not command this respect. Without this, the rest of the learning process is compromised.

I am privileged to have worked with The Mighty.

There are many stories that came out of his years of bold service to this medical center.

Years ago he was working on a difficult case in Room 16 when over the intercom came a request for help. It was none other than The Holy Ghost. The man that is considered by some to be the world's premier adult cardiac surgeon. The Holy Ghost called over the intercom requesting assistance with a complication that had arisen from the insertion of a device called an intraaortic balloon pump.

The pump was placed in the groin of the patient by the heart surgeons to assist with the function of his failing heart. The pump is advanced to the aortic arch and is a necessary but often quite invasive form of therapy. Blockage of flow to the leg distant to the site of insertion is a recognized complication of their insertion.

This patient had developed a cold leg over the past hour and was in need of an operation to retrieve a clot that was blocking blood flow to the leg. This was a procedure that The Holy Ghost's service was certainly capable of. Sometimes the request for the vascular surgeons to take care of their complications with a procedure that they already know how to do is seen as a form of dumping or even disrespect.

The Mighty was never anyone's boy.

The Holy Ghost's voice projected through the room, "we have a patient that I wonder if you could help us with Mighty Hoss."

The Holy Ghost went on to explain how the patient had clotted his leg as a result of the balloon pump.

The Mighty Hoss paused then inquired, "You ever been to the circus?"

"Yes," replied The Holy Ghost.

"You know those elephants that go along in the parade?" continued Mighty.

"Yes Mighty," replied The Holy Ghost.

"You know the guys that follow along and clean up those huge piles of crap that those elephants leave?"

"Yes Mighty."

"Well I'm not fucking one of them!!! Fix your own Goddamned complications!"

On went The Mighty, pounding away at his operation, not missing a beat. His proud team followed.

The Mighty was not afraid to speak his mind.

A great case that circulated around involved an awful abdominal aortic aneurysm repair. The patient was bleeding badly and somehow the intestines were opened and stool flowed into the field to the dismay of the Mighty and his followers. Mighty had his head down in the wound and was sewing furiously, all the while yelling out "Suck, God damnit."

A nervous medical student's single role in life at that point was to suck blood or anything in The Mighty's way. He nervously and incorrectly placed his magic suck wand into The Mighty Hoss' left ear, complete with a kernel of Grade A southern dukey on the tip.

Mighty paused and began to shake. The residents froze. "Do you mean to tell me that you just stuck that Goddamned shit-laden sucker in my ear?????!!!!"

The student did the thing that primal fear deemed most appropriate and ran out of the room.

The Mighty recovered and saved the patient. Whether the student's ego could be saved was another issue.

The Mighty did not trust particular anesthesiologists at the VA Hospital. This mistrust was based on her having "killed more veterans than the German Army!" It was true.

We all did what the Mighty said, and he taught us that "vascular surgery for the not frail of heart."

"Boy, if I tell you that a piss ant can pull a plow...hitch him up!!!"

My experience on the Gold Service with two folks sporting the combined power of Superman and The Mighty was one of avoiding the performance of lethal insult. I was there to not actively kill their patients. The correct answer was "yes sir." I was there to listen and to learn. My sphincter was appropriately tight to the point of necrosis for a 70-day period. The act of flatulence could potentially upset all dogs within a one-mile radius.

One day The Mighty and Superman both had great cases. Superman was removing a large thyroid goiter. The Mighty had a femoral to femoral bypass graft that I knew he would let me do.

I took a step in what was, in retrospect, the incorrect direction by scrubbing with The Mighty. I figured that I would get useful vascular experience and get a chance to be with The Mighty who had been out of town. I was slated to be a heart surgeon after all.

Wrong move. The femoral to femoral bypass went well, but the thyroid case went extremely well. It was one of those rare goiters where the sternum (breastbone) had to be split in order to fully remove it. This involved in making a sternotomy (dividing the breast bone-just like I was to be doing in cardiac surgery). I had missed a jewel by trying to think too much. Superman appropriately ribbed me about this for the remainder of the rotation. Any time a good case would come up, he would ask if I wanted to go scrub with someone else other than the Chairman of the Department.

Abdominal aortic aneurysms are the best time to be with The Mighty. "Go Ahead and Get Started, I'll be in there after a while" is his way of telling you that it is time to grow up.

This was the "old school." He was tough and you wanted to be him.

Time to bow up, get after those bootleggers.

Grandma Gets Naked

I am a private person. Tonight my walking out into the kitchen butt naked into the presence of my brother-in-law only reinforces that feeling. It also reminds me of the strong desire I have not to see my relatives naked. That desire was also betrayed around this time when my grandmother was visiting from out of state. She was in her early nineties, had skinny little legs, and a big round body with a barrel chest with giant breasts that hung down to her waist. She had become quite top heavy, and not designed for good solid walking.....

I am at Jimmy Ray's Barbecue picking up an order when the call comes in.....

Grandma down, on your deck, probable hip crack...

Oh shit.....A dash back to the house, an ambulance trip to my hospital, a rush into radiology to diagnose what I know may be a smashed hip and perhaps the end of granny.

Then, the true pathology strikes....

A look out of the corner of my eye as I pass by the x-ray suite, and there she is.....all granny, all nude.

More than I wanted.

I call on my objectivity in this time of need, but it is smashed. My mind races.

I guess I knew that she looked like that on the inside. I have seen a thousand grannies naked when I operate on them. Somehow you block the anatomy of your own family out.

I must stay focused.

Granny gets a hip operation a few days later. She does okay, then slips into the postop, ninety-year-old confused, picking berries out of the sky, delirium that has no cure to my knowledge.

I felt sorry for the sitter (who, incidentally, was being paid better than me as a surgery resident) and wanted to let her relax for a night at my home. I made the mistake of spending a night in the room with granny in a very small cot. This was at the height of her confusion. She would cry out that she "...CAN'T REST!"

I got so frustrated at her cries that I began to cuss at my own grandma.

"God Damnit, just rest. The conditions are perfect. The lights are out, you are tired, and you sure as hell seem to want rest. Let's do it!!"

Then I would draw back in horror at my own impatience with this poor ailing woman. I would then reassure myself that my ugliness would not be remembered once the berry picking went away.

I'll bet nobody will want to see me naked by the time I am 50.

## Seventh Year of General Surgery Residency......Blue Surgery Service

Hours:         Every other night home call; 100 hours per week
To work:       6 AM, Monday through Saturday; 6 AM Sunday
Home:          Average 8 PM during week; 2 PM Saturday;
               Noon Sunday
Note:          Chief call (protected by a junior resident, but on
               every night)

               Gross Pay Rate ...........................$6.15
               Net Pay Rate ..............................$4.66

El Toro headed up this service. He is the most experienced member of our general surgery department. He was trained in Mexico City and the Mayo Clinic. He came to the Bayview Hospital in the late 1960s along with The Father. He was asked by The Father to help set up a first class general surgery program.

He is the one who first attempted liver transplantation at Bayview. Liver transplantation was in its infancy at that time. There was not yet a solid regimen to prevent the bane of all transplant surgeons, acute rejection. It was not until the introduction of the medication cyclosporine that results became good enough to make liver transplantation an everyday reality The actual technique of liver transplantation was also in its infancy. It was El Toro's courage that enabled him to take on such a difficult problem. The liver transplant program at Bayview is now in the top five in the United States, performing close to 100 transplantations per year and having the best results of any center.

El Toro is one of the bravest general surgeons at Bayview. He was not afraid to cut into something, even if he was not 100% sure what it was. He knew that he could fix, whatever it was. There was the potential for much blood loss in his big cases, but you never felt like things were out of control. I loved operating with El Toro because he was fearless. I truly believed in him, and he was one of the guys that believed in me when I came to interview at Bayview in the summer of 1992.

El Toro always thought that I had potential because I was a Merit Scholar. I was a late bloomer in his eyes. It took the same courage and foresight to believe in me that it took for him to establish liver transplantation and indeed general surgery with the help of a few others at Bayview.

Dr. Simmons was another veteran of the General Surgery Service. He is a very good guy, and a terrific surgeon. A very tall and gentle, sensitive man. He was proof that you can be nice and be on staff at a killer program. You just had better be very smart.

He lets you do the operation. Dr. Simmons trained here at Bayview and under Dr. Patton. I always enjoy working on his service.

Dr. Simmons seems to have the best looking and nicest wife of all of the attendings. I believe that this is the result of his personality and he may have it more together than all of us. He also tackled those fat cases like Dr. Holly. I just could not handle that.

Dr. Hopkins was our expert in pancreatic surgery. As an African-American, he serves as a role model to the minority residents and applicants under the probably correct assumption that someone who is not both white, and male will be watched under more of a microscope, in a self-fulfilling prophecy kind of way.

I have a great deal of respect for this man. He is a guy that truly wants to contribute. The world seems to open up for those who do.

I performed a tremendous amount of cases on the gallbladder, pancreas and liver during my 10 weeks on this rotation. There were no cases that stick out as I write this. I guess that that is a good thing.

*Exit Mr. Sexy*

*Sex drive waning. Turns out that Fred was an old dog, even when we got him from the pound. He began to lose weight. He stopped eating. Then he bit Charles (the one that was poisoned) in the face.*

*No big deal. A few stitches, a plastic surgeon, and we were golden.*

*The dog had to go to the vet to see why he was losing weight.*

*Huge cancer of the esophagus. They put Mr. Sexy down.*

*We gave him a good year. He certainly lived life to the fullest.*

**Seventh Year of General Surgery Residency......Trauma Service**

Hours:          Every third night in-house call; 110 hours per week
To work:        5 AM, Monday through Saturday; 6 AM Sunday
Home:           Average 6 PM during week; 2 PM Saturday;
                2 PM Sunday

                Gross Pay Rate ...........................$5.59
                Net Pay Rate ..............................$4.23

It was my seventh and final year as a general surgery resident at the Bayview Hospital. The last challenge that I had to face was my Chief Resident rotation on the Trauma Service. My experiences here serve as enough motivation to write this book. I do not need any more. I hope that I can do someone that comes after me some good.

I spent eight weeks on the service. The first 2 weeks consisted of every other night call, because the third Chief Resident was on vacation. I would be at work at 0515 and would stay up all night taking trauma call. I would go home around 6 to 7 PM the next night. 38 hours on, 10 hours off. It took about ten minutes to drive home. This schedule, carried out for two weeks, runs to a total of about 120 hours awake and in the hospital per week. Add to this the constant threat of ridicule that you receive with every move, medical or personal, and you have the formula for misery.

I had already matched into a cardiothoracic surgery spot at Big City University. I was very careful not to flaunt it. I was leaving Bayview shortly. In some sort of sick way I was going to miss it. I had ranked Bayview as my second choice for cardiothoracic surgery, and would have been well trained there as well.

*Dead Man Disimpacted*

*I was quite the pro at relieving rectal impactions (stool rocks, often with high-pressure brown rivers behind them). I was not afraid. One of my best disimpactions came from a 95% burn patient that no one noticed had not had a bowel movement in a couple of weeks.*

*Stories about the relief that I obtained on this man circulated.*

*He had a rock holding off the storm. I pulled the rock out. It was hard enough that it tore my glove (unbeknownst to me) and I got it all up under my fingernails and onto my forearm. The stool was of such magnitude that I considered consulting the OB-GYNs to get an "APGAR score" (a measure of the functional status of a newborn infant) on the specimen. It was a powerful disimpaction, and a good lesson for the junior guys on the importance of a thorough physical exam on every patient every day.*

*It was also a moment of beauty to show Tidy Goldberg what I had done. He was such a tidy guy. "Quite atrocious, that bulging, almost animate mass of putrid material. Quite hideous. There there, carry on. Wash, wash."*

*I know the square root of every number to the 10th digit. That statement stands alone. Tidy Goldberg loved to show my skills off to other residents.*

I picked up where I had left off with respect to the AWs. I was trying to make it a positive experience. I was a set up from the start, so was my friend Stan, who had matched at Baylor. The phrase "kid gloves" fits well. I busted my butt for the entire 8 weeks on that rotation. I tried to stay out of trouble when possible, and to do extra to help out other services when needed. Miss Kitty was a continuous source of major screw-ups that were pissing the staff off. Guess who got to hear about it? The guys that stick around and accept responsibility are the ones that hear about the screw-ups.

There are 4 attendings that work in the Trauma office. Three of these are rested at any given time. You are always tired. Tidy Goldberg is the head guy. The rested ones like to go after the tired guys in the morning when you present your overnight disasters. It was for our education, and also filled whatever pathologic need they had to make us look stupid. It frustrated me very much being one of the poster children for BOHICA.

The events surrounding a resident's demise on the Trauma Service:

*We constantly have to gauge how the weather is with Stone Cold. He is so moody that keeping him from exploding is a full time chore.*

*Miss Kitty is a fourth year resident and was one of our Chiefs. She screwed up so badly that I was asked to step forward and fuse her surgical service with my own. The junior resident Damien was adequate to be promoted to taking Chief call. She was dropped to the responsibility of a junior resident.*

*Her demotion stemmed from her management of a patient that was shot in the back. She was told to study the patient with a CT scan (This is an unconventional approach to this problem, but not totally out the realm of effective care. There are papers written about this approach, it is called "selective management," where you study patients and try to avoid unnecessary operations; but as is so often the case, the people that write the papers don't do the operations.) The CT scan showed a large amount of blood in the back of the abdomen on the right. Usually, a gunshot wound to the back is an indication for an operation. This was a clear indication for operation. The trajectory of the bullet was such that it crossed the pelvis, endangering the iliac vessels, possibly a source of fatal internal hemorrhage. It was certainly inappropriate to watch this gunshot wound. Never mind that the attending on call told her to get the CT scan and was nowhere to be found at morning report when it came time to defend the decision to watch the patient instead of operating.*

*I found the patient on the 10th floor the next morning, having abdominal pain. I operated on the patient with another attending the next morning. There was only blood in the retroperitoneum, and the patient did well, despite the selective approach. The exploration was certainly appropriate to rule out injury.*

Kitty was hung out to dry after this case. Stone Cold came in and found this problem and stated "Can't I ever come in just one fucking morning and there not be a disaster waiting for me?"

Blood was in the water. It was acute on chronic. The attendings attacked and ridiculed her constantly. They crushed what little confidence that she had left. Everyone else, including myself just sort of backed away, the way that you do when someone passes gas in the cafeteria in grade school. She was officially "it." Nobody wanted to be "it." It is sort of like the sheep running up the rear in the herd and getting snagged by the wolves. No other sheep wants to be associated with that one, lest they be eaten as well. She was dangerous, there was no doubt, but there were softer ways of dealing with it. As it is, I tried to remind myself that it is my wife, my kids, and myself against the rigors of the residency process.

There was an understood custom within the Trauma culture that if the "it" gets killed, someone else has to step up and be the new "it." So you at least want the "it" not to bleed too much, just enough to stay wounded and alive.

Damien, meanwhile, took the reigns of his new chiefdom and ran hard with them. He loved to be in charge. We would actually get quite excited when there were medical disasters on the service. We ran hard. So hard in fact, that we were separated at the midpoint of the rotation to spread out the workforce.

One of my favorite stories was the night that Damien was on call and called me in. It had been a grueling 36 hours of call in which I had not slept. Two more traumas came in that needed to go to the OR. I was open to leave. I stayed. I did not want to leave my post when the team was getting waxed. Besides, Damien was a newly appointed Chief and was going to have to go to the OR with Stone Cold. The awake total was now 42 hours when I went home early that morning.

I was going to serve as some kind of buffer since I was the one who was on a roll with Stone Cold (for now at least, having busted my butt for six weeks and having kept Miss Kitty from knocking off the patients).

Stone Cold and I were smoking buddies on the "porch" that sat outside of the Trauma Office. We were equals on the porch. He reminded me of my younger brother in some select ways. He kept a dead bobcat in his camouflaged truck one weekend, just like Lee might. Lee just didn't do that mercenary thing. Stone Cold would tell me about his childhood that was in some ways very similar to my own. There was a friendship of sorts developing. Was I selling out to avoid death? Did I really like him? Some of both. It was the pig in me that appealed to him. It was also my ability to be his whipping boy that also kept me close. Pathologic surely. I was just trying to survive.

It was sort of a feeling.. "You hate the world Patrick?"

"Yup."

"Me too. Want a smoke?"

"Yup."

Anyhow, I scrubbed those two cases with Stone Cold and Damien. They went well. I finally got home at 1 am, scheduled to be up again at five.

Two more gunshots came in, however. Damien called me at 2 AM. I was in a coma.... "Are they stable?"

"No, they are shot and they are unstable and I am with Miss Kitty (the demoted former Chief), help."

"Are they okay though?" Sleep gaining again.

"No, they are young and they are shot and they are bleeding."

"Where are they bleeding from, um, did it stop?"

"No, you need to help me..."

I came in. I arrived in the ER at 0215 with my hair sticking up, but ready to help out. They were shot all right. One was shot in the leg and had no pulses below the wound. One was shot in the abdomen and was dropping his blood pressure. Damien said "Stone Cold wants us to go get started on the gunshot to the abdomen, and then he would get the gunshot to the leg with the cold foot in behind us."

I assumed that that meant that I was on my own for this one. It was just me, the exalted porch friend of Stone Cold, and Damien. Finally it was paying off. Let's go for it.

I went for it in the form of letting Damien do the case with my assistance. The patient was shot in the abdomen, was stable, but had an entrance in the left lower abdomen and an exit through the back that could mean aortic injury and the risk of massive bleeding. I opened this guy up, then packed off the retroperitoneum, and sewed up the small bowel. I did it the way any trauma surgeon would do it. I was a stud. I was free. I was letting Damien run. I was a leader...

I wasn't shit........ A 6 foot 6 shadow came across my back. I was about to instruct Damien to call Stone Cold when I heard a voice behind me (and in front of my anesthesia colleagues, nurses, fellow junior resident, and a medical student that had wanted to go into surgery up to this point):

"What in the FUCK are you doing?," said the towering shadow.

"Do you have any idea of the magnitude of what you have done? If I had two knives right now, I would stab you both in the fucking head!" Giggles from behind the anesthesia drape.

My temper begins to flare at their pleasure. The aquatic assassins (anesthesia) chirping down from the cheap seats. What I wanted to say is "you boys want to be on Gunsmoke, strap on your pistol, otherwise shut up!" They were the drunks hiding behind the saloon curtains. There is a certain pride in taking an AW and only responding "yes sir."

I was silent in my rage at such disrespectful and inappropriate treatment in the presence of a dying patient. I took it, but it did not go away.

I wrote a book.

Stone Cold continued... "You are both fucking idiots! What in the fuck are you trying to do? This is it, this is not even a training program. You two are just out in LaLa land. Thank you for giving me a reason to finally quit. Get the fuck out of the way."

I remained silent. A major AW had come.

Let it flow through you, Luke. Don't stab him with that knife. Do not give in to fear and the Dark Side.

There was a miscommunication. Stone Cold wanted to be called when we went to the OR. My junior guy Damien was probably too scared to ask Stone Cold to clarify that when he talked to him the first time. It was likely that he was yelling at Damien for some other trivial piece of information. The basic problem was a total lack of communication. Nobody functions under such conditions. Don't try to tell me that this is some form of training strategy. It is the bullshit whimpering of an unhappy person.

This is not the "old school." This is not training.

This is life. This is surgery. This is serious. It is a time for clear communication and peak performance.

The rest of that night was mostly a blur. The anesthesiologists laughed it up as did the nurses all of that week. Damien and I saved this boy's life, and were totally hammered by Stone Cold because we did not call him into the operating room when we entered. I am fully confident in my ability to handle trauma laparotomies. I was misinformed that Stone Cold wanted me to get started.

Stone Cold said that I was lucky this time. I did not feel so lucky. He rode me and ridiculed me like this on essentially every case, despite the fact that he was a three-time loser on the general surgery board exam, and I routinely make in the 90th percentile. I got along with the staff, ancillary, and other medical services and he did not. I felt at the end of that night that I had been dogged out and had done a lifesaving job.

"How was your night honey?."......

"It sucked, to be honest."

The usual chain of events occurred in the Trauma Office. Stone Cold would look all pissed off in the morning so that when Tidy Goldberg innocently asks "what happened," he could tell the whole animated story to the delighted audience. Tidy Goldberg would then call me into his office and innocently ask "what happened with you and Stone Cold?" My account and demeanor would then be transmitted back to Stone Cold between wild laughter that we could often hear through their closed office doors.

Then there was morbidity and mortality conference within the section on Thursday. It was an opportunity for us to talk about it in front of the ancillary staff, nurses, the million fucking coordinators of nothing, and the medical students. This completes the round of ridicule that permeates the section, and that you are subjected to daily. Paranoia runs amuck in the Section, and it starts with the chief. Everyone wants to keep him from getting mad. Everyone acts so loyal until they are out of his sight. He has earned my respect for his clinical ability, but that is it.

The patient that Damien and I had saved did well. He went home in four days, and thanked me for saving him. Stone Cold never talked to me again except for the day before he went out of town. He said, "you are too much of a dickhead for me to stay mad at you." The sick thing is that Stone Cold was probably never really mad at me. He just wanted to show off to the other staff that he was riding me. I know that he liked me, sort of the way a father likes the son that he smacks around. I was merely a catharsis for his personal unhappiness.

This type of deal happened over and over to some of the residents. It was a terrible cycle in which the true mission of a teaching hospital and an institution where we are supposed to hold up the ideals of the Hippocratic Oath are trashed by people with their own personality issues being satisfied with our misery.

*I am ready for some smart people, removed from the process enough to where they are not acting out of their own previous painful experience, to come in and inject some sense into the working conditions that we are having to endure. We already gave the business guys our incomes. They can use that as their consulting fee.*

I almost threw in the towel that night. It was so unfair and so embarrassing and so bad for the patient.

I am numb to the fact that such bizarre things go on in the office like Tidy Goldberg's infatuation with the CIA and Army Intelligence. Tidy Goldberg thinks that he is in the CIA, or at least tries to impress us with a folder with the CIA label on it that he keeps on his desk. My buddy Stan, who is going into cardiothoracic surgery at Baylor in Houston, saw the contents of the "top secret briefing folder" and was disappointed to find that it did not contain any secret documents about the Gulf War or international espionage. There were pieces of junk mail and reminders of the times for blood draws on the weekends. Tidy Goldberg says that he knows that Stone Cold was not a mercenary, because he has CIA informants. Stone Cold says the Navy Seals are pussies compared to his secret battalion. I say that the whole group is a bunch of misfit sick children that are tragically placed in charge of my training in trauma and critical care. Thanks, I'll just read the books and learn it on my own or from someone else, assholes.

*Is he going to be okay doc?*

*No matter how gruesome your description of a dead trauma patient's injury, the first thing the family will ask is ........... "Is he going to be okay doc?"*
*"No sir he's dead."*
*"OHHHHHHHHHHHHHHHH   GOOODDDDDDDDDDDDDDDDD, OHHHHHHHHHHHHHHHHHH JEEEEEEEEEEESUS"*
*I just try to stay near the door so that I don't get hit with any furniture.*

*"Ma'am, I am sorry, but your son was shot in the head six times with a 45 caliber pistol and came in essentially lifeless. There is nothing we can do. I am very sorry."*
*"How is he now doctor?"*
*"Uh, I'm very sorry but his wounds were just too severe."*
*"So how is he now?"*
*"He is dead ma'am"*
*"OHHHHHHHHHHHHHHHH   GOOODDDDDDDDDDDDDDDDD, OHHHHHHHHHHHHHHHHHH JEEEEEEEEEEESUS"*

*Sometimes they sort of know that he is dead and think that asking in a positive way will change the outcome....*
*"Your son was shot four times in the chest and twice in the head at close range sir. There was nothing we could do to save him."*
*"Tell me he's okay!!!!"*
*"I .......can't do that sir, he's dead"*
*It is an awful situation to see it hit the family. I do not like it when my patients die. It bothers me more than it should. Some say that you are supposed to remove yourself from the pain. I say stay in the game and go down with the patient. Never give up.*

The following will provide the reader with an insight into the general mentality of the Trauma Service. I believe that the culture of any organization starts at the top.

I was the Chief Resident for the Trauma Service the night that we had another load of blunt traumas come in. Among the casualties was a 52-year-old female that was the restrained passenger of a car that was struck broadside on the driver's side by a Mac truck. She was suffering from left chest wall pain and had difficulty breathing.

Our immediate response was to put a tracheal tube in her airway to protect her from any trouble with her breathing during what would certainly be a prolonged course of recovery, if she were to recover at all.

After placing the tracheal tube, we quickly took her to the CAT scanner to evaluate her entire body for the presence of any internal organ damage. Her vital signs were stable when she left the Trauma room. A patient should never be taken to the radiology department when he or she is unstable in any way. I felt that she would be safe, given her good vital signs, but I was a little bit nervous due to the severe nature of her injury mechanism.

She became unstable in the CAT scan room (where you have almost no help). I immediately made the decision to get her out of there. Nobody dies on my service in the radiology department. They die in the OR or the ICU if nothing can be found to operate on. I was forced to make a decision to stop her diagnostic study because she was in more danger by being in radiology than being in the Intensive Care Unit without a diagnosis.

I rapidly rolled her down to the Surgical ICU. Her labs revealed a hematocrit (blood count) of 20. A normal value is 40. She was bleeding rapidly from somewhere. I guessed the chest and placed a left sided chest tube. I was right. Two liters of blood came out immediately. Her blood volume is probably around 5 liters. She was aggressively resuscitated with all of the blood and IV access that I could give. We managed to keep her in a state of precarious stability. We were okay, but sitting on a really high fence. I also let the family know the same.

I was very open about the severity of her illness. It was upsetting to me because she had fairly young children who were very worried about their mother. My children have a mom too. Perhaps I invested too much in my interaction with the family for some, but I personally find that compassion for the person that you are treating, as well as for their family serves as all of the motivation that is needed to give it everything that I have.

Consider during this time that I also had a total of 15 admissions to the Trauma Service that night. All ranging from gunshots to neck stabs to your usual drunk driver butt holes. I was exhausted from the previous sleepless, Hell-laden nights of Trauma call. It was a very tough night. It was even tougher that I was on call with Stone Cold. He was not receptive to the idea of operating on this lady. In a way, he was right, at first. An operation in an unstable person is best to avoid if bleeding can be stopped with clotting factors in the ICU. But this lady's bleeding was turning out to be more mechanical. I was losing more blood with each hour. The phone calls to an irritated Stone Cold became more and more difficult over the hours. Finally I told (did not ask) him that we had to operate on this lady.

In comes Stone Cold. Pissed. We go to the OR. We perform a quick abdominal exploration, which is negative. Then we proceed with a left thoracotomy. We find a crushed left chest wall and scapula. There are also a large amount of lung contusions and lacerations are bleeding profusely.

"She's dead" proclaims Stone Cold.

The injury is not survivable.

Then the kicker.... "How long did this lady sit in the ICU with this severe of an injury?"

"For around four hours sir"

"Nice job Patrick, you killed her. Turn things off anesthesia. We'll talk in the morning, Patrick."

I was the one that kept this lady alive, and got him to come in. It was hard enough to tell the family that she was gone. Never mind defending myself against whatever Stone Cold would say to cover himself for being at the helm when she died. It was nobody's fault, not really even his. She was unfixable. I did not even feel like stooping down to defend myself or my actions. They speak for themselves. Everyone at the hospital knows who is solid and who is not. What hurt me most was the loss that this family incurred. To Hell with me and to Hell with the bastards that say they are trying to teach me something.

I guess that this is one that I still cannot write about objectively.

*How About A Shitty Round Of Golf On (The Only Opportunity That You Will Ever Have To Play) Augusta National To Cheer You Up?*

*I went to play the Augusta National course in April. It was one of the greatest moments of my life to get to play there, even though I shot a 94. Never mind that I had not played since the fall of 1997. It was a great experience. Caring what I shot is evidence that I am clearly too competitive.*

*I did not even try to get my professional hopes this time. Remember that comment about lowering your standards in stages (the quest for internal rather than external health). Here it is with respect to golf. It is just rationalization to justify your pitiful state.*

**Seventh Year of General Surgery Residency......Dustfart Private Hospital**

Hours:          Every other night home call; 80 hours per week
To work:      6 AM, Monday through Saturday; 6 AM Sunday
Home:        Average 5 PM during week; 2 PM Saturday;
                  Noon Sunday

            Gross Pay Rate ...........................$7.68
            Net Pay Rate ..............................$5.81

Greetings, and welcome to Dustfart! Fingers had left me a week-end's collection of stool and urine in the call room toilet that had been slow-incubated to a very ripe existence. What a thoughtful gift. This may have been his greatest moment.

Fixation.

Back I went to the decubitus ulcer palace. I was determined not to break my toe this time in response to my consultations.

*The Brain said that he wants the operative totals today. I am not crazy about him. Mostly because he is not crazy about me I suppose. It gets back to that wood carving comment that we started off with.*

*Miss Kitty got fired this weekend, but she came to work Monday. Nobody wants to ask her about it. I am going through a phase where I believe in the power of willpower to make yourself do things that you do not want to do. Convenience is not the answer; I have a Stairmaster in my bedroom, yet I hang clothes on it.*

*Today is 12/17/97. I did not do much new stuff today. The rumor continues to spread around Bayview that Kitty is gone. I raised Hell on the floor when Mr. Jack Buck looked poorly. I did a subtotal colectomy on him for bleeding. He vomited all last night and required a nasogastric tube to help him. After he became dehydrated at some point last night, his mouth popped open. This what happens to old people when they are ready to die, their mouth pops open. It is called the "O sign." When their tongue sticks out, it is called the "Q sign," and this is a very bad sign.*

*Anyway, I put Mr. Buck in the ICU. I am also in charge of keeping the daughter happy. She must not be very smart. She drives a Jaguar, yet has her beloved dad at this hospital instead of a good one.*

It was time for my Christmas vacation. We were given two weeks per year and one week at Christmas or New Year's. I liked Christmas.

Note: You can skip this if it is too painful. There is some entertainment value as you can laugh at my family and feel better about yourself.

*Typical Murrah Vacation*
*(12/30/97)*

*I finished the first portion of my rotation and left the service in Kitty's (still here) very capable, "I just got fired" hands. I have returned and was pleased to find that no one was killed. I will recap the week.*

*I got off work on a Friday at 4 PM, and of course drove directly to Disney World nonstop. We arrived at 3 AM and checked into the Contemporary Resort, hoping to slide out of that night for charges and only to be charged for Saturday night. It was looking good all through Saturday and really made us feel like we were smart travelers. Sunday morning's checkout corrected this bliss.*

*We had a great time because we really were advised not to go. The reasons were numerous; a) the kids were sick, b) the drive was too long, c) I was too tired; all combined with the fact that we were not in position to leverage buyout any corporations at this particular juncture. We felt like we were cheating. It was a very good move as it turns out. The children (us included) loved it. Mathew is in a phase of train obsession. He loved the train that runs around the resort, and the monorail, though he fell asleep every time we rode it. On Saturday we saw the Jungle Cruise, the Pirates of the Caribbean, and the Haunted Mansion.*

*We also went to the Hall of Presidents where we saw a live action Bill Clinton tell us about our diverse heritage. Maya Angelou narrated the movie this time, sorry, no live action figure for her. Maybe I am becoming a Democrat. I am very proud of it because every one else is going the other way it seems, at least in the medical profession. I played golf and gave it up to work hard and enter academics. My friends are finishing or finished with residency and are leaving the academic centers for an easier, more Republican existence that includes playing golf, subscribing to Cigar Magazine, and going to every Goddamned game that your Alma Mater plays, home or away. Yeah, okay, maybe I would be doing the same thing if my residency did not require me to finish the 30th grade (I counted it), but all of this wine bullshit is so cliché. Everyone is either buying a Goddamned farm or has a wine cellar. Where are we going with this? I'll tell you exactly where....... a pickle nosed red face gin blossom boozer on his third wife, the second one having taken that farm.*

*I am taking the high road, not even necessarily because I want to either. It makes great and admirable party conversation, you feel good about yourself, it is consistent with your religion and Hell, no one else is driving on it. I think the world needs people that care about other people. Why I care about other people may not be so noble. I was a favored son and was always worried about getting preferential treatment. This probably warped me into thinking that I had to worry about others for the rest of my life. This theory is probably not correct. People don't know how they are.*

*Anyway, back to the trip. We met my brother Lee and his fiancée at TGI Friday's. He is working hard, having just come off the disappointment of having Federal Express not send his application for PGA Tour School on time, even though it was guaranteed overnight delivery. I hope that he will be able to obtain a sponsor for the coming golf season.*

*We arrived on St. Simon's Island Sunday night. We made sure that Nana did not wait on us for dinner. She waits and then later blames by default if you do not cover yourself for your location at any of the three major meal times. We proceeded correctly.*

*The next day I tried to have an oyster roast. The woods were wet and it was impossible to get the fire going without some good help. Don't use gasoline to help fires, it has more of an explosive nature. JP4 or kerosene burns much more smoothly or safely if you will. The oysters were okay, but slow roasted and a little chilly. Everyone enjoyed them anyway. I left the island that Tuesday morning. David thought that I was quite stressed and asked if I had ever considered taking medication for my ailment, which I assume he diagnosed as depression/anxiety. I learned from my trip that telling your family about your problems only makes them worry; you work it out; they probably continue to dwell on it. I resolved not to share the crap of my job. I chose it after all. Manhood can be preserved by not whining. If you whine, you lose it all.*

*The tractor was broken. We mostly hung out by the fire then went to go see Aunt Rosa. On the way there, we noticed that Bridey the mule that used to belong to my grandparents was part of a nativity scene in front of the church by the airport. I looked over and saw Davis Love holding his son on his shoulders. Bridey's penis would go in and out during the peaks of the beautiful music. This was the feature that I noticed and it made me laugh. My grandmother did not think it was funny and she told me that it was very serious.*

*We left for Alison's family reunion next. This helped me to recover some good feelings about my own. It was great to see all of them. They all meet at a cousin's mountain compound. Some of the group could not come. I will leave it at that, Alison can write her own book and confess her own family's fun activities. This meant that we did not have enough players for the annual nerf football game.*

*We then drove back to The Big City and enjoyed Christmas. We went out on the 26th with friends to a French restaurant named Anis owned by a rather effeminate guy that used to date our friend's sister. You make the joke, and pronounce Anis any way you like. Our friends are great folks, and I can always count on them to keep me up on style trends taking place in the non-medical world. This time we brought our own wine. I thought that this must have been Anis' theme, but it turns out that we were just being fancy, and that I had once again lost touch with even identifying anything fancy. My knowledge of fine cuisine begins and ends with my mastery of the numbers of the combos at McDonald's. Sometimes I have what are called "Titusville moments," when I have a heightened sense of self-awareness with respect to my small town of origin. Getting tipsy on wine that I had brought to Anis and discussing it's merits with the waiter brought this state out pretty well.*

*There were some Christmas parties later that week. They were great. Charles showed us his 2 handed leg on the wall thunder dunk. There was a train going around the tree. It was great.*

*We finally made it back to Bayview City on Saturday night. Tired. But glad we did it.*

The family reunions are always fun. Funny that you think that everyone else's family is screwed up but yours, until you read about your own.

*What it feels like to have a patient die:*

*I operated on Bob Sellers; he was thirty-six, obese, nice enough. We took out an inflamed piece of colon that had ruptured. I was his doctor and his friend.*

*I remember sending him home. He was so appreciative. We had done everything right. We knew that there was a risk with a primary closure of the colectomy, but there was an equal risk of trouble with his colostomy, given his large amount of fat.*

*I operated on Bob a second time when he developed peritonitis. The anastomosis (where you hook the bowel together) was intact. There was another hole in the bowel.*

*Everything is okay Mrs. Sellers, no need for you and the kids to worry. This is a recognized complication of surgery for this bad of a disease. This time he got a colostomy. He did well. We talked about football.*

*Bob died on the second postoperative night of a massive pulmonary embolus on the floor. I got a phone call that they were coding him. It was New Year's night. I sped to the hospital through the back roads of*

*Bayview. I was frantic. The interstates were jammed with partiers.*

*I made it to the hospital in record time. There was a medicine intern sticking a needle in his chest when I arrived, a sure marker for death in my opinion. He was dead. I told them to stop.*

*I called the family in, not telling them precisely what had happened. They had no clue. I did not want them to wreck on the way in.*

*Bob's dad was so sickly already that all he could do is grunt. He did not have the strength to weep. He had just gotten out of the hospital and was courageously coming to see his only son. He was crushed. This was all that they had. The mother said plainly to her husband, "That's it, I will never be happy again."*

*It was the three of us in the room alone with a nurse. I cried too. This was their only child. I prayed to God to help me to tell them. He helped me.*

*The wife arrived next. She asked, "Is he worse?."*

*I said that he was dead. I cannot escape a sense of responsibility for the death of Bob, though everything was done by the book. All measures of postoperative care were carried out compulsively. I do not accept the death of a patient. I will not detach myself. I am their safe keeper. The last word.*

*I do not like the statement "we did our best." He is dead and I cannot let it out of my thinking. I think about life in such a mechanical sense. I want my heart to beat until my children and wife are set. Alison can take care of herself; the children need a father.*

The lawsuit came about a month later. This is a rough overview of the details of the events surrounding my most recent trip into the world of baseless accusations coming from incompetent lawyers trying to use the state's system of "jackpot justice" and the emotions of a grieving family to cash in big on my name. This sixth and last lawsuit would go through the painful process of deposition to two lawyers (that looked like drunks in suits) and result in me being dropped from the suit, only after I had had my name dragged through the mud some more.

I was taken off of the suit, thanks to the State Supreme Court and the terrific group of attorneys in Bayview that represented me. Another bush-league law firm had come after me again because of my institutional insurance policy that makes me a deep pocket. This is number six. They have all been dropped. Thank God for lawyers and a legal system that protects the individual. This is getting a little old to say the least. There is no time to grieve over the death of your patient. You have to turn right around and defend yourself against (in this case) some amazingly wild accusations.

Guess what guys, I may just come after your name now. Who says the doctor has to sit back and take it?

**Seventh Year of General Surgery Residency......Vascular Surgery Service**

Hours:          Every night home call; 110 hours per week
To work:        5 AM, Monday through Saturday; 6 AM Sunday
Home:           Average 9-10 PM during week; 2 PM Saturday;
                2 PM Sunday
Note:           Chief call (protected by a junior resident, but on
                every night)

                Gross Pay Rate ...........................$5.59
                Net Pay Rate ...............................$4.23

Next I rotated on the very busy Vascular Surgery Service. I had a very good experience on this service. We worked hard during the week. The disease is hardening of the arteries and we lived in the fast food belt. The weekends were usually filled by dumps from outside hospitals. Surgeons from all around the state loved to dump patients onto our service for holidays, weekends, and any sticky legal occasions. We were basically the garbage men for the state.

The following is a typical FAD (Friday afternoon dump).

*The case of Mr. Buff was interesting. He was a 58-year-old diabetic black male who was sent from a small town in the southern portion of the state with "bleeding from a left leg graft that I just cannot get to stop." I asked the surgeon on the phone if the graft was infected. He insisted, "No." I knew full well that the patient's graft had to be infected in order for it not to be able to stop bleeding. The surgeon sent the patient and he ended up having an infected right leg femoral to popliteal artery graft, even with hospital cultures to that effect. The patient had grown Methicillin resistant Staphylococcus Aureus (MRSA) from his wound. So the transferring physician (I use that term loosely) had lied to us.*

*The real reason that he was sent was that there was a real possibility that the patient was going to lose his leg and had no idea about it. This is a frequent tactic. It makes us have to be the bad guy and cut the leg off. I spent all of one Saturday night away from my family, in the ER and OR dealing with reality for Mr. Buff and his wife. We removed the infected graft and cut his leg off three days later when all of the blood supply was gone. The surgeon had tried to sew the infected graft back onto the artery and it partially dehisced itself and was ready to blow when we took it out. He had also clipped the main artery going to the thigh in order to increase flow through his graft. This is a terrible idea, because the leg was left with no flow to the leg when the infected graft came out. So the transferring surgeon was directly responsible for the problem and dumped it on us. I cannot tell you how many nights that we had to deal with the anxious family (justifiably so) and listen to their threats of legal action. They have now come to accept the loss of his right leg, and have confidence in us.*

*I believe in the legal system in this country because it protects the rights of people who may not be as smart as their surgeon. It treats them as equals. I do my best to stay out of harm's way by being a good and caring physician. Sometimes I get screwed and I get sued. But in general, I do okay. My mission is one of service, so I do not fear that sect of attorneys that I know are out there to suck mine and any other physician's blood. We physicians should clean our own house, and get rid of losers like the guy that transferred this poor man.*

Another example of a Friday afternoon dump (FAD) follows:

*Another sweet transfer was that of Mrs. Snort from an eastern part of the state. She had a right femoral artery to popliteal artery graft for claudication (leg cramps with exercise). She was otherwise extremely healthy, though 75. She came to my ER one Friday night (after I had worked around 100 hours during the previous 5 days) when her physician called me telling me that the family had lost confidence in him. In the OR that night I found out why. He had sewn the graft into a spot before the narrowing in the artery. He had not bypassed the lesion. The family had lost confidence in him because he refused to come in and see her after 5 unsuccessful operations to declot the leg. Her leg had been without blood supply for over 11 hours when she arrived in the emergency department. The family was so happy to see us when she arrived at Bayview that they cried.*

*We took Mrs. Snort to the OR and redid her graft past the narrowing. We also did fasciotomies (cut the leg open to relieve pressure from swelling damaged muscle) to relieve the pressure in her legs. Fasciotomies are done by cutting the membranes of fascia in the leg with scissors and allowing the swollen muscle to bulge out. She did okay and kept her leg after a long bout with rehabilitation. I felt very satisfied that we had saved her, but at the same time I am only as good as my next deed in surgery. The next patient does not know anything about my previous acts and has to rely on me performing at 100% that time. So I am liable just as that gimp that transferred him is. You do not get any good deed points. You get a sense that you have done some good for your fellow man. That counts when you go to sleep, and that is enough.*

My protection from the rigors of the service was a low grade/functional insanity that was encouraged by my third year resident, Blood Gas Man. He and I had the job of opening and exposing the pathology (abdominal aortic aneurysms, carotid artery lesions) each morning. There was a period of about 1 hour in the OR before the attending would arrive. It was all that we needed to recall and sing our versions of the worst pop songs from the late 1970s and 1980s.

We were left to our own devices in big Room 16........with knives.

We would try very hard to outdo each other......his Mac Davis rendition would be destroyed by a big reach and a Dr. Hook classic... "Baby Makes Her Blue Jeans Talk."

"Not so fast Murrah. Have you have forgotten 'Will To Power's remake/fusion of Freebird and that Peter Frampton song." Blood Gas Man would belt out a few bars to the scrub nurse's (who was looking for that perfect interval to actually be able to hand off an instrument) delight.

"Hmmm. Nice work Blood Gas Man. I am foiled and helpless! ...But wait! The lights go down. You are sipping wine coolers and 'Muskrat Love' suddenly and gently fills the room."

"Nice jab Murrah. I guess I'll just put my 'Total Eclipse of the Heart, Turn Around Bright Eyes' 45 away."

The final conclusion derived from our 8 week investigation of 80s pop culture was that, when the song and video are combined, "Dead or Alive" spun us all "right round baby right round" and ruled the roost. The power of the cross-dressing lead singer's finale...."I want your luu-uuuuuu.......uh–uh–uh.......uh–uh–uh.........-ove."

We could find nothing more pathetic. Of course, there was always us.

(Note: Donny Osmond's "comeback song" entitled "Soldier of Love"—complete with dance mix automated drum beat and 1980s big punk hair—was identified, after much open debate in the OR, as the worst song in the history of mankind. No, Donny's not back. He's repulsive.)

Honorable mention: Don't Pay the Ferryman... "....don't even fix a price..." ...No. Just don't buy the record.

Honorable mention: All songs by the band "Heart" whose band

members have become so repulsively fat that they have recently changed their names to "Fart."

### Seventh Year of General Surgery Residency......VA Vascular Surgery

Hours:        Every night home call; 100 hours per week
To work:     6 AM, Monday through Saturday; 6 AM Sunday
Home:       Average 8 PM during week; 2 PM Saturday;
                Noon Sunday
Note:        Chief call (protected by a junior resident, but on
                every night)

Gross Pay Rate ...........................$6.15
Net Pay Rate ...............................$4.66

"Fem-pop, chop-chop, hop-hop." Quality care for America's heroes.

"Fem-pop" (a femoral artery to popliteal artery bypass done to treat atherosclerotic disease of the legs...sometimes a futile effort in these patients who often continue to smoke right up until their operation, and as soon as they can after it.),

"Chop-chop" (the leg amputations that follow the failed bypasses that results from the smoking.)

"Hop-hop" (the necessary mode of ambulation following the above sequence; at least until the prosthesis comes in).

I did my best to avoid this morbid sequence and a service that resembled a war hospital scene from "Gone with the Wind." The VA has certainly progressed past that point; at least to the level of The Korean Conflict.

I then spent eight weeks practicing vascular surgery at the VA Hospital. Things went very well. I was good enough where I could help the veterans simply by working hard. I had been trained well by Dr. Will. I fixed 7 or 8 aneurysms and an aortic arch lesion in a man that limped his way up here from the southern part of the state.

*Doing Rich People Quality Work on Poor People*

*We did some good today. I performed a bypass of the right innominate artery today on a man that had been basically lost to follow-up in the huge VA Clinic and was refused by the doctors in his own hometown. He drove himself up, around 200 miles, with a totally blocked left internal carotid artery, and almost no flow on the other side. He was weak from a partial stroke, broke, and desperate. He could hardly speak due to his symptoms. I almost blew him off in the clinic myself. But then I looked at the results of his Doppler study and thought that he might have a very dangerous blockage in the innominate artery on the right.*

*I realized that this was a very sick man. We got an immediate arteriogram. It confirmed our fears. He was then discovered to have significant coronary artery disease. We did the aggressive thing today and did a jump graft off of the aortic arch and then let the cardiac guys do a triple bypass procedure.*

*He did very well and went home. The beauty is that this guy got the best of care and nobody cared that he was down on his luck and poor.*

*By the way, he was 38. I'd say he has some living to do. I told him to drop by and see the doctors that sent him down here.*

### Seventh Year of General Surgery Residency......Blue Surgery Service

Hours:          Every other night home call; 100 hours per week
To work:        6 AM, Monday through Saturday; 6 AM Sunday
Home:           Average 8 PM during week; 2 PM Saturday;
                Noon Sunday
Note:           Chief call (protected by a junior resident, but on
                every other night)

                Gross Pay Rate ...........................$6.15
                Net Pay Rate ...............................$4.66

I completed one more general (gastrointestinal) surgery rotation at Bayview Hospital. This was an excellent rotation that consisted of many gastrointestinal delights. There were also more foreign bodies of the butt.

*I was eating barbecue with my family when I was called to evaluate a young retarded boy with "something in his anus." I responded by having my wife drop me off in the ER and circle while I descended on the pathology of this most unsettled patient. It was big and wide, it was a chicken breast bone. I cut it in half with scissors to get it out of his rear end. His mom thanked me. I do not want to know if it came from the mouth (very unlikely, more likely to happen at an alligator farm), or the reverse route. Personally, my anus is an exit only device, but that is just me. We never went back to the restaurant, Alison just casually picked me up and I told her another story of the surreal that is our life.*

**Seventh Year of General Surgery Residency......The County Hospital**

Hours:          Every night home call; 100 hours per week
To work:        6 AM, Monday through Saturday; 6 AM Sunday
Home:           average 6 PM during week; 2 PM Saturday;
                Noon Sunday
Note:           Chief call (protected by a junior resident, but on
                every night)

                Gross Pay Rate ...........................$6.15
                Net Pay Rate ...............................$4.66

All that I can say to summarize this patient population is that one patient told Dr. Bubba that she had "Fireballs of the uterus" (fibroids I presume). This was my last rotation.

It was purgatory. I was ready to go. I have a lot of unrest to settle. Had Jesus shown up in the past seven years, I might not have noticed. I guess that there is CNN in the patient rooms. Speaking of religion:

*Missing Church*

*God must have come to the hospital, or I would not be here today. My two children, Charles and Anna, were both christened in the Episcopal Church. It was very hard to get to church. I made it to their christening, and I made it to Christmas Eve service most of the seven years of general surgery residency.*

*These were the hardest times that Alison and I had ever faced. One of the things about religion that appeals to me is the belief in a higher power. If you truly believe that there is a much greater power, then you also believe that we are a lower power. We're like a bunch of ants, or even sub-ants (What's a sub-ant? That's not the point). It makes any differences perceived between us seem as small and ridiculous as we are.*

*We get so educated. We have so much more knowledge (about medicine) than our patients. This may sound as bad as the concluding comment at the end of a Jerry Springer scrap show, but the perception that we are all basically the same is very important to me. It is also a necessary fundamental belief for the physician. This belief powers a sense of compassion for the "dirtbag" that shows up drunk in the ER at 2 AM with a real problem.*

Now begins my play by play dictation of the last thirty days of what felt like Hell to me. It will allow the reader to get into my head and feel some of the things that I have been talking about. Once again pardon the cynicism. There is nothing politically correct about the following.

*May 24th*

*Okay. We are starting. We are going to call this, 30-day countdown to escape from Hell. My name is Patrick Murrah and I am dictating this.... summary to describe the last 30 days of my residency and how it feels to be finishing my general surgery residency. I fear that I will not be able to capture the intensity of the emotions if I do not include the events as they happen.*

Let's make some rounds…

*Today is Sunday, a day of rest. I have 30 days to go and I am finished with my general surgery residency. I have until June 23rd before I can get out of here. 30 days to freedom from the Bayview Hospital General Surgery Residency Program. This has to be, without a doubt, the hardest General Surgery Residency Program in the United States. I have endured some things that may seem tough now, but will probably seem unbelievable in the next few years, when I have left and hopefully found a peaceful place to practice.*

*Yes, I have been through it. I made it through, sort of like a marine getting to come off of Paris Island, except my Paris Island lasted seven years...and I have to wear a tie to work. The end is in sight. I must keep my head down so as not to anticipate and let down my defenses. Hard work makes the time pass.*

*I am also going to give recollections about the past along with what is happening in front of me. Generally it is better for me to do my dictating into this K-Mart recorder in the morning, when I have had my coffee-induced blast of optimism. Things do not look as good in the afternoon, and I come down a little.*

*I am doing a rotation at The County Hospital. This hospital is run by the Cumberland County Commission for the indigent in this city. That is a very large and needing population. This morning I came in a little late for a Sunday...7 AM.*

*Cliff and Mark are my residents. They are good guys, and we have formed a great disease fighting team. Our mission, to help the patient, by stamping out disease and any ER doctors that might foil our mission along the way. We went around and took a look at all of the patients this morning. It is good clinical medicine. No CAT scans, no ultrasound, no MRI, just you, the patient, the nurses, and the OR on the weekend.*

*You damn well better do a good operation here. There is not much therapeutic or diagnostic technology to be found here. There are no CAT scan guided needle biopsies or drainages of anything; in fact there often are no radiologists. This reminds me of a popular saying among surgeons....It is called the "three laws of surgery":*

*Never have sex with animals*
*Never buy a Corvette*
*Never trust a radiologist*

*My folks are doing all right today.*

*Let's start up in the ICU. They do not call it an ICU, they call it "'7 South" with a breath of refreshing honesty. The letters "ICU" stand for "Intensive Care Unit." ICU used in the context of The County Hospital would falsely bring images of actual intensive care. Pulling the covers up over a patient and seeing if he floats or sinks is not intensive care in my book. This is the land of the end-stage call that goes something like this...*

*"We're coding Mr. Jenkins," or "Mr. Jenkins don't look so good," or occasionally "Mr. Jenkins is dead." What can you say from your bed in your underwear? You may feel the fleeting urge to mount a flamethrower and purge the whole unit as you speed to the hospital, but you don't. You cool as you come in. You deal with the problem. You say hello. You take the slow elephant ride and try to salvage the patient.*

*We have a 450-pound lady that graced us with her presence in the ER yesterday. She was so round that the medicine doctors and the ER hit men could not get an IV in her. I placed a catheter in her right internal jugular vein. The landmarks are not good in someone that fat. Everything is tougher in a fat person, but they still seem to be able to reproduce.*

*Gee, that was ugly. I should be glad to push back the Law of Natural Selection for a while longer. After all, she can't help it if she has pizza delivered directly into her bed after she pays through her bedside window. The ER nurse told me of this arrangement.*

*This lady had one of those fat operations by Dr. Holley. Her stomach was reduced to a 30-milliliter size, but she has broken through that barrier by eating heavy syrups. She has gained another 50 pounds. She presents with the complaint of throwing up blood. She can't stop eating, and now she is almost dead. Man is one of the few species that can eat its way into the grave. She is well on her way.*

*I remember feeding my grandma's dog Baron a whole 72 pack of Vienna Fingers in the Airstream out back, but I think that this lady is more impressive in her behavior. I suspect that she has something stuck.*

*I don't know or want to know what it is, but I'll bet that it is there. I have my intern Mark, who is an Army Ranger, with me. He helped arrest Noriega, I'll bet he has a good chance to conquer this consult.*

*Mark says "Patrick, I just cannot get a central line in this lady."*

*I go to see her and sure enough there she is slumped over, inviting me to try to stick her.... a formidable challenge. It is like sticking a BMW bowling ball. Where do you stick her? On the B? There are no landmarks. Usually you use a subclavian stick approach. But I cannot see that she has a clavicle.*

*I went for the only landmark, the neck. Everybody has to have a "neck area" if they have a head. The "fleas" (internal medicine doctors- called fleas because they are the last thing to come off of a dead dog) admit her with the diagnosis of an upper gastrointestinal bleed. I thought that she had what is called a bezoar, or more commonly stated, something "stuck" in her stomach.*

*The next couple of days she refuses to have the endoscopy to allow us to look down the great interstate that is known as her gullet. She wants to talk to Dr. Kennedy. He is a doctor and also the head of the hospital. He is an inner city missionary of sorts with a Harvard degree and a social conscience. I give him a great deal of credit for his combination of talent and generosity. He embodies what this place needs, in addition to a few more million dollars a year on its budget. Anyway, she wanted to talk to Dr. Kennedy before anything was done.*

*I said, "Ma'am, how do you feel about bleeding out of your mouth?"*

*She said, "Not good, I don't feel really good about it. I want Dr. Kennedy, some Maalox, and some ice."*

*I agreed to all of her terms with no reservations." We can do those things, but I think we need to put a scope in you. We will get Dr. Kennedy to come by and he will give his opinion on things. We'll give you some Maalox and some ice, then we will put the scope in for you."*

*"Okay"*

*She got her Maalox and ice, she got the promise of Dr. Kennedy, and later she got the scope. First patient seen.*

*The next guy is Mr. Pounder on the seventh floor. Rumor has it that Mr. Pounder murdered somebody. He is up there at the end of the hall with his shackles on. The guard has a bouffant hairdo, 7 teeth, a fat rear end, and scariest of all, a pistol. I consider it common courtesy to wake her up before I go in to see the prisoner on rounds.*

*The patient was admitted to the hospital with right upper quadrant abdominal pain. I always remember that the guys that are able to get to the ER from the prison are usually quite sick. The prison doctors like to let those ulcers and appendices rupture to a good solid fester before they allow them to come to the hospital. That is another reason not to break the law. There is another group of patients from the prisons that fake pain in order to get codeine. These guys represent the other extreme, but usually are exposed or chicken out before they are evaluated by a surgeon.*

*I examine Mr. Pounder's abdomen. He is sort of the scary type. He has a cold way about him. There does not seem to be a lot behind those eyes. He could almost pass for a normal guy. You know, the Jeffrey Dahmer slightly nerdy look. I have not asked the guards what he did, but I will guess that there is a good chance that he did murder somebody. Finding out what the prisoner did is truly a big concern, on non-cafeteria/Jerry Springer hours.*

*We scoped him and he had some gastritis and duodenitis (inflammation of the stomach and the duodenum). We did not really have much else in the way of a diagnosis. He probably has symptomatic gallstones. This morning he threw up his breakfast.*

*I am not surprised that he threw up the stuff since breakfast around here consists of bread with sliced American cheese process on it that they call cheese toast. It is convenient for them to put the already square cheese on the already square bread. I am surprised that they even take the wrapper off of the cheese given their immense energy in the cafeteria. They lay it on the bread, then put it in the microwave. Microwaving ensures that there is no possible way that it can be crispy. They give the patients grits each morning also. Now that is easy to prepare because they can fire them up in a big vat. Less work, more food. They also make some eggs.*

*Well, my prisoner vomited all of this today. Mr. Pounder is going to get fixed but we are not allowed to tell him when so he cannot "plan his escape." I will let you in on the top-secret affair. We are going to do him this coming Tuesday. Monday is a holiday, Memorial Day. We can't take care of the patients on a holiday, holy Hell no. We can't get the radiologists to come in because they have to go barbecue somewhere. Meanwhile the surgeons are in here every day, rounding, in clinic, or in the operating room. We have to wait for those people. (Hey HMOs, if you are reading this, cut their salary if you want a piece of the doctors. They don't do anything helpful. Hire people to transmit the x-rays and studies over the internet to major centers of excellence).*

*I come in every stinking morning...Look at me. I was so touchy feely only a couple of paragraphs ago. Reminding myself of how certain parts of the world are does this to me. I need to work on my forgiveness, or have my butt enlarged so that BOHICA won't hurt so badly.*

*We will get the radiologists to ultrasound his gallbladder when they*

*show up. We will then bust (perform a laparotomy or laparoscopy) him
and pull out his bag (gallbladder) and send him home (prison) by
Friday. The pistol wielding Pinkerton, Spice Girl guard insisted that I not
inform him, "so he won't be able to plan his escape." It is more likely that
she will go into DTs over lack of honey buns. Never mind that he is in a
bed shackled to the sides and behind a deadbolted door with no windows.*

*That's patient number 2. By the way, he cut his wife's head....OFF
...with a buck knife.*

*The medicine doctors consulted me on a guy with AIDS and a CD4
count in the undetectable range (<200 is bad news). He has some lymph
nodes in his chest that are smaller than the size of my patience at this
point, and that ain't much. The nodes are also in an area that is not
accessible. They are simply a finding on CAT scan. Never mind that they
are tucked behind the aorta and esophagus and there is no way to get
to them...why would you want to operate on this guy anyway?*

*"Can you come and biopsy this for us, we are weak," says the flea.*

*The man is dying. They are asking us to spear him in the chest just
to finish him off and then to be pallbearers. Not if it's my dying brother.
I will not assassinate the man. Life is tough enough. Just say no..... fleas
(I rest my case on the appropriateness of the term).*

*Miss Candy is back. She is a severely alcoholic 28-year-old black
female that was dropped off by the family because she was bleeding
from her esophageal varices (varices are large, tortuous, veins that form
at the end of the esophagus or in the stomach as a result of excessive
consumption of Mad Dog 20/20. The family has a pattern of dropping
her off around holidays and weekends when they perhaps have something else going on. The attendings that work full time here, and see her
over and over again say that that is the case. She bleeds out of her
esophageal varices every time that she goes on a drinking binge or vom-
its one of those vessels into rupturing. I am thinking along the lines of
Mad Dog 20 20 or Thunderbird. I hope they use a shower curtain for
their furniture on those weekends that she inconveniences them with
her bleeding presence.*

*Poor Miss Candy is very scary looking. I think that I can tell what a
person with viruses looks like, be it HIV, or hepatitis. If she bleeds hard
and the fleas come calling again, I am recommending that they place a
Blakemore tube down her esophagus. That is a tube that initially goes
into the stomach, you blow it up, and pull it back until it presses on the
gastroesophageal junction. This pressure effect is usually adequate to
stop the bleeding. There is another balloon in the esophagus that goes up
if this gastric one does not do the job. The whole device usually needs to*

*be held in place with weights or...a football helmet. The sight of the patients with their helmets on is a little shocking, especially if you are a fresh medical student. I hope that it does not come to a Blakemore tube. What this lady needs is to move down the street and get herself a liver at the University, but that will never happen as long as she continues to drink.*

*Next case.*

*We received a consultation to see a patient by the name of Mr. Bigon. He has a calcium of 19 (normal 8.5 to 10.5) and a huge abdominal mass seen on CAT scan. The fleas asked us to come and biopsy the mass and give them a tissue diagnosis. We did it and the pathology returned as a squamous cell carcinoma, metastatic from we don't know where. Poor old guy. The nice ones die. The stubborn ones do the best.*

*I posed Mr. Bigon the simple question on rounds this morning... "Do you understand why you are here and what has happened to you?"*

*Of course he said "no."*

*I proceeded to tell him that he has cancer in his belly, that we don't know where it came from, and that he is probably going to die. I spent about ten minutes with him. I think that he appreciated my candor. People are afraid to tell someone that they are going to die. I think that most people that are going to die would like to know. They deserve it. Another tip for the budding doctor: Sit down when you talk to your patient, especially if you are telling them that they are going die. I know that you are busy, but this is their only visit of the day from you. That is about it for the medicine floor.*

*We now drop down to the 4th floor where our regular non-consult patients are located. Our first patient is about a 450-pound lady who had a huge spleen that was causing abdominal pain and pressing on her stomach. She had an uneventful splenectomy but dropped her platelet count to 26,000 (normal being greater than 100,000). She says that she has been bleeding from her vagina today. I am sympathetic but would bet that neither she nor her husband has seen her vagina in 20 years. There probably is some blood coming from somewhere down there. We're going to give her a pad, put her on her hormones, and see what happens. Hope that those platelets will come on up.*

*The next patient has severe diverticulitis of the left colon. We resected the inflamed area and performed an end to end anastomosis. We hooked the thing back up rather than performing a colostomy. I let Emily do the operation. She is only a third year resident and it takes a fair amount of confidence from the Chief to let her do that big of an operation.*

*I am going into cardiothoracic surgery, but continue to have an interest in general surgery. I have a hard time believing that one can be a good jet pilot if he can't drive his car to the airfield. Some of the guys that go into cardiothoracic surgery disrespect general surgery. They are mistaken. The general surgery residency is the place where you learn how to take care of sick patients. You also learn the general principles of setting up an operation. Those same principles apply to any field, including cardiothoracic surgery. The junior residents want to operate with me because I feel secure enough to allow them to do the operation.*

*That is Mr. Green. He is doing okay today. He is tired of his naso-gastric tube, but continues to be patient. I find him some days looking out of the window at the less than scenic old downtown, but that seems to be enough for him. He will take another day to open up. I think that he is doing pretty well overall.*

*Another case down the hall is that of Mrs. Ridmore. She is a 73-year-old lady that is hooked on Valium. We wrapped her stomach for reflux (Nissen fundoplication) and all that she complained about postoperatively was the itching. She cried and cried for days that she was itching, despite every effort to treat her. The operation should help relieve her symptoms of reflux. She would wake up when we came into the room and start crying. We liked to sneak up on her while she was asleep to reassure ourselves that at some of this is coming from the head. It was probably the morphine.*

*Shadie Williams has about 3 feet of small bowel and half of her colon left. She has a little peephole in her midline wound through which you can see the intestines. That seems to be healing up well. She is now only postoperative day number 170-something.*

*We are in the park now. I am swinging Charles and dictating these things into this recorder. I don't know if it is so good to hear all of this. At least I am here.*

*"Mommy's coming back, okay?"*

*Another case we have in the hospital is a guy with a huge perirectal abscess. His scrotum was huge. The abscess was all around his butt. He was dangerously close to getting what is called Fournier's gangrene, which is essentially ass and scrotum rot. I really wanted to get in on this case because I wanted to see the release of pus under pressure. I stabbed his butt and got just a huge amount of pus out...*

*"That's really good water Jackson." My dog is drinking from a mystery puddle.*

*One more guy has abdominal pain and probable pancreatitis. That's about it for the service.*

So close, hang on....walking around the track in a focused train of thought....

*In today's 12-step program, I told Alison that there is nothing that can be done to change things when they suck. What takes a long time to get into takes a long time to get out of. There are only 30 more days. Everything is great for us in the long term. In the short term it is just a bone up the rear end. Alison gets "Mommy mommy mommy" all day. I get the same crap from multiple sources all day. Still I consider myself a strong resident. I am proud, just beat.*

*It is funny how a man in desperation has a new plan of escape each day. He has a theme to help to deal with the harsh realities that he faces. He constantly plots his escape until he loses hope and gives up. This is learned helplessness, when you stop trying to get up. I am not down to that yet. I have another lame theory. I told Alison that there is nothing that you can do in bad times. I proposed a mental experiment: think about tough and miserable dilemmas that have occurred in your life. They went away eventually. Was there ever anything that you consciously did that ever resulted in that problem going away? I don't think so.*

*The situation is tough now. Suck it up. At least take consolation in the fact that there is nothing that you can do, or should do. That is today's deal.*

*This morning's coffee-induced positive thought. One should always try to avoid grouping of individuals. I have been in a constant struggle to come to terms with lawyers. I went for a year without saying bad things about them and saying that I had lost my anger towards them. It all shot out when lawsuit #6 came down the pike and I realized that it was them against my family. My struggle against my own anger continues. I know that lawyers are as diverse a group as doctors are. I have 2 great in-laws that are lawyers, as direct evidence of what great people they can be. I just get sloppy now and then. Anger is wasted energy, and God knows I need to conserve.*

Lawsuits from my perspective...

*There was the case of a patient who underwent a third kidney transplantation, having rejected the previous two grafts. I assisted on this third transplantation. The patient suffered a severe rejection of this graft, resulting ultimately in a wound dehiscence (separation of the wound edges). The patient was taken to the operating room and was closed with much difficulty given the multiple previous operations. The field was a mess and a laparotomy pad was inadvertently left in the abdomen. I did not scrub on this case. The lap pad was removed without event the following day by the operative team. There were no adverse effects on the clinical course of this patient.*

*Because the insurance policy that covers the residents makes us a deep pocket, the plaintiff's attorneys tried to tie me into the case by alleging that the laparotomy pad was left in during the first case. They took it a step further and tried to say that since the pad was left in the abdomen on the first case that it caused his rejection and any of the pain and suffering of having to have dialysis.*

*The major events in the case, the rejection and the dehiscence, had nothing to do with the lap pad. The pad was an unfortunate side deal that had zero impact on the case. The lawyer (a disgruntled ex nurse that went to law school) tried to say that the lap pad made him lose his kidney and caused him to have the morbidity of dialysis, though the rejection was the primary event. This man was already predisposed to rejection due to his previous episodes.*

*The hospital settled for a small amount to save costs. I was on the suit as far as the National Practitioner Data Bank is concerned. Nobody will ever see anything other than the fact that I was named in a lawsuit that was settled. That is a large crock of brown dukey. I like my name. I don't like being sued. They call this the state of "Jackpot Justice." This is the state that allowed a jury to award a plaintiff $ 50,000,000 in punitive damages against a car company that deceived him by re-painting a used BMW without his knowledge prior to the sale.*

*Being sued in redneck land makes me suspicious that this is not how the rest of the world does things. It would seem to reason that bad people are more able to get away with things in, how do I say, "less advanced" ("stupid" actually seems to work better) states. Sort of like the tale of the Old West. Perhaps it would feel better if some New York firm jammed it up my rear end instead? I try to think positive about these things.*

*I have been trying to overcome these feelings. I did so well for a while. The bad feelings were eating me up. The restraint recently broke down again when I was involved in a case in which a lap pad was actually left in somebody. The patient was completely saved by the original procedure. The patient had a ruptured abdominal aortic aneurysm. The procedure carried 50% mortality in a guy with good lungs. This guy's lungs were like something from an R.J. Reynolds lawsuit. He was on oxygen at home.*

*We fixed him. His aorta had eroded into his inferior vena cava and spine. Postoperative day number twenty something we got him off of the ventilator. He had horrible lungs. He had a persistent ileus (slow or absent bowel activity) which we could not explain. We found evidence of a lap pad on his abdominal x-ray and took it out without incident. We will probably get sued. I beat myself up really hard for doing this. But the lap count of the nurses was correct and the attending was there. Nobody saw it. There was so much blood. He was so fat. This goes to show that you can never fully trust anyone when someone's life is on the line.*

Us and them:

*I want to take a moment to clarify something. I do not think that people realize the differences in the intensity of the training process for different types of doctors.*

*The general surgery residents work very hard in the hospital, and do so for from 5 to 7 years, depending on whether they do research. The general surgery residents are the workers in the hospital. That is the way that it has been from the days of Dr. Halsted at The Johns Hopkins Hospital. Among surgery residents, Bayview is one of the toughest residency programs in the world. I talked to you about The Father and I talked to you about Superman. This place busts your butt. There is no doubt about it. It is one of the last holdouts in the country. They do give a damn about you but they don't treat you that way. Superman keeps it all together, he is tough, but he is fair and expects no more from you than he does from himself. It is a well thought out training process.*

*So now let's talk about different specialties within the hospital. Let's talk about the misconceptions that people have.*

*What is this...ER? This ain't ER. This is the Dirty Dozen.*

Let me begin my description of the mentality that makes me feel so warmly about the "studs down in the basement."

May, 1999

Mrs. Griffin

The Chief of Cardiothoracic Surgery at W. T. G. Morton Hospital is named Dr. Hakkin' Mika. He just called me and said, "Pat, I just got a call about a little old lady that I operated on a few months ago named Mrs. Griffin. The home health nurse said that she has been short of breath. I told her not to worry and to come to the ER. Would you mind taking a look at her and letting me know what the problem is?"

"Yes sir," I stated between each couple of sentences.

"You might give the ER a call and let them know that she is coming."

I proceeded to call the ER as a quick courtesy to them.

"ER, can I help you?"

"Yes, this is Dr. Murrah, I am one of the cardiothoracic surgery fellows. I need to speak to someone about a patient that may be coming to your ER," I stated. I had spent the last 8 hours doing busy work on the floor and in the ICU that Saturday morning. I had faithfully responded to 23 pages in the past four hours from three nursing stations. I was in a disciplined state of calm. I wanted this to continue. I am too principled to effectively deal with lazy people for an extended period when it comes to patient care.

"You need to talk to the charge nurse."...............Two minutes pass.

"This is Betty."

"Yes, this is Dr. Murrah, I am one of the cardiothoracic surgery fellows. I need to speak to someone about a patient that may be coming to your ER," I stated in a helpful, disciplined state of calm. I continued, "She is 75 years old and had coronary bypass surgery a few months ago. Her name is Mrs. Griffin. She is a patient of Dr. Hakkin' Mika. If you could please get a chest x-ray and a CBC and chem-7 and give me a call I will come and see her."

"Mrs. Hakkin' Mika? Who is the surgeon?"

"No. The surgeon is Dr. Hakkin' Mika. Her name is Mrs. Griffin."

"Uh, sir, we do not take verbal orders over the phone. You will have to talk to Dr. Prakash Dickshit," said the helpful and appreciative nurse.

"Could I talk to him please?" I asked in a disciplined state of calm.

"Hold on a minute."...............Two minutes pass.

"This is Dr. Dickshit."

"Yes, this is Dr. Murrah, I am one of the cardiothoracic surgery fellows. I need to speak to someone about a patient that may be coming to your ER," I stated in a helpful, disciplined state of calm. I continued, "She is 75 years old and had coronary bypass surgery a few months ago. Her name is Mrs. Griffin. She is a patient of Dr. Hakkin' Mika. If you could please get a chest x-ray and a CBC and chem-7 and give me a call I will come see her."

"Uh, sir, we do not take verbal orders over the phone," said the helpful and appreciative physician.

"Can you not just get an x-ray to save time when the patient arrives? I will come and see her right away."

"I will call you when the patient arrives. I cannot take a verbal order."

Primal anger swelling, a new vein on my forehead....... "Thank you."

Gosh, I would hate to make them see a patient. From now on I just will not call and try to help them by giving them a heads up on a patient coming to the ER. I will just let them perform their clinical mastery that they have developed with years of exercising such an "I don't give a shit" attitude.

Thank you for shopping K-Mart. We are talking about human beings.

*Looking back on the following discourse, I almost cannot recognize the person who wrote this passage. I leave it in the text because I want to tell the truth about the way that I felt during my residency. This is the "near death experience" of my idealism. Perhaps I was becoming the organism that Robert Marion was referring to when he stated in his book "Learning to Play God" that "Many of these house officers, who just a few years before were themselves medical students, have, through a combination of exhaustion, a consequence of spending every third or fourth night on call in the hospital without any sleep, and depression, the cumulative result of all the miseries with which they must deal on a daily basis, becomes jaded, bitter, and angry-angry at the hospital for demanding that they work so hard, and angry at the patients, whom they come to view as their natural enemies, depriving them of the chance to lead anything resembling a normal life."*

*It is clear that my idealism was "in a flat spin with both rudders out".......*

*I remember hearing a radio talk show host say "those ER doctors are the adrenaline junkies." No they are not. They are sissies. They are Phil Donahue Junkies if anything. They are nineties men. In touch with Oprah, not busting your ass like we do.*

*I don't think that that radio talk show host understood hospital dynamics very well. I don't think that most people do. The ER doctors are just triage personnel that call us when the fire starts (and sometimes when they smell smoke). Some of the ER doctors can be helpful, ...by yielding. When it comes to the sick and the traumatized patients in the ER, they yield, lest they get in the way.*

*If they want to be in charge of the patient in the ER, then I welcome them. As long as they can: 1) Help (unlikely stretch of reality); 2) see the patients in the hospital early each morning; 3) discharge them/fill out their prescriptions; 4) field their calls from home asking for more damned pain medicine.*

*The ER heroes are always changing shifts. I often see 4 sets of ER docs during a two-day work run. They are weak clinically, partly because they don't stick around long enough, and partly because they probably breast fed into their teens.*

*They may be the most inept people in our hospital. I think about this show "ER." I do not know where this notion of ER heroes comes from. Maybe things are different in other parts of the country. I can say with 100% certainty that the show is not based on my hospital. Here at Bayview, the surgery residents handle every sick patient.*

*The other specialties work these tiny little hours. They write these little 'I'm so stressed' books. I have never seen one written by the ones that actually do the work, the surgery residents. Try 136 hours/week like I did for 8 weeks at the Children's Hospital. Try every other night call in house. The other specialties are popping off at every fourth or fifth night.*

*Most of the other non-surgical specialties go around in scrubs; they go home in scrubs. Funny, I never see them in the OR. I wonder why they wear them? To look cool I guess. I especially like the scrub top, conventional clothed bottom, or the two different color scrub shirt and pant combination. That makes them look really respectable.*

*We are fired if we wear scrubs out of the hospital...on the spot. We must be dressed in a tie that is pulled up and a shirt that must be buttoned at the top. Our coats must be buttoned to the top. There are one hundred medicine residents. There are about 20 surgery residents. That's a tough ratio. We cover way more patients. Some of the other specialties have adopted a "clock in and clock out" mentality as a result of their skimpy hours. Most of the other specialties come in around 0730 and leave around 3 PM if they are not on call. We get here at 5 am on the average, and leave around 9 PM on the average. They are less well trained as a result, and are less able to take care of sick patients, do a procedure, or make a decision as well as we can. I think that it is remarkable that they are seen as the ones that do the stressful work in the hospital. We run circles around them.*

*Some of the other specialties represent another extreme. I do not want surgical training to be anything like it is for the ER doctors. Surgical training programs should still have long hours, but within reason. There should be a day thrown in each week where you are completely off. My current fellowship is that way. We are ranked in the top five in the United States and still manage to treat the residents well. I went to work every day during my residency except for the two weeks per year that we were given vacation, plus one week at Christmas. Going to work at 0430 to 0500 every day for nine months gets old.*

*Heart surgeons are the last word in the hospital. They had to do a general surgery residency to get there. Stan is going to Baylor; I am going to The Big City. These are 2 of the top spots in the United States. He goes to the home of Michael DeBakey, I go to the clinical machine. The Big City is doing the second largest number of cases in the United States right now.*

*OB-GYN. There is a general perception that the roller-derby women are taking this one over. The guys that practice this specialty lean more towards wearing those "Little Dutch Boy" sissy clogs on their feet. "Some" surgical training seems as logical as "some" flight training. It's surgery with a kinder, gentler, more medical touch. It's the answer for the medical student that tells you that he "likes surgery, but do not want to put in all of the work to do it." So skippity skip, yee hee, let's learn it half assed and call ourselves surgeons. We can still wear the scrubs around and look really cool. We'll be the "Phil Donahues of medicine," we'll be "Housewives with Knives." Come on you wild and crazy "Susie Surgeons" let's go have some fun!!!.......God I am pathetic, this is all funny for a while (perhaps not quite as funny as the things that they call us), but in the end it is all a bunch or horse crap coming out of the mouth of a guy that wish that he had not sold himself.*

*Nothing is good enough for the "power-cynic."......What other specialties are there to talk about? Plastic surgeons. I am jealous of the cleanliness and more elective nature of the plastic surgeon's schedule. I see their life and I am briefly comforted in a pathetic way by calling them "so lazy that they have been known to marry pregnant women just to save the effort."*

*Alison says that we can't all do the same thing. I know that she is right. It is just the angry general surgeon that felt proud (and at the same time hated) to be the last word for every fucking sick surgical patient in the hospital.*

*I am jealous of the schedule of the ENT doctor. They get to go home and see their families. I can only draw some transient, pathetic satisfaction from calling them "bugger pickers." The cheap thrill clears, and the fact remains that I am still in the hospital (occasionally picking my nose). There is nothing wrong with choosing an easier life style. It just makes me feel better about my miserable schedule to ridicule them. I wish that I could play golf.*

*The orthopedic guys work hard and are pretty good guys. They get their AWs handed to them just like we do. They are more physical. They are more athletic. They are more well rounded people. They are good folks. They have done pretty well with their programs.*

*Now let's talk about the proud and the miserable. Who gets trodden on the most? That would be the general surgery resident. They are accountable for their patients (not that others aren't. We just never leave). They are the downtrodden, the cynical .*

(Is that evident here?)

*They are proud yet at the pinnacle of misery. The question for them is...will you pass your wrecked life on to the next generation, or suck it up, be nice to your juniors, and move on? What's all the fuss with these attendings? You are just operating on doo doo. It may seem like I have sold out to the former, but trust me; I have just arrived at the fence and am in an acute phase. Acute means reversible. I will probably be okay. Only a month to go. It will be close.*

*We (the general surgery residents) get in trouble and get yelled at. I felt like I was in trouble for seven years. The medicine residents get chastised, but nobody deals out any AWs, they probably just get extra time at spiritual retreat camp. We do research. We do a longer residency. We work more weeks and more hours per week. I am 33 years old and I have gone straight through. 4 of high school. 4 of college as a Merit Scholar. 4 of medical school. 7 of general surgery. 27th grade. I've got 3 to go to be a cardiothoracic surgeon. 30th grade.*

*I am taking my wife home and my kids to their grandparents (The Big City). I can make it. I could not have gotten through without them.*

What's up with this show "ER"? Can some of them come down here and use their heroics to help me?

*I want to make a quick comment on a case that I just received a call about. My intern was called to the ER to see a man who had been walking around with a hole in his shoe for 2 weeks and had a sore great toe in the exposed area. My intern saw it and said, "sure enough, that is a sore toe." This referral came from the ER doctor, a man that makes $125 per hour. I make $3.00 per hour. I have a hard time believing that he is 41.6 times better than I am. I have a harder time believing that this man could be on the "ER" show. I want to submit this as exhibit A in the evidence of my case that there is such poor training amongst the ER physicians in my state.*

*My proposed solution to this problem? Make them do a real residency. How about making them spend some time (seven years) taking care of sick people like I have. Perhaps the man with the hole in the shoe is equally victimized by the poorly trained ER doctor as I am by the second rate attorneys that whimsically take pot shots at my name. They ought to all be board certified, board eligible, or not taking care of patients.*

*There is really nothing that I can do. My existence is similar to that of a prolonged prisoner. I am not excited to get out. I have lost the will to run from the gate. I am numb. Morgan Freeman called it being 'institutionalized' in the movie 'The Shawshank Redemption'.*

*If you just sort of hang on, things will pass. If you look back at the times that you had horrible conflicts in your life, they went away in the absence of anything that you did. They just went away. I am hoping that this residency and this blah feeling will go away. I have 30 days to go. I think about the things that I have given up. I apologize to the reader, but these are my feelings, and I feel worse today than other days.*

*I have not done anything outside since Augusta 1 month ago. You sort of think that life was going to be a little less predictable. No other good cases have come in. I am just sort of hanging out with Alison. Waiting for them to call me. Thinking about getting through the end of the day.*

*Memorial Day.*

*29 days out. Today is my day off. I only worked eight hours. I feel best when I am going home and have had my coffee. A patient with AIDS has nodes in his chest. They are too small to hit. I told you about him. AIDS is such a dreadful disease. Every turn of the needle makes me think about it.*

*We scoped that big lady today. She did have a bezoar (a gastric scumball) as I had guessed. She is so fat that the pizza man puts the pizza in the window so that she does not have to get out of bed. Only in America does this happen, you eat until you get so fat that you may die. Then you are saved by the government and a surgeon with an operation to control the size of your stomach. Then you eat continuous small meals and slowly increase the size of your pouch until it can hold a liter of high calorie shit. Then the shit clogs up and forms what is called a bezoar, a name for the scum that cannot be digested and lingers and obstructs the stomach (Like the stuff shown in the pipe in the Liquid Plumber commercial). We dug out the bezoar today. Now she can go back to her bed. I am not going to get paid for it of course.*

*Shadie Williams goes home today. She goes to Hanover House today. She is postoperative day #171. She survived the assault of 4 Chief Residents. She has about 3 feet of small bowel and half of her colon left. She has a colostomy. She made it out while on my watch. She said goodbye to me today. I cannot be paid in any better way than to see her make it out. Good job Dr. Bubba.*

*Mrs. Ridmore is the next patient. She is the opposite of Shadie, rash-eaten and complaining all of the way. We wrapped Mrs. Pridmore's esophagus with her stomach to treat her gastroesophageal reflux disease. We should have wrapped her mouth. She will do fine. I will slash my wrists. We round on her and she is asleep. We wake her up and she starts crying and saying that we are torturing her. Don't tempt me lady.*

*Time changes things and makes the bad go away. I cannot control some of the forces in my life. I can throw a better stitch. Bald headed Steven Covey may be right. Put yourself in the stream of correct principles. Since you are a surgeon, you can make those up. God did. Honesty, hard work, the right to have a 0730 start time and run 2 rooms. There are a few bad things that plague my mind:*

*1) lawsuits*
*2) being out of shape*
*3) giving up golf*
*4) giving up flying*
*5) being more poor than your friends of the same age that you dominated in all respects*
*6) being antisocial*
*7) I worry about Lee. I want to help him so badly to get on the PGA Tour*

It is all worth it…God carries you when you think that you are alone

*The bad feelings left the day that I sewed up an abdominal aortic aneurysm in 90 minutes skin to skin. I knew that this lady needed a quick operation. The feeling of saving someone's life makes every miserable minute worthwhile. This lady gets to see her grandkids, and vice versa…*

*The nurses said that they had never seen nor heard of a case being done that quickly. For that moment in time and intermittently thereafter, problems 1-7 were gone. It takes a man to move on to a different life. It takes a man to be a father and a husband first.*

*Sometimes I feel like I deserve 1-7 though, like there is something wrong with me. I feel like my predicament is unfair. But it is hard to get ahead in life. You have to tread through the unfair, and do more than the others do. The insurance companies and their cutbacks on one side, the drive to practice defensive medicine on another, the at-times unreasonable expectations of your superiors. You have to be a whole different kind of tough. If you make it through and sacrifice your soul, if come out an unprincipled man, you have lost. I try my hardest to do the right thing and keep the patient in the center. Things that are not in line with correct principles will not stay with me. Your self-image suffers through this all. I sleep well...but maybe the messed up hours helps that too.*

*You learn not to hope for too much. You take it. I am afraid to hope sometimes for fear that it will never get better. I am going to stop talking.*

On doctors' need to take charge of their own fate, rather than selling it and complaining...

*Doctors are in a bad position. Let's say that I am Chief of Staff or even CEO of The County Hospital. I still work for the County. John Israel (a member of the County Commission assigned to watch over The County Hospital), who went to a local average college, is my boss. Suppose that I am the CEO and went to Harvard. The Harvard guy has to give up medicine to pursue a job as a City Councilman or a State Representative. It all works together for the average college guy. The Harvard guy ends up getting told what to do by the average college guy.*

*The answer (if the Harvard guy does not want to be told what to do by the other guy) is to run for office. I was once told by the president of the American Bar Association that the lobby for medicine in Washington leaves something to be desired, to use a good phrase. I believe him. Especially after seeing the President of the AMA on C-SPAN and being quite underwhelmed. I could not understand what that person was talking about. It was one of those "what you are shouts so loudly that I cannot hear your words" moments. The challenge of the future is to be more like Dr. William Frist. Senator William Frist. Heart Transplantation William Frist. The public wants it too. It just takes hard work. Physicians have many strengths that make them the natural leaders of health care reform. First and foremost, they are the ones directly taking care of the patients. There is also the objective honesty of the scientific method. Physicians are bound by the principles of the Hippocratic Oath.*

*John Israel was probably an okay student. He wanted to do public service and ended up where he is now. He is to be commended. The world promotes those who want to lead and serve. The world works against those who want to promote themselves, you have to trick it. It is hard for the doctors because they serve their fellow man all day and all night. The world wants a little of that service in the public, outside of the hospital. There does not seem to be enough time. Don't blame John for being in charge. Blame yourself doctor. Whip his butt, whatever, but do something...besides complaining and hiding.*

*I am a liberal when I have had coffee and/or rest. The fear mentality creeps in when I fatigue down. It never gets so bad that I like Rush Limbaugh. But I am often quite cynical, and at the same time ashamed of my cynicism. I told myself the other day that I would look at 1 person at a time. Today I don't care. I am now and often like one of those 'Old French Whores' on Saturday Night Live...damaged goods.*

## Day 28

*I always feel better in the morning. Tidy Goldberg (Chief of Trauma) got an 8.7 million-dollar grant. He is to be congratulated. I am glad to be leaving. Alison said that she is going to The Big City and may just stay a while. That was just to get my rare attention. She feels better this morning and so do I. She has to watch the Casey Junior cartoon all day every day. Last night I did not care what happened. I am better now.*

## CLINIC CAM

*Gracie Shotts...incarcerated hernia. Wants to stay in the house because she is poor. Wants me to fill out her foodstamp card.*

*Mrs. Honeybutt...unresectable cancer, blissful ignorance... "We are going to have radiate your bottom ma'am."*

*"Okay doctor...whatever you say."*

*This poor and sweet lady. She would be the one to have unresectable cancer. It is not fair. Oh what the heck, I can't think about that now...next...*

*Man/child molester/pornographer/overall cesspool of psychopathology from prison with right inguinal hernia...name not to be released for fear of reprisal:*

*'Hey Mr. Dirtypicture how are doing?'*

*"I had a spell with my heart this Friday, I went to UB...uh Universe..uh...I had this spell where my heart was hurting me...I had two heart attacks...but I am better, what's my problem is that I got a hernia...it's hurtin' me real bad"*

*"How old are you"*

*"45"*

*"You want to just drop your pants and let me look at that thing? What have you been lifting?"*

*"I ain't been lifting nothing for a long time"*

*"When was your last heart attack?"*

*"I had one January 15th"*

*"Cough..........Cough........Cough.....let me stick my finger up here.....Cough"*

*"You can stop coughing now"*

*"Stop coughing Mr. Dirtypicture."*

*"It bothers me all of the time."*

*"Which side? Right side?"*

*"Yessir. I had one fixed a long time ago and they did not fix it right...they put that stoppin' mash in there."*

*"Does your sack ever get bigger? Do your, you know, your balls ever grow?"*

*"Yessir."*

*"These balls hurt me so bad that I can't hardly walk upstairs."*

*"Where is the scar?... There it is... Who did the operation?"*

*"Doctor down in Russelville."*

*"Do you work now?"*

*"What it is... I have had a lot of problems... I've done some bad bad things..."*

*"Do you have someone to take care of you if I do this operation?"*

*"Yessir...I am not going to lie to you...I was framed...I am a Christian...I have been in prison and ...I am not going to lie to you...sir ...I love my children...and sir I am not going to lie to you...they beat me up in prison because they caught me at home...they planted them dirty pictures...and they said that I mistreated my children...I am not going to lie to you...I love my children and they beat me and gave me thirty stitches in my head...I had me skuuuuull busted ...I lacked that much... A man brought filthy movies to my house, I told him that I did not believe in that filth...stay out of my house...I ain't goin' to lie to you sir...I had the scarlet fever and hepatitis...I am not going to lie to you."*

*"Do you have any allergies sir?"*

*"No...and I am not going to lie to you sir...they put me in that jail and I am a Christian...they had that man in the jail...he was locked up in the prison...he played with himself...they won't let me drive a car, I've been in 39 states ...ain't had but 1 ticket."*

*"Have you had any other operations?... Don't cry it's okay... I (can) fix that hernia for free and you will feel better... I'll treat you like any other person sir...it's okay"*

*"God love you son....praise Jesus thank you...praise Jesus"*

*"Yes sir"*

*Coming out of the room... "Truss" (a non-operative therapy for hernias)*

Severe fatigue improves slowly with coffee and the cortisol that your body releases around 6 AM that makes the all nighters that a resident pulls possible.

*May 30th*

*I am getting called in to see a patient at 5 o'clock in the morning. It is some BS abdominal pain patient. Something unique about Bayview is that you are on 24 hours a day call for the last 2 years. This formidable stretch is interrupted only by the lumped together, often pre-scheduled 2 weeks that you get each year. This is unusual for a program. A previous Chief Resident called this "taking a bite of the Bayview shit sandwich." He may be right, but I also call it the price you pay for a lifetime of practicing good medicine.*

*I am in charge of the 0700 Saturday Conference. I run it and Superman comes. It is a very good conference.*

*I have come a very long way. I have come from being the new 2nd year resident, of questionable ability out of a private program in Florida...to now being the best of the batch. I am tired of my residency...but I did it.*

*I don't think that I will transcribe the remainder of my 5 am deposition on some specific complaints that I so eloquently described. Suffice it to say that we all have to blow some steam off.*

*7 AM conference was great...it was 'Acid Base Disorders', given by my friend Blood Gas Man. He wrote the chapter in a current edition of a leading surgical text. Alphonso talked about butt lesions and showed some anal pictures worthy of the raunchiest website. Theme taken from the conference... "Don't stick yourself and get AIDS, or this could be your butt."*

*A case that my co-CV Surgery friend Stan did comes to mind today. I tell it to demonstrate the meaning of courage. A Chief Resident not to be named did not make it into the ER to see a patient who had a known abdominal aortic aneurysm, a tight abdomen, and hypotension (sounds like and was a ruptured abdominal aortic aneurysm). There was only the junior resident, and a man crashing fast in need of an aortic cross clamp to stop the bleeding. The Chief was nowhere to be found. He did not answer his pages. The intern just took the guy to the OR and called my friend Stan who was a fourth year surgery resident on a different service, and had never done a case like this before. He had read about it maybe 100 times. Stan came in from home. It was not his service or his responsibility. He was being a hero. He came in and took the guy to the OR immediately, calling the vascular attending on the way. There was no time. Stan was ready to make the incision, against all rules and legal precautions. He was doing it only to save the man's life. Just before Stan cut, Dr. Will, the attending, showed up. They saved the patient together. That took balls. You can get fired in that position if something goes wrong. Stan took the chance to save that guy's life. That Chief went on without ever being touched.*

*Stan and I have spent the last seven years accepting responsibility. Running in the high grass is an attempted policy of some of the residents here (though it rarely works). Being a hero is not really safe.*

*I just gave a case away to my junior resident. A subtotal colectomy. It takes a confident Chief to let those cases be done by a junior. The patient was a good guy, and he did well.*

*Did I mention today that I am ready to leave this program? You know how when you are super unhappy that you try to overhaul your life in repeated and failing attempts? It is the move of a desperate man. This ends with despair and reluctance to try again due to persistent failure. The saving philosophy from this has been spoken of earlier. ...Think of a dilemma that you had in the past. A seemingly horrible dilemma at the time. It went away. Was there any specific change that you made to get rid of it? Or did it just fade away independent of you?....I think the latter. Just let it go. Your life sucks now. Stop wasting your energy being miserable. Ride the elephant. Or ride behind the elephant and clean up in this case.*

This was a crappy day.

*June 1st*
*I think that I am going down the shitter. I feel sort of down today. I want to get out of here. Maybe I need some coffee. I do not think that I have ever felt this bad. That is scary because I am in the dark and do not necessarily know where the cliff is. Am I going to fall off?*

*I have always accepted responsibility, and not passed the shit down hill. At least not to my interns, perhaps more than a billion times to my wife. Maybe I should have. Maybe I would be less down. How can I care about my golf game? How can I care what I look like? My life is under assault. I am just trying to keep the desire to continue. I do not enjoy anything. I am so frustrated that I cannot help my brother.*

*June 2*
*The Mighty strikes again. He said that a certain anesthesiologist at the VA Hospital had killed more veterans than the German Army. I love his sayings*

*We should talk about some of our friends here in Bayview City.*

*There is this gossip line that goes from Shelley to Angela her daughter. The information is then phoned in to Alison. The phone company is behind their relationship I am certain. The Clark's are our good friends and we are grateful to have them. They are true friends to us. Those are very hard to come by.*

The jaded cynic whimpers for tort reform. Needs sleep......

*June 4*
*The vulgar comment weedeater has lead us forward by 2 days. June 3rd was nasty. Trust me, you don't want to hear it. I really don't want to type it. We are closing in on the end. I asked my wife today.. "What am I doing wrong?"*
*I am a solid Chief Resident. I am nice to my patients. I don't lie, cheat, steal, or do anything. What is the legal profession trying to do? What message are they trying to send? I am not perfect for sure, but why are they coming down so hard on me? Is it working here? Is malpractice working here, or is it knocking down a guy that is still in training? I am not even out yet. It is knocking me and many others from a framework of trust to mistrust. I just...I don't see the....is this working? Is this helping? ...Is this the way that it should be?...What am I doing wrong? I look back at myself...What am I doing that is fundamentally wrong?*
*I have been named in about 6 lawsuits now.*
*(Update: I was dropped from every Goddamned one of them as of May, 1999. This was not before I had to run the "let's take a pot shot at his name" cycle of depositions, and meetings with hostile, uninformed, sarcastic attorneys that looked like somebody that not even their mother would be proud of and I sure as Hell would not operate on without first drawing a liver profile.)*

*It is getting a little bit ridiculous. I am discouraged by it, personally. I propose that the legal climate that we are in now makes it difficult to function. I feel that I am being unjustly accused in a ridiculous system. I can not begin to tell you about the hassle that I have been through.*

Such a dreadfully tenuous happiness that you have built. Remember, you signed up for it:

*Saturday, 6/13*
*However bad you think things are or can be....they can always get worse. Just pretend that you are a resident, you get jabbed all day at*

*work, you get home and you get jabbed all day by your three and one year old. You and your wife don't have any time for yourselves. Pretend that your wife, whose car is not working, also gets jabbed 24 hours per day. Pretend that her car was not working because the kids play in it all day and they left the lights on. Pretend that your car is also not working. I went to K-Mart last night to get a battery charger. The battery would not charge while mounted in the car, another safety feature of the Volvo that makes life near fucking impossible. It keeps you from charging the battery, it's ....really....safe.*

*That's great. Anyway, we can't get that started, so I am going home from work Saturday, after having gone to Morbidity and Mortality conference. I figured that I would drop in and get some air in my tires and get some gas. ....My front tire exploded when I was putting air in it. I am sitting here, waiting for the insurance company tow truck to get me because I do not have a spare tire. The insurance company says that I do not have a policy with them anymore, but that they would cut me $50, so they said. I am going to get towed to the Firestone Station. Alison cannot come get me because her car is dead, the battery will not charge, and she can't get the battery unhooked because it is on there too tight. Then I have a consult for a guy with a hole in his leg. In the mean time, I talked to Cliff, who is my intern at The County Hospital. He said that he would come and get me at the gas station. I am going to go.....I don't know where I can go, I guess that I can take him back to The County Hospital, take his car back to the gas station, where the attendant is a male dancer and wears a big golden earring, and wait for the tow guy to come. He may never come, I don't know.*

*They have a Mrs. Winners across the street; I went to get a chicken sandwich. Then I waited. I called my wife, but she did not answer the phone for 1 hour, she was outside. She finally answered the phone and realized that I was broken down. I am not sure how much I can take. Alison says that she is ready to pull a Thelma and Louise, the only thing that I have to decide is whether I want to be Thelma or Louise. I can't take this fucking shit any more. I can't talk very loud because I am so embarrassed from talking into a fucking tape recorder in the middle of a parking lot in Bayview City.*

*Everybody is getting ice at this point. They are all getting ice because they are all going to the fucking golf course. They are going to fill up their cooler, and they are going to get fucking drunk, and laugh, and have fun. Oh boy, I am on call....hmmmmm. Hmmmm, okay, fine, I don't think that I can take much any more. I am sitting here and taking it though....*

*.....And it is hot. Very hot. This heat coming in, it is pounding me.*

*No, but I will be okay. I am waiting on Cliff. Sort of hoping that he will come. He is sort of a lifeline at this point. My Mrs. Winners Coke will be being poured down my shirt shortly. (Taking a drink of the Coke)...I don't think that it can get much worse than this. It is the old broken down car, double break down, hot weather, sitting in the parking lot, on call, man with a hole in the leg in the ER, routine seems to have really gotten the best of me this time.*

*I surrender, I surrender. I went to Grand Rounds this morning. They are talking about how there need to be prospective randomized trials to justify that what we are doing is correct. We have to explain ourselves to the HMOs, or they will not reimburse us. We have to prove that what we are doing is right. You know, I say let the lawyers sort it out. To Hell with the HMOs. Let the lawyers get the HMOs. I will stick to saving lives. Some day they will figure out that that is what is most important, and that physicians are the ones that can do that.*

*They can't (verb that starts with an F) with us that hard can they? You know, everybody knows that a jet plane trip is faster than a mule driven pull. Do we have to prove this with a prospective randomized trial? No we don't. What a waste to prove that one thing is better than the other when clinical judgment makes it obvious? I still say that the judgment of the surgeon is the one thing that we acquire, and hold, and it is the one thing that the HMOs do not have, and never will. And as long as we have that judgment, and it is good and honest, the public will want us to call the shots. Judgment, used in the most effective way possible. I contend that anyone who questions that judgment for their own gain will be stopped in short order by the attorneys, our newly found friends.*

*Aw shit, I don't see Cliff yet. If I die we won't call this thirty-day countdown; we will call it 20-day countdown.*

*Well, I have 10 days to go. I am sick of it.*

*Other things that are broken.... my computer. The 2 cars. My cellular phone. The cable does not work. Not that it has even been paid for. Fuck me.........*

Heat rising in the gas station parking lot. Tire still exploded. Frustration pooling, fear mentality taking control.......cynical alert!

*You know we don't live forever. I have already spent half of my life doing this crap. I am taking the last thirty years and doing whatever I want to do. I don't care anymore. I hereby say, to Hell with academics. To heck with anything but money and pleasure.*

*While I sit. You know I was thinking, one of the worst things about this program is, I forgot to mention it, it is not all of this shit. It is not all of the people, or the way that they treat you. It is the fact that you have a locked in conference at 0700, 0800, and 1045 on Saturday. Which means that you have to have the patients seen before that time. Which means that you have to get up around 0500. If you are an intern, you have to get up around 0430. On Saturday, Jesus Christ. That happens every Saturday. You cannot get out of that. So Saturday afternoon, after you get home from your clinical responsibilities, if you are not on call, then you are so tired that you don't do anything. Then you get up on Sunday and you do it again. You don't get days off in this program. No sir. Fuck that. You get 2 weeks of vacation a year. And you don't really get to schedule that. Maybe it is just me, but sometimes it feels like they don't give one fucking slimy shit about you at this place. I am......not pleased with my surroundings.*

My ride did come and things transiently got better.

*Well, I got my tires replaced. I forgot to tell you that my windows were rolled down and they sprayed into my car. So I tipped them $5 in standard Murrah "please take advantage of me" fashion. Well, we took our ride around the city. It was nice and got everyone relaxed. We got ourselves a slushy; the kids were about nodded off. We pulled back into our house. Alison had locked us out. So we don't have any keys to get in. We'll have to call the locksmith, but we can just do that tomorrow. My immediate response to this latest crisis is to call this day a bust, and to proceed directly to the hotel, where we frequently bail out. So we are headed there now. Alison is following me. It has been a really good day. Filled with ......joy. I can't recall a more frustrating day. But huh, there is always tomorrow.*

*Well, we are in our room now. It is the second time that we have been to the Embassy Suites this week. The last time as you may recall, we lost our power and had to duck in here to have life sustaining things available. This time we have succumbed to human error. But there are movies here, so hopes are rallying.*

Slow ascent to primal:

*30 seconds into arriving at the hotel, we notice that the batteries are dead for the remote control player. It is the only thing that we wanted to do is watch a movie. We all sat down to watch the movie and began to push the remote control, which of course did not function. The device is not functioning. The batteries are, in fact, dead. I am now putting my clothes back on and going back downstairs to get new batteries. I have not lost my shit externally yet. But I have lost it internally.*

(Blood pressure 150/95, pulse 110, slightly agitated)

*Well, now it is about 10 minutes later. Cliff just called me three times in 10 minutes. The first 2 calls were a zit on the arm that he popped and the second was a laceration to the arm that was inflicted by a scorned girlfriend. She took a rake to her drunk dog stinky boyfriend. He was not sure if he needed to bring the rake into the hospital.*
   *I said, "sew the goddamned thing up."*

(Blood pressure 190/110, pulse 130, sweating, shaking)

*So da de da, he sewed the fucking thing up. The third call that I got from Cliff 'THE....WALL' is, I mean literally a minute since the last call. The fucking ER doctor and this mother fucker better not have been in the ER for a very long time, has free air on his KUB. So I am going to the hospital to fix a hole in some drunk....society scourge pig's......abdomen. I ordered room service after just sitting down for a second, and finally getting a fucking channel changer that works so that I can watch a goddamned movie with my fucking family. And we are all excited that we are finally going to do something......*

(We're losing him sir! I think.....yes, we have primal!)

*... And here it comes, some fucking drunk ass stinker, with his........just fucking so goddamned drunk....says.......'Oh my stomach hurts'......well I wonder why, you have only been drinking for sixteen fucking straight hours, 'I wonder why my stomach hurts'. Sitting on the fucking porch!!!!!!! THIS DRIVES ME FUCKING CRAZY!!!!!! NOW I HAVE TO GO PATCH UP A HOLE IN THIS FUCKING PORK BELLY'S ABDOMEN!!!!!!*

*June 14th, Sunday*
   *Good morning it is July, June, I don't know what day it is. It is "post-ictal Pat," sporting the flattened affect that people have after suffering a seizure. It is Sunday. I only have 9 days to go. 9 days. Today is a chip shot because Dr. Short is on call with another resident. I have 8 real surgery days left and I am just as pleased as I can be to be getting done with this. I repaired that perforated ulcer last night and that was kind*

*of interesting. I am getting there. I am making it. I am feeling okay. I am going back to my hotel. My wife and kids are probably still asleep on the floor. YAWN. I feel better about life. I finished my work and I had some coffee. I feel better. Life's not so bad when I am done with work. You feel good. It is the feeling of having done something, and being on your way home. This is the best that I ever feel. That is about it.*

*You know that it is true that when I am tired and cynical, that my politics lean a little to the right, but at rest I am a little more to the left, and I care about the little guy. At rest, I have an abundance mentality; there is enough to go around. When I am run down, I am more like the militia guy that rips my ass on the Trauma Service, and I say to heck with them. I want my piece. So when I get my piece, I will be a liberal, that's not very noble,.......oh well.*

*We are down at the house now. We just got out of the hotel. I allowed my kids to watch Starship Troopers a couple of times. This movie pits overgrown alien bugs against human Starship Troopers who somehow ended up with only M-16s in the distant future. It is a gunfest certainly fit for my 1 and 3 year olds. But they hold still when it is on. There will be no moral argument here.*

*"Hey do you want to talk Charles?"*

*"No No, it's spider."*

*"The spider? Where? Shoot him, Shoot him."*

*That's what we are doing. Our dog is inside looking at us. We are still locked out and waiting for the locksmith. I hope that Jackson's prostate is okay. He has been in the house for 12 hours now. This all began as a little, ...where were we going last night honey?..... We were going to go for a drive last night. And now we are waiting. The temperature is climbing to about that on the surface of Mars, and we are ......uh....back where we started.*

*"Mommy.... it's locked."*

*"That's right."*

*So we are waiting on the locksmith to come. Then we will be done. He said he would be here from 1015 to 1030 right?...It is 1020, he will probably be late. Can't you just see us sitting in the driveway for an hour? I can, it would be par for the course. None of the kids have shoes. We do have diapers because we went to Bruno's last night. Alison does not have shoes. I do not have socks. I did the operation last night without socks. I've got athlete's foot. I operated on the guy last night without socks.....I just put on my scrubs, saved his life and came back to my hotel. Sounds dramatic, but it is true.*

*"Oh doody, look Anna, that's good. Oh you stink. Do you want to say something?"*

*Charles wants chick chick and French fries. The station wagon is their play toy....*

One last push of primal cynicism:

*9 days until I am finished with this program. The Bulls just won their sixth consecutive championship. Well, sixth championship in 8 years. I am going to get a movie. The guy with the power and the money controls the definition of virtue. It is the "Golden Rule," the person with the gold makes the rules. Michael Jordan is not my role model. I have worked my ass off. I save people's lives, he wins basketball games.*

*I am going to write all of this down. I don't know how I am going to make it into a book, but I probably can. Just clever writing. Make it entertaining, amusing, well written. I think that I have enough stuff here to at least do something with it. I'll spend a few years on it. Put it out.*

*9 more days to go. There is a party the night of the 23rd. Rest assured that I will leave after that party. I will get into my car and I will drive AWAY, never to come to this town again. Sure the residency program did not do it to me. It didn't help. I want to record the misery that I feel. As to the actual cause, you may not be convinced that this residency was so bad, but I am 33. I have been the best at everything that I have done. Ever since I was a kid. I am ready to get a reward from society. I am ready for money. I am ready for recognition. I am ready for respect. I am ready for good hours. I am ready for the freedom to do things that I want to do. I am ready for society to reward me with things, like time with my family, money, security, peace, power. I have none of these. All that I have is LIABILITY, DEBT, DEPRESSION, ANGER.*

*Three more years and I will be a heart surgeon. I think I am right. Those who try to predict what will be a lucrative specialty in the future are wrong. What you can predict is that if you pay the up front price, if you do the hard thing....what is the hardest thing in medicine?......CAR-DIOTHORACIC SURGERY. ........You will be rewarded. That is why I want to do cardiothoracic surgery.....because it is hard. There were a lot of guys that did radiology, ophthalmology, or other relatively easy (boring) specialties coming out of medical school. But the opportunities diminished in those fields. Where are they now? I took the hard road. Three years. Three years.*

*Monday June 15th*
*You know I am to the point........somebody is (adverb) honking at me...that's not (adverb) cool. My rear view mirror is gone because my*

*kids picked it off of the window. I am driving to work. I can't imagine what is wrong with me. It is never a good sign when they honk at you though. There is probably a human body hanging off of my car. No, he turned. So there is nothing, thank God. I was really concerned. No really, honestly, I am shell shot right now and I wonder what is going to happen next. I just can't take it anymore. I just can't take it anymore. This is just painful. I'll go do a couple of zit pops today and, I don't know, ...I am just sick of it.*

*What the hell am I supposed to do with this crap? This ain't interesting, it is just a guy complaining on a fucking tape....Yawn.....It is a bright beautiful day. I had the whole weekend off.....what did I do......not jack shit. Fly to Indonesia like my friend Mike?....No, I didn't do jack. Beautiful weather outside. Look, there goes a soccer mom, passing me on my left. Going about 80 in her Suburban, yeah. Uh huh.*

*I am leaving this state. I ain't coming back. It's really nice outside, but you know what that means. It means that it is horrible.....oh driving, driving, driving, please fucking drive. God damnit. I am so sick of these Goddamned retards around here. Well, turning right into The County Hospital. Oh boy, I am loving it. I am loving it. As I pull into The County Hospital. mmmmm.....mmmmmm. It is like time stands still in the parking lot. It's party time, get me some of that cheese toast!*

The last day happened. I was the Chief at The County Hospital. There was a party for the Chiefs at the Pinnacle Club at the top of the tallest building in the city. All of us were to be there at 7 PM. I had to go to the OR, naturally. There was some guy that a resident had done an aorto bifemoral bypass graft on. I had helped close one of the groin incisions. That groin bled, just in time to fuck up my last evening.

Two days earlier, I had a conversation with The Brain in which he told me that he could not sign my certificate for completion of the general surgery program. I would have to find more of the operative notes to verify that I had actually done the cases that I had recorded in the computer system. It was one last mad dash to get the requirements to get this residency over with.

I had been keeping a meticulous record of my cases on an Excel computer program, and then entering them directly onto the Residency Review Committee's new computer format. I had been putting the copies of the operative notes that medical records sent me in a big stack in my living room at home. I did not rely on the copies that I was sent from medical records. That would mean relying on the people in the Medical Records Office to keep my totals. I did not even notice when in 1997, they stopped sending copies of the notes to the resident's box unless they were requested. So when it came time to turn in the operative notes, I was missing the ones from late 1997 and 1998.

What irritated me was the matter of fact way that The Brain told me that I did not have enough cases. When he used the phrase "....these cases that you propose that you have done....," that set me off. I never said anything to him or anyone else about my anger, but what in the Hell did he think that I had been doing for the last seven years? As a former Chief used to say....."Take another bite of the Bayview shit sandwich."

All it took was a trip to the Medical Records department, where they printed out the last two years' notes. All of my numbers were okay as of the evening of the party. I had sucked it up one last time, remember Patrick? You and your family....I solved the problem by simply calling Medical Records and having them send my operative notes. The insult from The Brain was not necessary, but it was also not unexpected. I am sure that they had treated him the same objective way at his training program.

I went to the party. I sat across from Dr. Lipshave, the one that told me that he had serious questions about my future in the program. The Brain did sign my certificate. I got up and thanked them at the party for the good things that they had done for me. I do have a lot of appreciation for the guys that let me come back after my year in Florida, Superman, The Brain, and El Toro. I knew that I had been well trained.

I did not go home that night. I packed the kids and the wife, and left. Pete (the one that had to do his medical records while sick in the hospital bed) left that night too.

I was 33, still young enough to remember my abs, and old enough to realize that nothing much mattered more than getting the crew away from my pleasant little 11 year jaunt in Bayview City. I was driving East on I-20 and heading to The Big City, and hopefully, a better life.

# 18

# First Year of Cardiothoracic Surgery Fellowship

Total Years:     16 (1998-1999) ..................34 years old
Gross Salary/Debt:   $41,880 gross per year; $31,704 net per year;
                $60,000 debt
Hours:           Varied with rotation
Title:           "Mammary Bitch"

I had maintained my ideals, but was well on my way to losing my mind as the family rolled into The Big City. They break you down just to build you back up. The breaking down had gone just fine. I just needed a little more time to build back up.

So much work had gone into getting to this point. I had done an incredible job rehabilitating my curriculum vitae to the extent where I could pull this off. Getting a spot here meant that I was: 1) Training at the best cardiothoracic surgery program in the country (career covered); 2) Bringing Alison back home (though she never asked me to bring her back home); 3) Bringing my children closer to both sets of grandparents (baby sitters).

The Big City was my first choice for a cardiothoracic surgery fellowship. Bayview was my second choice. I made the decision to leave Bayview City, and it was much harder than I thought that it would be. I do not think that it was because I was going to miss the people that ingrained general surgery into my thick skull. I just felt like I was

leaving part of my hide (ass) behind. Everybody thinks about themselves more than anything else. That is human nature. It was the mem-
ories of the seven year AW that I had been provided with, and perhaps
even some of that "institutionalized" mentality, that made me go less
than 100 mph on the interstate heading east out of town five minutes
after the conclusion of the Chief Resident dinner.

**First Year of Cardiothoracic Surgery Fellowship......The Big City
University Hospital–Cardiothoracic Surgery**

Hours:          Every third night in-house call; 110 hours per week
To work:        6 AM, Monday through Saturday; 6 AM Sunday
Home:           Average 8 PM during week; 2 PM Saturday;
                Noon Sunday
Note:           Every third weekend off with pager turned off.
                One week vacation per 4 month rotation

                Gross Pay Rate ............................$7.55
                Net Pay Rate ...............................$5.71

I showed up one day early for work. It had all been big talk about
how I was going to be a heart surgeon. Now I had to learn how to be
a heart surgeon. All of the work and preparation to this point had covered everything but the actual performance of heart surgery. Dr.
Sternalpunch says that "heart surgery is not hard to do, it is hard to get
to do." I think that it is pretty hard to do.
    I arrived all dressed up in a blue blazer with a new tie, pressed
shirt, and a buzz cut. I met one of the outgoing fellows who was
amused by my inappropriate attire. It seemed that this was going to be
more of a come and go in scrubs situation. I went to the call room to
meet the second year fellow Ralph. Ralph was still in the bed and it
was 0600 AM. I thought that he must have overslept given the late hour
(in relation to my Bayview experience). I was very much encouraged
at the possibility of having a life when he just sort of rolled over and
began talking to me in a relaxed manner, seemingly unconcerned
about the time.
    "So you are from Bayview?"
    "That's right," I replied.
    "You are going to love it here. They treat you well, you operate all
of the time, and you get out of here when the surgery is over with."
    I was a little skeptical of this concept at first. I was used to the idea
of being the preoperative work-up, intraoperative assistant/watcher,

and the postoperative everything. The Father had set things up that way at Bayview. The Big City had a different style. The fellows are thrown into the OR early at The Big City University, and they either sink or swim. It is the responsibility of the fellow to get the patient opened up (a median sternotomy-sawing the chest open through the breast bone), take down the internal mammary artery, and get the patient on cardiopulmonary bypass safely and preferably in 45 minutes or less. The fellow spends much more time in the OR here than at other training programs. The fellows are also responsible for the preoperative and postoperative care, but within the framework of a team approach.

We have a great team here. The OR team is made up of perfusionists (who run the pump and can and do save your butt on a daily basis); physician's assistants (who are the ones that know what to do and hopefully are like my friend "The Cleaner" Kandrach and have the mercy to show you); and anesthesiology. The same anesthesiologists transition over to the Intensive Care Unit where there is a Critical Care Team made up of anesthesia attendings, residents, and physician's assistants that helps to respond to problems in the ICU (intensive care unit) that come up while we are operating. I think that this emphasis on the team approach makes for better patient care.

I was well trained in putting a pig on bypass, now I just had to do it on a human being. How hard could that be? I was brought up to speed by my second year fellow Ralph and my Chief Bufkin. It took about two weeks for me to get it down. I was very cautious. My overall goal was not to kill anybody and get sent back to Bayview.

One of the first landmarks is getting to where you are safely taking down the left internal mammary artery (LIMA) from the chest wall. This artery is used in most modern coronary artery bypass grafting (CABG) procedures and has been one of the factors responsible for heart surgery's superior long term benefit when compared to more short term therapies such as PTCA (angioplasty) and stent placement.

PTCA stands for "percutaneous transluminal coronary angioplasty," and represents a fancy term that means squashing the delicate, friable, atherosclerotic plaque against the inner wall of the coronary artery and hoping that it will stay open. It does not. God is smarter than that. He built the body well. He built the body to protect itself by scarring down wherever it gets squashed. The coronary artery is no exception. The cardiologists tried to trick the body again in 1987 when the world's first coronary artery "stent" was placed at The Big City University. This process involved not only squashing the coronary artery open, but also the placement of a small artificial tube in the newly traumatized artery to keep it from closing. God is still smarter than that. He built the body well. In addition to his building the body to protect itself by scarring down wherever it gets squashed, He also protects us by walling off foreign objects. The stents are walled off, and the lumen (opening) of the diseased coronary artery closes. The stents appear to be going the short term solution way of the angioplasty.

The results of these modalities have never been impressive in terms of long term outcome, but the practitioners of these procedures are clever. When confronted with the early failures of PTCA, the response is the promise of improved results with the stent. When confronted with the early failures of the PTCA/stent, the response is the promise of improved results with radiation of the PTCA/stent. A moving target is harder for science and the people that reimburse such procedures to hit. They will figure it out.

PTCA and stents appear to have a place in the management of patients that are too old or too sick to stand the stress of CABG. Their role in the management of everybody else seems sometimes to be driven more by profit motive than the science that has shown them to be long term losers. It ends up being much more expensive (and profitable for the physician) to angioplasty and stent a person repeatedly rather than to provide a long term solution such as CABG.

It is deja vu in the cath lab for the patient; or deja doo doo as it may be. The problem presently is that the average length of stay of a person in an HMO plan is slightly less than the length of time that it takes for a PTCA or stent to fail. I predict that the HMOs (independent of their demonstrated inspirational sense of humanity) will figure this purely financial problem out and recommend that CABG earlier in the course of patients with coronary artery disease.

Cardiopulmonary bypass (the "heart-lung machine") is the modality that cardiothoracic surgeons use to stop the heart and perform open heart operations such as CABG. The heart-lung machine was developed Dr. John Gibbon over the course of 20 years beginning in the early 1930s. His work culminated on May 6, 1953 when he used the heart-lung machine to close an atrial septal defect (a hole in a wall of the heart) in a patient at the Jefferson Medical College in Philadelphia, Pennsylvania. The heart-lung machine was further refined in the 1950s by The Father (now at Bayview) at The Mayo Clinic where he published the first successful series of open heart operations using the heart-lung machine. CABG was first done in the late 1960s by Dr.s Favaloro at The Cleveland Clinic and Sabiston at Duke University. Thirty years of hard work have seen remarkable improvement in the results of CABG despite a progressively sicker, older (and fatter) population.

CABG using the heart-lung machine (to replace the function of the heart and lungs during open heart operations), high powered telescopic lenses (to facilitate the surgeon's precision in sewing), improved cardioplegia (the solution given to stop and preserve the heart during open heart operations), and improved anesthesia and monitoring devices, have lead to some outstanding results. This precision approach presents a much more physiologic therapy for the patient.

CABG is used to bypass all segments of the three major coronary arteries. PTCA and stenting are commonly only useful for a single vessel. The internal mammary artery (from the chest wall), and saphenous veins (from the legs) are used as conduits to achieve the bypass of diseased segments. The saphenous veins are sewn to the aorta at their proximal extent and plugged into the coronary artery in a minimally diseased area that is past the blockage. 60-70% of these vein grafts are open at 10 years. The internal mammary artery is already connected to the aorta at its proximal extent and is plugged into the coronary artery in a minimally diseased area that is past the blockage. 90-95% of these grafts are open at 10 years, and their durability into the 20 year range appears to be promising.

Neither PTCA/stent or CABG (open heart surgery) cure the underlying process of atherosclerotic coronary artery disease (ASCAD). There is much ongoing research in prevention of the development of ASCAD. In the mean time, CABG makes more sense to me for long term results, especially with more than 1 vessel disease (there are 3 major coronary arteries on the heart). I am excited to be a part of such a promising future. The country is getting older and fatter. I am very excited about my future because CABG works, and it is more fun.

So as the first year fellow, it is your mission (should you accept it) to get that internal mammary down safely. You really do not want to "bugger up" the internal mammary artery and ruin the patient's chances at long term survival. You are the gatekeeper to the rest of the patient's life. The pressure is on. It is as good as any sport that you played as a kid. You are the "mammary bitch."

I worked hard for four months and became a good bitch. I worked my ass off. There was so much to learn. I had ascended to an incredible program that was extremely busy. I occasionally would reflect on the fact that I came from Titusville and was one of 2 people to go to medical school. I had really gotten myself in deep. My inability to say no to a challenge won't matter soon. There won't be any challenges left.

The attendings at The Big City University Hospital are all terrific. There is a notable absence of hazing in this institution. The do come when they are indicated, but the overall atmosphere seems to be one of teamwork between the specialties. I am very proud to be here.

My hero, Dr. Sternalpunch, has been extremely supportive. He is a very interesting person. I was not sure that all of this fast talking, fast moving, physical, hyper-aggressive but benevolent behavior was the real thing.

It is. It comes from inside. He doesn't just act like Superman-2. He is Superman-2. He never stops. It bothers me that he has more positive energy than me. I think I need to run more.

He gives me a push when he thinks I need one, and I proudly respond. Six months ago I approached him on the floor and asked if I could do anything to help out. I was dressed in scrubs with a surgical cap on my head. I had not shaven and had been awake for 36 hours.

Dr. Sternalpunch stopped for a moment, then looked at me and said, "You can shave. You represent me. You ought to be clean." With a characteristic snap of the fingers and a point in my direction, he was gone.

I immediately ran to the ICU where I grabbed a prep razor (used to shave the patients), then headed to the locker room where I dunked my head in the sink and washed my hair with that pink surgery soap. I then performed one of my patented dry shaves with the prep razor (guaranteed > 2 small face bleeders), changed into my dress clothes and went hunting for Dr. Sternalpunch. It was a pitiful sight, my running around at age 33 to please daddy.

I found Dr. Sternalpunch over in the clinic looking over some heart cath films. I sort of stood there, hoping that his peripheral vision would catch my newly rehabilitated appearance. He looked up, back at the film, then did a double take.

"What do you think sir?"

"Great Pat, I'm proud of you again. Damned glad you are here."

It has been six months since my fashion rehabilitation. I never have come to the hospital or left the hospital in scrubs since that time. I always carried out this practice at Bayview mainly because I would be fired by Superman if I did not. I cannot say that it was pride. I never got around to that. It was fear. I had gone a few months in the scrubs, but now had arisen with the sense of pride that Superman had exhibited and tried to convey to me at Bayview.

Two weeks later came another encounter... "Pick your head up, Pat. Get your shoulders back. You look embarrassed or something. God damn man, you're a heart surgeon. Chin up, shoulders back."

Subsequent encounters in the hallway over the next few weeks lead only to a six word exchange.

"Shoulders back, head up."

"Yes sir."

*The Aggressor*

*I cannot effectively incorporate the one thousand stories of the (usually) benevolent aggression of Dr. Sternalpunch. This is refreshing in a world of increasing politically correct sissies. This is the guy that you want on your side; if for no other reason than the fear of having him on the other side......*

*We place pacing wires on the surface of the heart at the conclusion of each open heart operation. These are loosely tied with a silk suture. They are generally removed with a pair of scissors. In the interest of time (speed), a fork from the patient's plate was as good as any pair of scissors for Dr. Sternalpunch.*

*The incisions over the chest were just a little bit bigger for Dr. Sternalpunch. "Big surgeon, big incision, big bills."*

*Dr. Sternalpunch completed his general surgery residency at The Massachusetts General Hospital. Many stories circulated there as well, including the way that he completely cleaned the entire caseload of the TB ward during his rotation on that service. There was nothing left for the next guy that came along. He loved to operate.*

*His presence is easy to detect. He whistles and clicks his fingers constantly as he moves from room to room telling his patients that "both you and I need to lose some weight" or that they are just plain "fat." His smoking rehabilitation is more direct. There are no support circles of co-miserating smokers. There are no Nicotrol patches. There is only his big index finger prodding into your fresh sternal wound reminding you that ......*

*"You (poke) need (poke) to stop (poke) smoking (poke)."*

*Around the time that I was interviewing for a spot in cardiothoracic surgery, a story was circulating around amongst the fellows at The Big City University.*

*The anesthesia attending began, "Dr. Sternalpunch, this is Dr. X, he is an applicant for a position in cardiac anesthesia."*

*Dr. Sternalpunch greeted the new anesthesia applicant with a characteristic punch to the chest (over the surgical drapes) with the words "Joe Sternalpunch, damned glad to see you!!" The force of the friendly gesture caught the applicant by surprise. He stumbled back, and then hit a tool box on the floor that sent him stumbling helplessly to the ground.*

*The very next week the exact same scenario arose. The applicant received the same greeting (to the chest wall) and was equally unprepared. "Joe Sternalpunch, damned glad to see you!!"*

*POW!!!*

*The applicant stumbled back initially, but was able to catch his balance.*

*Dr. Sternalpunch was apparently impressed as he remarked, "I like this one. You need to hire him, he didn't fall!!"*

I had a great four months and benefited greatly from the teaching of my senior residents, Ralph and Bufkin. Ralph came from the west coast and was very quick with his hands. Bufkin was from a small west Texas town "West of the Pecos." He was a smart kid that made good from a very small town. I have never been to west Texas, but I have an image of lots of armadillos and the movie "Tin Cup." He told me the story about falling off of a horse as a kid and breaking his arm. His dad simply told him to "get up." Bufkin's folks must have done something right. He has a very strong common sense about him that I have seen keep many a patient out of trouble; and the line between "in trouble" and "dead" is not very thick. My friend's dad that said that an attractive cardiothoracic surgery applicant is one that he would "trust to take his family across the plains in a wagon train in the days of the Old West" was right, and he was describing Bufkin.

My first four months was not without a few frustrating aspects. I was starting to feel my age. The middle of the night calls from the floor for Tylenol were starting to wear on me. Here I was in my eighth year after medical school, and once again unprotected by an intern to get these fucking calls. You may recall that I took out my left big toe with one of those consults five years ago. Nothing made the frustration of trying to interpret the multicultural (including Southeastern Redneck, and Soccer Mom—"I killed your dog") versions of .....

"Sorry to wake you Tylenol Bitch, but Mr. Johnson is constipated, has diarrhea, has a fever, is cold, is confused (picking berries out of the sky), won't wake up, can't sleep, has a headache, is nauseated, vomited, hasn't seen a doctor since he came to the hospital, (a definite marker for a pain in the ass patient), pulled out his.....Foley catheter, central line, IV,.... can't pee, is in atrial fibrillation, has a high blood pressure, has a low blood pressure, wants Ensure with his meals, and my personal favorite... "fell out of bed."

What I feel like saying at 3 AM (and must overcome in order to avoid this 18 year effort being converted to a 16 year effort and one pink slip)......

"That's okay, I can relate because I stopped giving a shit at 2 AM; life is, tough, sometimes we all get the squirts, cork him; stop taking his temperature; give him a GD blanket; I'm confused too; it's 3 AM, I'm a little groggy myself; can't sleep? What a foreign concept!; I have a headache too; standby, maybe he'll barf; he did barf, thanks for calling; he has been here for a week and I know that somebody had to have operated on him; what a stud, he did his own prostate ream-out operation; may God damn you and your first born son; (drop the phone into a trash can and beat it around some to the calling person's auditory delight); it is 3 AM, I can't pee either; (atrial fibrillation) gotta treat that one; I have high blood pressure now too, now that I am your personal "Tylenol Call Bitch;" (low blood pressure) gotta treat that one; why don't we just "sit tight" tonight on the pressing "Ensure issue" and take another look at that in the AM (The phrase "sit tight" is a good, polite—but nearly condescending—way to say "put your hands in the air, step away from the patient slowly."); put him back in the bed and "TIE HIS BUSTED ASS UP!!"

(Note: A bed spill is a guaranteed trip to the floor for the fellow—with closed or tightly squinting eyes and primal rage—where you must make sure that they have not broken anything other than your will to live. A little pink slip must be filled out for each spill.)

I was able to overcome the phone calls. Frequently by counting to ten or doing some push-ups before saying something ugly. "Sit tight" was a very useful phrase as well. It is a good, polite way to say "Put your hands in the air, step away from the patient slowly." It is a way to make "stop" sound like an activity for those that you know won't stop. It also sounds better than "Each time you open your mouth the sum total of all knowledge in the universe decreases."

I left this four month run knowing that I was going to make it. I had chosen the right place. We were operating day and night. The attendings were gentlemen. The facility and support staff were outstanding and it was all in my wife's hometown. The years of pig surgery and structured torture were all worth it. I was on my way back. I was a very good doctor. I had been well trained at Bayview. Superman had prepared me well. I was building a career.

### First Year of Cardiothoracic Surgery Fellowship......The Big City University Hospital–Thoracic Surgery

Hours:        Every third night in-house call; 115 hours per week
To work:      6 AM, Monday through Saturday; 6 AM Sunday
Home:         Average 9 PM during week; 2 PM Saturday;
              2 PM Sunday
Note:         Every third weekend off with pager turned off.
              One week vacation per 4 month rotation

              Gross Pay Rate ...........................$7.23
              Net Pay Rate ..............................$5.47

Two surgeons make up the Thoracic Surgery Service at The Big City University. The Viper and his disciple, Dr. Work

How good are these thoracic surgery guys?

Try operating every day on every form of thoracic pathology in a city of 3 million and every Friday Afternoon Dump/Medicolegal Disaster five days per week and for four months and have a death count of ....zero.

Oops. I forgot one. Do you remember that huge wedding that Alison and I were given 8 years ago? Our minister was the leader of the largest Presbyterian Church in the Free World and a close friend to three generations of Alison's family for 30 years. He was a force for good in his community. He served on a spiritual advisory panel to the President of the United States; and, of course, he died on my service.

This one came on fast. Dr. Good felt ill for around three months. One of the last funerals that he conducted was for Alison's grandmother down in the southwestern corner of the state. I remember Alison saying that he did not look well then. Dr. Good was admitted to a competitor hospital across the city for treatment of a worsening pneumonia.

Dr. Good's condition worsened shortly after his admission. His internist wanted to intubate him (place a breathing tube in his airway), but Dr. Good was not going to have that. He called my attending on the telephone from the ICU despite being very short of breath.

"Joe, this is Frank Good. I'm over...... (a few breaths)...... at St. Blows and they are trying to put that......(a few more breaths).....breathing tube in me."

"Now you just stay there Frank. I'll be right over."

It was the middle of the night, but this made no difference to Dr. Work. Frank was a man that had touched his life. Dr. Work had attended a separate Presbyterian church for years with his family, and at the end of the service had raced five miles through the Big City to sit on the back row of Dr. Good's church to hear his sermon. Dr. Work would then come over to the hospital to make rounds. The unbelievable level of motivation and idealism required to do this for so many years is surpassed only by the fact that he never told anybody about it. I only found out about his Sunday morning ritual when Dr. Good's wife mentioned it to me during a visit to her ailing husband's bedside. It was an impressive tribute to his humility and level of character.

Dr. Work made a trip to St. Blows where he picked up Frank and personally brought him back in the ambulance. He did have to intubate Dr. Good. He had a severe pneumonia that progressed to ARDS (acute respiratory distress syndrome). Dr. Work stayed at his bedside all night long.

My shiny, sorry butt showed up in the ICU at 6 AM, knowing nothing of what had transpired the night before. Dr. Work had outworked me again. He had allowed me to rest that night and had not called me in. I remember seeing the name of my minister on the ICU board and thinking "Please do not let that be who I think that is."

I checked the chart. Occupation...minister......

It was him. I could see his feet sticking out from around the corner in Room 4.

Damn.

I immediately called Alison and told her that "it had happened" (seeing and treating family friends) and asked her to pray for me to do the right thing.

Two months of aggressive treatment with antibiotics, chest tubes, tracheostomy, feeding tube placement, more antibiotics, 3 or 4 emergency races to the ICU for dying spells, more antibiotics, 35 consults, more antibiotics, hope, and a final slow deterioration that lead to a nightly procession of the Big City's most prominent (including my father-in-law) saying good-bye and praying at his bedside, ensued. I was worn out. Dr. Work was worn out. We did not give up. Even at the end, Dr. Work called the leaders of lung transplant centers around the world and asked if there was any way to stop the dying that was going on in Room 4.

There was nothing that we could do. Dr. Good's body was worn out from years of disease (including coronary bypass by Dr.

Sternalpunch and a successful recovery from lymphoma) combined with a work ethic that rivaled that of the man that was trying to save him.

I liked the way that Dr. Work gave it his all. Some say that you should remove yourself from emotional attachment in the event that you fail and go down with the patient. I say get in the game. Every patient, rich or poor, holy or demonic, deserves everything that you have. Fight for them even after those around you are shaking their heads (saying "let him go") and you are not "cool" anymore. Dr. Work had given Dr. Good everything, just as he had for every patient that had come before.

The end came in the first week of March. We had withdrawn support that morning as it became obvious that he was dying despite elevation of our efforts. The family understood that the fight was lost. Dr. Work was at the W.T.G. Morton Hospital across town and I had to scrub out of a case when I heard that Dr. Good was gone.

I felt a bit awkward coming into the room full of brilliant physicians and in essence saying; "Yep he's dead all right." It was another one of those self-awareness "I'm from Titusville" moments, but that is how Dr. Work wanted it.

I pronounced my minister dead.

I called Dr. Work on the telephone. I could hear the intense emotion in his voice.

I have always been (am always) afraid of knocking off any of my in-laws' friends. Perhaps even more sacred is a desire to never see anyone that attends their annual huge Christmas party naked.

0 for 1.

**First Year of Cardiothoracic Surgery Fellowship......The W. T. G. Morton Hospital–Cardiac Surgery**

Hours:          Every other night home call; 120 hours per week
To work:        6 AM, Monday through Saturday; 6 AM Sunday
Home:           Average 8 PM during week; 2 PM Saturday;
                Noon Sunday
Note:           No days off during week, but can take call from home.
                One week vacation per 4 month rotation

                Gross Pay Rate ...........................$6.60
                Net Pay Rate ...............................$4.99

Just another day at the office. I am going to write this as I take my last weekend of call at The W. T. G. Morton Hospital. I am going to finish my first year of cardiothoracic surgery fellowship on Wednesday. I have enjoyed the year tremendously, but I am left feeling very 34.

I am still in bad shape, and I know that this is my fault. Every evening (usually after a huge dinner that was a reaction to a normal breakfast and lunch that had represented a 12 hour attempt at "nutritional peace") I have promised myself that I will get up at 4 AM and run. Every morning I cannot get out of bed because I am too damned tired.

I have not played golf in 3 months, when I shot an embarrassing 99. I think I shot a 99 when I was 10 years old. It has taken quite a while to reverse the improvements that I made in my youth, but I finally accomplished that with the help of a wild swing and a dozen penalty strokes. I stubbornly maintain the dream of making the cut in a Senior PGA Tour event. I also stubbornly maintain that I do not have the lack of conscience that it would take to go play golf for 6 hours and spend $100 when I have Alison, Charles, and Anna waiting for me at home after such a long work week.

I was out of bed today at 4:30 AM. The only running that I did was to my car. I had 42 patients to see by 8:30 AM when I was to meet The Perfect Coronary Surgeon for rounds. My Chief Resident was in Lake Tahoe for a meeting. My junior resident was on her vacation. I had a guy from the lab to see some of the patients, but knew that the responsibility landed squarely on my head if there were problems.

2111 Grace.......
76 years old. CABG 5/25/99. 85 pounds preop (before surgery). She also has this depression with anxiety issue. These little old ladies with tiny bodies and no chest wall muscles have a hard time recovering from surgery. Recovering from a chest incision is comparable to a slow continuous exercise (like a brisk walk). Not everyone is up to it.

The jury is still out here.

Grace bled hard from a duodenal ulcer on the fifth postoperative day and almost died. She made it home about 10 days after her bleed. She then pulled some sort of an Elvis/Valsalva maneuver (straining that can kill you—probably the way that I will die) and almost died again. The Street Surgeons (EMTs) got to her at home and she lived through that too. Now she sits on the floor with that sort of washed out look that spells NHP (nursing home placement), our best efforts at assassination having failed. She also has some regurgitation across her mitral valve, making it easy for her to go into congestive heart failure.

She really has become a challenge. Can we get her to the nursing home? Can a human being survive on Boost nutritional supplements with ice? Would face-pillow therapy be more humane?

I am sure that there are worse ways to die. My EMT friend told me that some of her worst calls were to retrieve people that died in their Airstreams and melted in the Florida sun for a couple of days before being discovered. This is surpassed only by the smell generated by a person that craps a giant puddle of bloody stool (melena) into their bed and dies in it over a two day period. Bloody doo-doo is the only thing that smells worse than doo-doo.

Page (8:47 AM)—

"Mrs. Grace is breathing better now, but her saturation (blood oxygen measure) was much lower earlier."

"How low?"

"87% on 2 liters of oxygen."

"Thanks."

Page (10:41 AM)—

"Emergency cardiac cath"

Call the OR and "standby" in case the patient crashes and burns (needs to go to the OR).....standby........STAND BY......Are you standing by?...........Your kids are standing by at home.

Page (2:26 PM)—

"Mrs. Grace has a heme positive stool." (There is blood in her bowel movements).

"Send another hematocrit (blood count) on her please."

Page (2:58 PM)—

"Mrs. Grace gets very short of breath when she walks and her creatinine is up to 3" (this means that her kidneys are doing poorly as well).

"I know, she looks terrible. We are trying to diurese (remove fluid by inducing urination) her for her CHF (congestive heart failure), but are limited by her poor kidney function. Let's see what the blood count shows and sit tight until then."

"Okay."

Curbside (4:45 PM)—

"Her blood count is okay. She still says that she cannot breathe very well."

"Let's sit tight."

She is inches away from cardiac drugs (like dobutamine), and a trip to the ICU.

I finally break down and consult cardiology to help manage her failure. She is still hanging in there, but I have not made her any better this morning.

2112 Johnson.....

40 years old. CABG 6/24/99.

"I'm doing great, doc. No problems here."

I pulled out the pacing wires on his heart and asked him to lie in bed for a few hours in case his heart starts bleeding.

Page (2:30 PM)—

"Mr. Johnson in 2112 can't hear out of his left ear.".....

"I was just in there. He said he was fine."

"I guess he did not hear you."

Back into the room with Mr. Johnson.

"I can't hear out of my left ear." Blank look at me (Save me).

I examine the ear. No abnormality. Smallest stroke in the world, wax, sinus congestion. A communist plot to make me quit. I just do not know.

"Okay, sir, it looks okay. We'll watch that."

"I can't hear out of my left ear." Blank look at me (Save me).

"Okay sir, it looks okay. We'll watch that."

Blank look. (You did not save me).

Page (3:00 PM)—

This occurs just as I am pulling into my house, feeling the blunted effect that one must feel after just having a seizure.

"Mr. Johnson wants to know when you are going to come by and talk to him some more about his hearing."

"Could you please tell him that I just got home and will see him again when I am back in the hospital this afternoon? I am sure that I will be there."

"Okay. He just wanted to hear that from a physician."

Visit to bedside (5:00 PM)—

I approach the ear lacking an otoscope; thinking that anyone dumb enough to think that I am going to focus only on his fucking ear when he is surrounded with a hospital full of dying hearts, probably will not notice that I do not have the right equipment.

I give him a cozy, family practitioner once over......

"Let's have a look at that ear" said the doctor that does not know jack shit about ears. "Hmmmm. Yes, very interesting. Hmmmm. Very interesting indeed."

"What does it look like, doc?"

I say, "I think that your eustachian tube is clogged," thinking that a big word like eustachian will further dazzle him and leave him helpless.

"Is that bad?"

"No, sir (the hook is delivered), that should get better with Afrin nasal spray." I draw from my own history of sinusitis.

"Thanks doc."

"You're welcome." (and I might further ask that you refrain from breeding in order to preserve the quality of mankind's genepool).

Page (8:00 PM)—

Of course, the fever call must come in.

"Dr. Murrah, Mr. Johnson in 2112 has a temperature of 101."

"You can give him some Tylenol."

"Thanks."

"Okay."

"Great."

2114 Hawks......

No insurance. Diabetic. Can't talk because his larynx got pulled out at The County Hospital in Bayview City. Depressed. Preop for surgery Tuesday.......Responds to "Lucky."

I did him the favor of untying his battery operated talk box that was tangled up in the armrail of his bed this morning. This, along with the presence of diapers in any patient preoperatively, is a poor prognostic indicator.

Page (7:15 PM)—

"Dr. Murrah. Does Mr. Hawkes need his telemetry?"

"No."

"Can we discontinue his IV; it is old and I am worried about it getting infected."

"Okay."

Curbside (9:10 PM)—

"Can Mr. Hawks have a Fleet's enema?"

"Yes."

Curbside (9:12 PM)—
   "Is Mr. Hawks going to surgery Monday?"
   "No. He is going Tuesday."
   "Okay."

Page (9: 14 PM)—Sunday
   Meaty Flashknife calls. "What cases do I have tomorrow?"
   "None for the time being, but you are on call tomorrow."
   "You can, however, come in and help me tie a patient of Dr. Nopump's down."
   "That's okay. I'll see you tomorrow."

Page (9:39 PM)—Sunday
   Dr. Hakkin' Mika calls. "What cases do I have for tomorrow?"
   "You have Mr. Wright. He is going to be a redo." (A redo is a second or even third heart operation. There is a greater risk because you have to saw the chest bone open and the heart is stuck to the back of the bone. There is a finite risk of sawing into the heart and making a mess.)
   "Okay. I'll see you tomorrow."
   "Yes sir."

2116 Williams...
   Lung biopsy for diagnosis of lung condition. Steroid dependent. On lots of drugs.....Methadone (Boy George's choice), morphine, Percocet. Going home. Attractive daughter...in high school. Next patient.
   We discharge her home and a new guy (Mr. Right) arrives in the room about 4 hours later. He is a preop for surgery Monday for Dr. Hakkin' Mika.

Curbside (8:48 PM)—
   "Can Mr. Wright have some Ativan for 'his nerves'?"
   "Yes."

2117 Dickinson...
   62 year old 4 days out from Mitral valve replacement for rheumatic disease as a child. Patient of the chairman. Flying.

Curbside (5:00 PM)—
   "Cardiology came by and wanted her telemetry left on since she has a valve."

"Okay."

I am only doing this "okay" because somebody, somewhere, asked me if we could stop the telemetry. I escaped from this with an "okay."

Curbside (5:05 PM)—

"Can we get rid of her IV?," said the nurse to the "okay" donor.
"Okay."
"I am going to murder you now, Dr. Murrah."
"Okay."

Curbside (6:30 PM)—

"Can Mrs. Dickinson have a suppository?"
Yes. Give her a Dulcolax."
"Thanks."
"Okay."
"Great."
"Great."

2118 Hicks....

67 year old. Diabetes. Emphysema. High blood pressure. Postmenopausal mustache. They are pretty sick when the 'stache gets that thick. Doing okay.

2119 Ferry...
CABG 5/4/99. Stroke 5/5/99.

He is family of a nurse at the hospital. This is a risk factor for disaster. The stroke came swiftly and silently, like a big string of drool coming from the corner of someone's mouth. He got better very slowly.

Next came the air in the bladder from an unknown source. I maintain that Dr. Hakkin' Mika's PA (Phil) was blowing air into his catheter. We had general surgery see him for a possible alternative diagnosis. No diagnosis was reached despite an operation and a 30 foot restraining order against Phil.

Next came the prep for the nursing home/extended care facility......tracheostomy and feeding tube......The washout from the above leaves him in the nursing home where he gets sick again......Now he is back.

Page (1:56 PM)—
"Dr. Murrah."

"This is general surgery. You can pull his PEG tube out any time that you like."

The PEG is his feeding tube that got infected at the nursing home. He is not using it because he is starting to eat well.

"Thanks."

Page (10:04 PM)—

"Dr. Murrah, Mr. Ferry needs something for agitation."

"Did he take anything at the nursing home?"

"His daughter said yes, but she is not sure what it is."

"Give him Ativan 1 mg by mouth every six hours as needed."

"Thanks."

2120 Ranger....

58 year old. CABG 6/25. Flying. Must get him out of the hospital. Likes whiskey. Will withdraw. Not picking berries or yelling yet.

Page (3:45 PM)—

"Mr. Ranger needs something to calm his nerves."

It starts. The long slippery slope of the alcoholic pulled off of his drinking schedule by open heart surgery.

"Start him on scheduled Ativan."

"Thanks."

Page (4:45 PM)—

It is Dr. Nopump. He has the world's largest series of cardiac cath data supporting the success of the new rage in cardiac surgery—"off-pump" CABG. These procedures involve direct suturing on the beating heart without use of the heart-lung machine.

The compulsive young attending strikes again. It is his third phone call to me (there would be two more the following day), and he is not even on call. Once again I reiterate the refreshing concern for the patients' welfare. I am hoping, however, that tonight's party for the out-going Chief Residents will lead to a couple of stiff ones and perhaps turn his attention to something else, like sex. The party could have the opposite effect and open the flood gates on his functional obsession with cardiac surgery and "off-pump" cardiac surgery leading to another phone call.

"Pat, how is Mr. Ranger?"

"He's doing great."

"Great."

"Okay."
"Great."
"Okay then. Great. Any other problems?"
"No sir.."
"Great."
"Okay."
"Okay."

Page (7:09 PM)—

"Dr. Murrah, Mr. Grainger wants to talk to you about having a cardiac cath tomorrow. Could you please call him directly in his room?"
"Okay."

Dr. Nopump does another cardiac cath to check the patency of his bypass grafts after doing "off pump" CABG (this is a coronary bypass procedure done on the beating heart without use of the heart–lung machine). This has been an institutional policy at W.T.G. Morton Hospital to ensure that the bypass grafts of this new procedure are of good quality. The policy also means another test, and another stick in the groin for the patient.

This guy is a bit anxious about going back to the cath lab. I cannot blame him.

"Hello."

"This is Dr. Murrah, you were worried about having a heart cath Monday?"

"Not really, I just want to know why you are doing it."

"To ensure that the results of this new technique are good."

"Okay." (He is using my patented response technique.)

"I want you to understand that it is your body, and you do not have to consent to anything. This test helps us to get a baseline idea of your new coronary anatomy, and it also helps us to ensure the quality of our work. Again, it is your body. You do not have to have the cath."

"Okay."

"Think about it tonight, and I will talk to you about it again in the morning. I support you either way."

"Thanks doc."

Page (8:35 PM)—

Here we go.

"Mr. Grainger is pulling out his IVs, says that we are trying to kill him."

It starts. Whiskey river take my mind. We already have the wife crying (step 5 of the ten step postop whiskey convalescence).

"I'll be right there." (To talk to him, medicate him, tie his ass up if necessary so that he won't leave and die.)

The kicker is delivered by my 4 year old son Charles as I rush to the car with my coat over my shoulder.....

Charles opens the side door and looks out. He is as naked as a Jaybird...... "Thanks for dropping by dad!!"

Gee, after missing playing baseball in the yard (he played with mom), his swimming lesson, and everything else that he did today; that didn't hurt too much...

I rush to the hospital. I arrive on the floor and find Mr. Grainger standing in the hall surrounded by security guards.

"Tell me what's going on Mr. Grainger."

"I'm going home."

His wife is standing by her side weeping and pleading with him not to go.

"Why do you want to go home?"

"I want to find somebody that will take care of me."

"We are trying to take care of you sir."

"You are trying to kill me." (more tears from the wife)

"No we are not. It is my job to do everything that I can to help you. I will do anything for you to get you home safely, but this is too early. You are not ready to go."

"I'm going."

"No, you are not. I am not going to let you go. I can convince you to be smart and stay on your own volition, medicate you, or have these guys help me tie you to the bed, but you are not going home. I am the guy that is entrusted with your care and I take my job very seriously."

"Mmmmm"

"Why don't you just take it easy. I'll do anything for you."

"Let me go home."

"Except for that."

"Why don't we talk, honey," says the wife.

A private conference ensues. I take time to talk to the security guards and tell them to try not to hurt his sternal incision if we go for the "WWF Stone Cold Steve Austin Throwdown."

He returns to the room and sits in the corner. The wife calls their son in South Carolina. He is the one that Mr. Grainger will listen to.

"Mr. Grainger's son wants to talk to you."

"What's wrong with my dad?"

(He's a fucking drunk)

In an effort not to state the above: "I am not sure. I do know that he is very confused. He may be having a reaction to some medication, or he may just be disoriented from having such a big operation and not being in familiar surroundings for a while."

"Is he ready to go home?"

"No. I am worried that he would die if he went home early. His oxygen saturation is 87%, and yours is probably 99%. He is not ready to go home."

"Okay. What is your name, doctor? (So I can focus my lawsuit more effectively when I sue your ass if anything happens to my dad)

"Dr. Murrah"

"How do you spell that?"

"M U R R A H"

"Thanks."

"Okay."

STAND DOWN MEN

I must give the son credit. He got dad to go to bed without leather restraints.

I think that the gung ho security guards were ready for a fight. I appreciated their presence.

I also ordered a beer with his meals as needed and called the pharmacy to ensure that they had some alcohol available.

"Uh, sir, you will have to talk to my supervisor about that. I have never heard of giving a patient a beer."

"It happens all of the time. If you can't get any, I'll go home and get a few long necks out of the fridge (a challenge to their domain)."

The security guards like the direct beer approach. They are laughing and asking if I will be their primary care physician. "Mine isn't as hip as you, doc."

The guards also offer to go to The Grady's (the local indigent hospital) where this sort of therapy is very commonplace.

I walk into the resting angel's room... "Mr. Grainger, do you want a drink? I will be glad to get it for you."

"No. I am okay."

Good job South Carolina son........

I wait anxiously for the next phase........Stone Cold Tiedown Texas Barbed Wire Death Match. Stay tuned.....

2 Pages (9:35 PM, 9:38 PM) come in from pharmacy and the nursing supervisor who are still lathered up by the "beer therapist." I tell them to relax for now.

2123 Whitmore...
85 years old. CABG. Tough. Will beat Whiskey Man home.

Page (6:45 PM)—
"Mr. Whitmore's IV infiltrated (blew), do we have to restart it?"
"That's fine."
"Thanks."
"Great."
"Great."
"Okay."

2125 Harris.....
64 years old. Mitral valve replacement and CABG 10/98 at an outside institution. All bypass grafts closed (clotted). He shopped for a new doc and found us via the TV. 3 days out from CABG. Doing well.

Page (12:00 PM)—
My attending calls to check on the anticoagulation state of his patient.
He wants 10 or 12 mg of Coumadin given to get his blood thinner given that he has a valve in place. He is a good and compulsive physician, treating his patient the way that I would want to be treated.
I say that I will handle it.
I handle it.
Just checking on things. I am getting the general impression that I am the focal point where most of the medical universe goes to "check on things."
I love the expression "Edward Scissorhands by day, Michael DeBakey (a famous heart surgeon) by night." This signifies the elevation of your importance or perceived value when you are in the hospital when nobody else wants to be there; such as the middle of the night, weekends, and holidays. They will be back Monday morning to look at my work. My status will drop to Scissorhands again, and they will ask "How was your weekend." I will bite my lower lip (which I am beginning to do even in the absence of stress) and respond.... "Okay."....then write another chapter about the work epic that my life has turned into.

2128 Hudman...
60 year old. "Redo" CABG on Monday. Ready. No chest pain last night.
"When is my surgery?"

"Tuesday."

"I thought it was Monday. I need to know because my family is flying in from all over."

Chart check. "It is Tuesday."

The ensuing 12 hours are paraphrased in the following few sentences.

"I want to go home."

"You can't, you are on antibiotics for an arm infection. That is what Dr. Nopump wants."

"Can he do my operation on Monday?"

"He will be in Minnesota."

"Can I get a day pass?"

"Yes."

I write a day pass for him.

Another page comes in. It is Dr. Nopump. "Discharge Mr. Hudman on oral antibiotics."

"Yes sir."

"You can go home Mr. Hudman, but I have to write a bunch of your prescriptions so that you can take them while you are out."

I write for around 15 medications, under the impression that he is going to be discharged. I come down to his room to explain the medications to him. He is singing in the shower.

I wait a while. He comes out and decides that .......

"I would rather just go home on a pass and not be discharged. The nurses said that that will keep me from having to go back through admissions."

"Okay."

Somehow, I feel like this is not over with.


2134 Lower....

He had CABG one week ago. He is 78 years old and on hemodialysis 3 times per week. 12 hours after arriving home, he returns just "not feeling well."

Dr. Hakkin' Mika (Chief of cardiothoracic surgery at W.T.G. Morton Hospital) wants to bring him in.

I bring him in, and start him on antibiotics. I am very worried about an occult presentation of mediastinitis. Old diabetic patients with kidney failure and new wound pain are a "red flag."

Many clues in medicine must be extracted and are not blasted into you like the stereo commercial with the guy sitting in the chair getting blown away by his stereo. You have to dig for clues and diagnoses that could save the patient's life.

Page (1:00 PM)—
  Dr. Hakkin' Mika: "Pat, could you please admit Mr. Lower. He just
is not doing well."
  "Yes sir." (Good answer).
  "Okay."
  "Yes sir."
  "Great."

Page (5:03 PM)—
  "Mr. Lower has a temperature of 101."
  "Okay. Let's get some blood cultures."

Phil (Dr. Hakkin' Mika's physician's assistant) calls in from home
and orders IV antibiotics on Mr. Lower. He has spoken to the Infectious
Disease team and found out that Mr. Lower had some positive blood
cultures that grew out in the lab after his discharge. Phil must be feeling very guilty about being the one that discharged this 12 hour
"bounceback" to the hospital. He is great to work with because he
takes responsibility. It could also be that Dr. Hakkin' Mika called him
at home to inform him of the rapid bounceback of his admission. Well,
that is all good, but it leads to another problem (and another ride to
the hospital for me).

Page (7:10 PM)—
  "We can't get an IV in Mr. Lower."
  "Okay," said the numb, hateful person.
  I roll into the hospital and pop in a line (while holding my breath
to impress the nurse), check an x-ray and get back out before the
guy with the ear knows that I am around.

2138 Webber...
  2 days out from CABG. Rolling. Pacing wires pulled out.

Page (3:00 PM)—
  "Mr. Webber has a fever of 101. Do you want blood cultures?"
  "No. Just give him Tylenol and make him breathe."
  "Thanks."

Curbside Hit (7:05 PM)—
  "Mr. Webber's platelet count is low....69,000"
  "I think he is okay since he is not bleeding."

Outside Call (7:52 PM)—
  To paraphrase:
  "Give me some Percocet."
  "No."
  "Give me some Darvocet."
  "No."
  "Give me some morphine."
  "No."
  "Why am I shaking so?"
  "Because you are a drug addict."
  "Thank you."
  "Thank you."
  "Okay."
  "Okay."
  "Great."
Four more people would call that weekend asking for narcotics.
Four similar rejections would follow.

2139 Beller....
  2 days out from CABG. Rolling. Pacing wires pulled out.

Page (9:23 PM)—
  "Dr. Murrah, Mr. Beller has a temperature of 101.2, do you want
cultures or Tylenol?"
  "Give him some Tylenol please."
  "Thanks."
  "Okay."

2140 Cannon....
  78 year old "dried up granny lady." She has reached the point of
developing that characteristic "man face" that results from years without estrogen. What do you do when your wife gets a thick mustache,
and starts to look like one of your fishing buddies? True love must prevail; take her fishing with you.
  Anyway, she is 3 days after CABG. Rolling.

2141 Lower...
  3 days out from CABG. Rolling. We used the new "off pump" technique on him as well. He wanted it because he saw us on TV. The
internet, TV, and The Wall Street Journal are effective advertisers to
smart people. A little knowledge is a dangerous thing, and the unfortunate and dangerous reality is that these are not scientific forums. Dr.

Nopump seems to be the only one in the country that is looking at this in a truly scientific manner. The scientific method tends to outlast fads.

2103 Ross....
3 days out from CABG. Rolling. "Off pump" again. Biscuit poisoning (fat). Going home. Has memorized the "Krystal Creed."

Page (3:54 PM)—
"Can Mr. Ross still go home? He has a temperature of 100.4."
"Yes."
"Thanks."

2104 Harris...
2 days out from off pump CABG. Rolling......

Page (3:35 PM)—
"Mr. Harris feels nervous."
Ativan.

Page (1:14 AM)—
It's the "2 days postop fever/Tylenol call."
Tylenol.

2105 Hale...
75 year old one day out from an aortic valve replacement. She has made it to the floor from the ICU.

Page (6:33 PM)—
"I am so sorry to call you again Dr. Murrah. Mrs. Hale is in rapid atrial fibrillation at 160 beats per minute."
"That's okay (I was just gouging my right eye out with my thumb), you can call me for anything. Give her Digoxin 0.25 mg as a load, and 0.25 mg every 4 hours times two, then give her a daily dose of 0.125 mg. Also give her Cardizem 10 mg IV over 2 minutes, then start a Cardizem drip at 10 mg/hour."
"Thanks."

Curbside (7:00 PM)—
"Can we give her Lasix to her as an IV?"
"Yes."

These folks were all seen for the first time on Saturday morning over the course of 3 hours.....Now the ICU. I have to hurry because The Perfect Coronary Surgeon will be here shortly.

I run around with my junior guy who saw the ICU patients (he sees them because he was up all night last night with them).

Bed 1 Jones...

Day 1 after open lung biopsy for metastatic cancer. The original lesion was a leiomyosarcoma located on his leg. Leiomyosarcoma is a low grade, slow growing tumor that has a tendency to recur months to years after resection of 'the original lesion. It is this slow, relentless process that takes its toll on the patient's mind and body.

This guy is a stock broker. I talked with him about his work and my work. He wants to read my book. I took his phone number and told him that I would send a copy when it gets published.

I learned from him that the while the stock broker may have the edge on physicians during this time of record market growth, we have security. I am too quick to point out the negative aspects of my profession. Being a doctor is the best way to guarantee that you will have a good job with good pay. People are always going to be sick.

He looks great. He goes to the floor.

Page (8:15 PM)—

"Mr. Jones says that he was on Zestril at home and wants to take it again today."

"Restart him on 10 mg by mouth daily."

"Thanks."

Bed 2 Louis....

IV drug abuser. On dialysis. His dialysis graft got infected and stuck to his valve. The vegetations grew on the valve (endocarditis) and then started shooting clots to his head. He came into the hospital in a comatosed state. Dr. Hakkin' Mika replaced the valve, but he is not really waking up. He remains on the breathing machine, and will be until something gives. He remains on powerful antibiotics for his infection.

This guy worked as a security guard downtown.

Bed 3 Kitchen...

CABG 2 weeks ago. Her developed mediastinitis (infection of the chest/incision/heart) early in his postoperative course. The plastic surgeons had to open his chest and place a piece of abdominal omentum (fatty material in which the blood vessels travel) in the defect after debriding out all of the pus and "gradoo." He remains as sick as hell.

Call (2:25 PM)—

"Mr. Kitchen has poor urine output."

I order IV fluids given the large amount of inflammation that is going on in his body.

Bed 4 Brooken...

65 year old lady that had shock therapy for her depression and then came to our service where she staged an escape from the hospital before letting us cut her open. She is 4 days out from CABG. She pulled her breathing tube, central line, and most of her IV's out during this admission. We're just waiting for the next break in reality.

Bed 5 Hayes...

CABG yesterday. Doing well. Going to the floor.

Bed 6 Kolit...

CABG yesterday. Doing well. Going to the floor.

Bed 7 Williams...

CABG yesterday. Doing well. Going to the floor.

Bed 8 Moore...

CABG yesterday. Doing well. Going to the floor.

Bed 9 Johnson...

2 weeks out from a mitral valve replacement. She is a school teacher and had a massive stroke after surgery. Her husband and 2 young sons come by and hold her hand. She can only move the right side of her body. She has a feeding tube and a tracheostomy. We do not know how she developed her stroke. It is most likely that some clot broke loose from her heart and traveled up to her brain. She is making a slow recovery. Thank goodness. How much neurologic function that will be left is a mystery.

Page (2:43 PM)—

"Her Coumadin (blood thinner used when a patient receives a mechanical heart valve) was not ordered."

"Give her 5 mg tonight."

"Do you want a chest x-ray in the morning?"

"Yes"

"Do you want labs ordered in the morning?"

"Yes"

Bed 10 Walker...

This is a young girl with sickle cell anemia that is three days out from mitral valve replacement for endocarditis. She had to return to the operating room when she began bleeding immediately after surgery. She remains on full ventilator support. Valve surgery seems to take a whole lot more out of these patients. They have a higher incidence of strikes and bleeding after these procedures.

Page (2:41 PM)—

"Her Coumadin (blood thinner used when a patient receives a mechanical heart valve) was not ordered."

"Give her 5 mg tonight"

"Do you want her on full ventilator support tonight?"

"Yes. Try to get the tube out in the morning."

I then proceed to see about ten "outliers" that are getting ready for surgery on Monday. I come back downstairs and am given a doughnut by the nurses. They have been tremendously supportive of my cause. Without them, my ship is sunk. I remember always that my mom was a nurse. I remember how hard she worked and I appreciate their work. They spend more time with the patient than anyone else in the hospital. They can make or break a patient with their efforts. They can make or break a resident with their efforts.

Nurses

I cannot begin to thank all of the nurses that helped me make it through this process. There are too many. I should start with the person that became a nurse so that I could go to school to become a doctor. Mom. I have done some pretty discipline-oriented things on my road to becoming a heart surgeon; but beginning to study after the four kids went to bed is something that I am not sure that I could do.

A nurse brought me into this world.

The nurses have got it right in so many ways. Their approach to the patient is much less mechanical than that of many physicians. They can serve as a go-between when a doctor is not spending enough time talking to the family, or is just generally being a "rear-end." They can be the search-engine for other sources of help when the resident on-call clearly does not know what the hell he is doing. They are the ones that spend the most time with the patient. They've got it right.

This was just one day's efforts on call at The W. T. G. Morton Hospital. To get the full effect, you have to multiply that times two. Then you get to work until 7 or 8 PM Monday.

We are the weekend warriors. Why does the resident do what it takes a team of workers to do during the week? We are cheap labor. We are part of the solution for their financial problems. We have already been factored into the equation. The physician's assistants used to take call like we do on the weekends, but that was discontinued because the hospital did not want to pay for them (and they weren't so keen on getting an average of 100 pages over a 2 day period). The residents are the glue that fills in the financial holes for the system. You can call it education if you like. I begin to have my doubts as I field the fifth call from a wacked-out patient asking me to "call in" his prescription for narcotics.

This year has come to a close and I am certain that I have learned more in the span of 12 months then I have ever learned in my life. It is getting harder to be a "boy" when you are 34. Being back on the bottom has been the hardest thing about the year, but I made it. I am still on the recovery from my Bayview experience, but can now see the light at the end of the tunnel.

# 19

# Second Year of Cardiothoracic Surgery Fellowship

Total Years:    17 (1999-2000) .................35 years old
Gross Salary/Debt:    $41,880 gross per year; $31,704 net per year;
                      $60,000 debt
Hours:          Varied with rotation

**Second Year of Cardiothoracic Surgery Fellowship......The Big City Children's Hospital–Congenital Heart Surgery**

Hours:          Every third night in-house call; 100 hours per week
To work:        6:30 AM Monday through Friday;
                7:30 AM Saturday and Sunday
Home:           Average 7 PM during week; 11 AM Saturday and
                Sunday
Note:           Every third weekend off with pager turned off.
                One week vacation per 4 month rotation

                Gross Pay Rate ...........................$7.90
                Net Pay Rate ...............................$5.98

   I started my second year of cardiothoracic surgery fellowship at
The Children's Hospital. It was evident that I was entering into an orga-
nized system. Our work schedules are much less intense than those at
W.T.G. Morton Hospital and University Hospital. We are there to learn.

There is so much more help available. You don't get the impression that anything would change if you were not even there.

You don't feel like cheap labor.

This situation can be seen as an opportunity to slack off or an opportunity to have a clear mind, think, and operate. I have chosen the latter. I am feeling like I have fallen behind with respect to my personal discipline. I have been making myself move every second of every day (at home and at work), and I have stayed off of coffee. There is a satisfaction that comes from doing things that you know that you should do but do not want to do. There is a sense of satisfaction that comes from enduring pain to get something worthwhile done.

I conclude that if I am going to lead my family through this quest for heart surgery (that I have gotten them into), I must be a more disciplined man. My family did not volunteer for this. My kids, and Alison (amazingly enough - lucky me) do not give a damn if I am a heart surgeon or a garbage man. They do care if I am too tired or mentally fucked up to spend time with them. I accept the challenge and responsibility of having a family and must make myself a few notches more disciplined than my job requires. This is a heavy load. This is a lot of discipline. This is also my choice.

I took my first night of call last night in the Cardiac ICU. We had a kid with a condition called Hypoplastic Left Heart Syndrome. It is a disorder in which the left ventricle and the aorta are malformed and requires a very complex procedure called the Norwood Operation to keep her alive. The child was born here in the city and was immediately transferred to the CICU at Children's Hospital. The mom (no dad) had no insurance and appeared to be some sort of a gypsy.

"Mrs. DeVille, your daughter has a very serious condition that will require a very complex operation with a very high degree of risk...."

"There will be no operation."

"Okay.....There will be no operation."

"We heal him and we pray."

"Okay."

In comes the religious figure, dressed in flowing robes. He is what I envisioned the Dalai Lama from Caddyshack to look like. He performed what I can only describe as a faith healing on the child's heart.

"Ma'am, I must emphasize how sick your child is. We respect your feelings, but at the same time want you to understand the risk of delaying surgery."

"Now you look with your machines to show the healing of my baby's heart."

"Okay....Now we look with our machines to show the healing."

Hmmmmm.

Sorry, no dice. She still has Hypoplastic Left Heart Syndrome.

"Ma'am, I must emphasize how sick your child is. We respect your feelings, but at the same time want you to understand the risk of delaying surgery...."

"We would like to be transferred to Michigan."

"......and we'll be sending for the jet shortly....."

The Cessna Citation arrives from the University of Michigan to pick the nice (uninsured) family up. I see a fellow from the University of Michigan (just like me), and I feel sorry for the load that he just took on.

"We would like to ride in the jet," says mom.

"No. They have an airline flight arranged for you."

"We would like to ride in the jet."

"No."

I liked this guy already.

And now the reason that I wrote this little story down for you.......

"You......go to the Devil.....I curse you......go to the Devil."

The tired fellow looks at her.....

"Thank you so much.... We'll do everything that we can to save your child."

There was a collective sigh of relief when the entourage left the CICU. It seems a little misdirected to try to pull an uninsured, unappreciative, gypsy-curser's child (with little hope for much quality of life) out of the fire, and then fly them around the country for free. There are a lot of things that I can imagine doing with that money, including the feeding of some local kids. Oh well, I guess that you have to make the call when it is put in your face.

*The Name Game*

*They used to name their children after their doctors. I know a thoracic surgeon that trained at Charity Hospital in New Orleans. He delivered a tremendous number of indigent children (a former colleague used the term "democrats") during his OB-GYN rotation in medical school. It was an honor to have your doctor name the child. This guy named them all the same names....Joe or Josephine. He estimated that there must be 200 of them scattered around the country by now.*

*I took an interest in the names of some of the children that come to this hospital. A little research and curbside interviews of some of the long-term workers at The Children's Hospital brought the following list of names...*

*Orlando Fudge*
*Mahogany Rainforest*
*Miracle Whip*
*Siryitnoj (acronym for "Satan I rebuke you in the name of Jesus")*
*Little McLucy McCloud*
*Nacerima ("America" spelled backwards)*
*Abcde (Pronounced "abucida")*
*Marta Bus (Marta is the name of Atlanta's rapid transit authority)*
*Amiracle Kelly*
*Theend (The sworn last child of this family)*
*Chevy Shead*
*Precious Glorious*
*Female (pronounced "fe-mal-e")*
*Tequila Chase (who had fetal alcohol syndrome)*
*Lemonjello and Orangello (siblings)*

*All names can be altered by adding "avious," "la," "isha," "iquia," and "quarrious." ...I think that every child should have a good shot at success in his or her lifetime. A good solid name like one of the above helps. Things can be further optimized by the sperm donor (father) sticking around long enough to see him/her grow.*

The kids that were admitted to the Cardiac Intensive Care Unit (CICU) at The Big City Children's Hospital were often quite sick and terrible looking. Frequently they had an unhealthy "blue" look about them. Some were able to be resuscitated. Some of those made it to surgery for correction of their often complex heart defects. A few died after a long fight in the CICU. A few just died.

El-Dude (A fellow from Israel that is spending a year here) had one of the latter last night. This child came in septic (a condition that can result from bacteria in the blood) and bleeding out of every orifice. The poor baby had her nose packed with blood-soaked gauze, a tracheal tube in place with blood streaming out into the ventilator circuit, and bright red blood blowing out of her rectum. She was in what Meaty Flashknife (one of our cardiothoracic surgery attendings that you will meet soon) would call "a flat spin with no both rudders out." Death came quickly and mercifully last night, despite El-Dude's best efforts.

I don't like it when kids die. El-Dude didn't either. I think that this children's heart stuff might just have the potential to eat a person up. When they took all of the crap out of her and wiped all of the blood off and put a bow in her hair, she looked much better.

Even though she happened to be dead.

One That Looked Exactly Like My Son.

*Consent.*

*"The risk of the procedure is minimal. The likelihood of success is very good. There is a small risk of bleeding and infection. There are very rarely strokes that can occur from being on the heart-lung machine....."*

*"He should do fine."*

*What else can they do but hope that is the case. They have done their homework. They have chosen the best heart surgeons in the country.*

*On bypass. Stop the heart. Close the defect.*

*Everything is perfect......*

*...The randomness of life strikes, the heart begins to beat, sending air into the left side of the circulation. Air goes to the head.*

*A flat tire on my way home, and I happen to hit a telephone pole on the side of the road....It just happens.*

*Everything was perfect.*

*Slow to wake up in the ICU.......He has some spastic type movements.*

*"He has been doing that since he was a baby. He looks at us when we speak to him."*

*"Mommy and daddy are here..."*

*Slow improvement.*

*"He looks better, thank you doctors for everything."*

*To the floor......worse again overnight. Rigid, somnolent. This is a reach that the parents cannot overcome with their incredible optimism.*

*Emergent CT scan of the head...massive cerebral edema, areas of stroke.*

*"Your child has had a large stroke"*

*Back to the ICU. EEGs, neuro exams, neurosurgeons, heart surgeons, cardiologists, terrific nurses.......All kinds of medical stuff sticking out of our son's head.*

*The parents stand by and watch. Nothing else to do. It is as if they are in a dream that they will soon wake up from. He continues to slip slowly away.*

*We are approaching irreversibility.*

We need a couple of good days.

A bad day. Another change in mental status. Another CT scan of the head.

*A huge stroke. The dream does not end.*

*"Let him go."*

*Flowers from the parents at the front desk of the CICU made me think of this today.*

**Second Year of Cardiothoracic Surgery Fellowship......The Big City University Hospital—Cardiac Surgery**

| | |
|---|---|
| Hours: | Every third night in-house call; 110 hours per week |
| To work: | 6 AM, Monday through Saturday; 6 AM Sunday |
| Home: | Average 8 PM during week; 2 PM Saturday; Noon Sunday |
| Note: | Every third weekend off with pager turned off. One week vacation per 4 month rotation |

Gross Pay Rate ...........................$7.55
Net Pay Rate ...............................$5.71

More of the same bullshit patient population.........

Social History:

Causey: "Any alcohol?"

Preop cardiac surgery patient: "2 quarts of Canadian Mist per day. Some beer."

Causey (hoping the answer will be no): "Do you work?"

Patient: "Instructor in Taggart's Driving School."

This is the start of my serious push to actually know how to do heart surgery. "Heart surgery is not hard, it is hard to get to do," says my boss. I have pretty much passed through the "hard to get to do" part. I will have to say that it isn't so damned easy either.

Case in point. I am the second year resident on the service and now the guy that opens the "redos." A "redo" is a heart surgery case that is done on a patient for the second (or greater) time. When the sternum (breastbone) is divided at the first operation with the sternal saw, the risk of sawing into the heart is not nearly as great. The second operation usually comes several years after the first operation. The heart has had time to stick to the backside of the sternum. The space between the back of the sternum and the front of the heart can be anywhere from a few millimeters to zero, and you are supposed to avoid bridging that gap with your big hot saw. There is therefore a finite risk that you will saw into the heart when you go back in for the redo. There is a certain amount of pressure that comes along with the responsibility of opening a redo. It is a growth experience for sure. I really do not want to saw into the guy's heart. The thrill of getting a guy open safely is in many ways comparable to playing an intense golf match. It is in many ways more intense than even the best golf match because somebody dies if you screw up. In golf, short of sustaining a rattlesnake bite in the deep rough, nobody dies and you just throw your club or curse a little.

I helped out on a hero's (we will call him The Hero) redo operation this week. The Hero was one of the men that stormed Omaha Beach in June of 1941. He has a scar on his right shoulder that looks a lot like a pacemaker scar. It was actually a shrapnel wound that he had sustained on the beach. He had made it through a coronary bypass in 1988, but was having recurrent symptoms. He had a bad feeling about going through the process again. He was convinced that he was going to die, and had related the feeling to his wife. These intuitions that patients get about their impending doom are quite scary and are best heeded by the wise surgeon. This man had seen death first hand, and been around it all of his life. He was not scared and hysterical. He was calm and sober and reserved about his intuition. Perhaps he had used up all of his luck this time.

He told his wife good-bye in the preoperative holding area.

I told myself that I was not going to be the dumb ass that killed this man. I was charged with my first real solo redo opening. I had rehearsed it over and over for the previous 24 hours. I knew just what to do for every conceivable disaster.

You saw in to the heart and it bleeds like hell.........go to the groin and get him onto bypass through the femoral artery and vein (quickly!).

Get the pursestring stitches in early in case you goon the heart while dissecting out the scar tissue. That way you can go on bypass and finish the dissection under cardiopulmonary bypass....and the guy doesn't die.

First do no harm, a great principle. Don't kill the patient.

I am blessed by the presence of "The Cleaner"—the Physician's Assistant that has tons of experience and has taught me a ton over the past 12 months.

We get through the case without too much trouble. The operation lasted 7 hours. The Hero pulls through the operation on the wings of 3 well placed bypass grafts. The last operation had used up most of his "conduit" (leg veins that are used for bypass grafts), so we used the artery from his left arm.

I spoke to The Hero this morning. He is still on the ventilator (breathing machine), but will probably be under his own power by morning.

A few more antlers bud out of my head, and for a brief moment I am able to experience the rewards of what at times has seemed like an 18-year bullshit cruise.

I am energized by the amount of good that I can do for people on a daily basis.

The experience on this service was much like it was at W.T.G. Morton Hospital. I do however, want to leave with an account of another HMO horror story that took place yesterday. This happens all of the time, and I think that I skip telling the reader because I am so numb to the injustice of it all.

The Perfect Coronary Surgeon's third case for Monday was transferred to a relatively unknown medical center on the coast because his insurance refused to pay for The Perfect Coronary Surgeon to do the case.

It was a huge insult to the patient. It was a medical risk to transfer a patient via ambulance when he has such critical narrowing of his coronary arteries. Going to an unknown center from here is akin to going from Prime Rib to a month old Krystal burger that was found in the corner of the fridge behind the pickles. It both worried and irritated the living crap out of me, the patient, and everybody here at The Big City University who were forced to take up his cause try to keep him here. It pisses me off that there is such unbelievable accountability on the way that surgeons with 20 years of training and another 25 years of experience make highly complex decisions, yet there is no accountability for the dumb ass that may have killed this nice and very sick man.

There was nothing that we could do and he was transferred out. I anxiously await the wave of lawsuits that is coming to balance this injustice.

Things are getting busier and busier on the service. Last night was one of the hardest call nights of my residency experience (many nights seem that way, and that sinking feeling comes around 4 A.M. when you realize that you are not going to get any sleep). We fixed a guy's post-infarction VSD (a hole in the heart that occurs after a heart attack), and he limped into the ICU at around 11 PM. I was placed in charge of his care last night just about the same time that Mr. Little sat up in bed and said that he "can't breathe." He was suffering from the end stages of endocarditis (infection of the heart). He originally had developed a pneumonia that sent bugs (bacteria) into the blood and caught hold of his mitral valve. He went through two mitral valve replacements and tonight was the night that the whole thing fell apart.

"I can't breathe."

The agitated condition and upright, panting posture of a man who is suffocating.

Get momma out of the room.... "If you will please wait outside."

Get him to lie back. His eyes roll into the back of his head. He finally passes out.

Call the code.....Get the fucking tube in his airway.

To the ICU.......Every line known to man is put in his body in rapid-fire fashion, just like you learned to do on the Thirsten and Duncan Teabag Endowed Trauma Service at Bayview.

"Damn son, that was fast."

It is good to be good at something, even if it isn't the ability to stiff a 1-iron into a strong wind.

A long night is spent alternating between "hole in the heart man" and "blown up valve man." It was not easy giving the morbid updates to the families either. "We're doing everything we can means we're losing.

By 4 AM this morning it was PBTBKLO (pine box to bedside, keep lid open) for hole in the heart man. I was proud that I had kept him alive overnight as I presented him on 7 AM rounds to my Chief Resident.

The Chief turned off the balloon pump that was supporting his heart and noted that there was no activity. With a stroke of irreverence (though not intended) towards my salvage efforts he stated, "he's dead."

"He's not dead."

"When I turn this pump off there is nothing underneath...he's dead."

"Hmmm, he may be dead."

"He peed 6 cc last hour," said the nurse.

A private transient thought from the fatigued mind of a post-call veteran, "Is it possible for a dead person to tee tee?"

He was not dead.....but he did not make it another 4 hours.

Dr. Sternalpunch continues to inspire me. He skipped a two-day delay on a patient's heart surgery by pulling 3 loose teeth out of a patient's mouth on rounds with a hemostat this weekend.

This may sound cruel, but it did not hurt the patient (very much) and it prevented a delay in his critical heart operation in the name of the two-day dance of the tooth fairies (oral surgeons) who would surely make an event of it.

He gave the old guy a wet rag and told him to bite down on it, then rinse his mouth out in the bathroom.

Big ones......

"Big surgeon, big incision, big bills!" Somebody has to make the call; make a decision, sometimes heart surgeons do not have the luxury of time.

A Great Day for a Heart Surgery Resident

I stayed up all weekend because I was the in-house dog. That is a 48-hour run that includes little sleep and many calls from the floor regarding an urgent need for anything from Tylenol to suppositories, to what I like to call a "weather update" (just statements of fact—at 3 A.M.—that have no real urgency or even importance other than serving to bring the aneurysm in your brain a few millimeters closer to blowing). I was very tired and mowed right into Monday's cases.

I was given the last case of the day. It was a disaster that lasted until around midnight. We had done it all to this 47 year-old high-risk reoperation. She was very sick to begin with. She was fat. She had 50 other medical problems. Her heart was stuck to the back of her sternum and we had to spend 3 hours carving the terrible pulsating scar that was her heart. We finally had to put a cannula in her groin to get everything exposed. We still could not see very well and had to shut the pump off before we could see well enough to sew the new mitral valve in. When we restarted the heart, the bleeding began. The bleeding, or my fight to stop it would take me into my 60th hour of being "awake." Things were so bad at one point during the operation, and the word sent up to the waiting room had become so grim, that the family actually thought that she was dead.

"Dr. Murrah, the family thinks that the patient is dead. What do you want me to tell them?"

"Let me look at the heart.......hmmmm, ......no, she is not dead."

I had been too busy working on this lady to realize that we had saved the shit out of her. My Chief Resident relieved me near the end of the battle.

I went to Krystal and got a "Number 4...Biggie sized with a Coke" and an extra four Double Cheese Krystals. I wolfed down what I could on the drive home, fed the rest to my dog (who wolfed them down even faster than even I could), had sex with my wife, got up 3 hours later and started doing heart surgery again....

I may look back on my present state and laugh. It seems more normal now than it will later.....I hope.

I Drive A Piece of Shit

My car. A piece of shit.

No rear view mirror (melted and fell off the windshield last year)

-left turn signal (I have to click it intermittently to simulate a signal)

-left windshield wiper (it scrapes metal on glass, better to just let the rain hit and disperse, or lean to the right side of the car to see past the good wiper when the hard rain comes)

-radio (it comes on in the summer when the car gets really hot...which leads to my next item..)

-air conditioner

-glove compartment (gutted and gone...I don't remember where it went)

-left rear tail light (waiting for the ticket, which leads to my next item...)

-Driver's License (last renewed in Bayview a few years back).

I am not ashamed. My car has character. I'm pretty much not interested in the beast doing anything more than getting me to the hospital and back home fast. The car has reached that threshold where repairs are futile. It has reached the point where you don't give a damn if you floor it. It has reached the point where you put oil in it when you hear the valves click or start to smell the engine burning.

I am sure that my dad is flipping cartwheels reading this one. I seem to like my car being a piece of shit. I abuse it the way some fat people eat ham sandwiches and ice cream when they get stressed out.

I am not ashamed....

Cliff Notes on a Code From Hell

"Mr. Leaker fell down, we can't get him up," says the floor nurse on that very, very lonely Saturday.

"I'll be right over."

Man down, lying in the hallway, covered with urine and shit (including on his socks where I had grabbed his feet with my bare hands to lift his legs up).

"Aw God Damnit."

I lift his legs up and try to get blood flow to his head. He passes out and stops breathing. All of this in a 350 pound man who is on the floor (covered in shit).

One, two, three....ten people that I recruited by screaming lift him onto a stretcher......we run to the ICU with a rather large woman pumping air into his lungs at the head of the bed. She is running backwards, ...for a while....then she trips and lands in the hallway on her back too. She looks much like a turtle that has been flipped over in the desert sun. A devolved couch potato that is all of a sudden asked to move.

"Push her out of the way!!!" was my bold and politically incorrect statement. They push her out of the way. We make it to the unit.

Endotracheal tube. Arterial line.

CPR.

Central line.

CPR.

Intraaortic balloon pump.

The attendings gather to see my mess and help with the code. For this is the father of a VIP (of course).

God damned mess. A huge stroke.

They never show the doo doo on "E.R."

"And by the way Dr. Murrah, that nurse got her feelings hurt when you told them to push her out of the way."

I made an apology... with my tail between my legs.

Mr. Leaker dies in front of me and his family over the next 12 hours.

"How was your day honey."

The scrotal free space.

Our surgical gowns are big green hot robes that we wear during the cases, which average around four hours in length.

The scrotal free space is a region that intermittently becomes inflamed as I stand during the long cardiac surgery cases. It is a zone that is bound anteriorly by the back wall of the scrotum. Posteriorly and laterally, it is bounded by the posterior aspects of the upper inner thigh. I wear boxers (mainly because of the reduction in skid marks as compared to the tight whiteys when worn over the two days spent in the hospital on call), and this creates a potential "terrarium" (the little plastic greenhouses that came in boxes of Super Sugar Crisp when I was a kid) effect. You are asked to stand still for long periods of time in the OR (especially when you are dealing with the micro-surgical techniques of the coronary arteries). That lack of motion combined with the heat of the OR and the heat of the double cover of the gown as well as the scrubs makes for a very hot environment in the scrotal free space. Sweat invariably drips down off of your bag onto your legs. There is also the potential for gas jet damage from the anal orifice, which is located just posterior and superior to this region. Some fungal elements can grow in this region if left unchecked. Occasional motion with frictional forces applied to these areas can cause great pain. Intermittent erections (some spontaneous, some secondary to a good LAD anastomosis) give the scrotum a boggy/post venous engorgement quality, furthering the humidification/rotting process.

Moisture, heat, organisms and time (lots of time) leads to the rash from hell, located on the inner thighs. It is a rash that resembles the area under the giant breast where that fat lady kept her turkey sandwich. Some call the area between the anus and the genitals the "Taint"—'taint your asshole, 'taint your bag. I like to include the airspace in between as well and name this the scrotal free space. Perhaps I will have to resort to the tight whitey, skid mark era of my childhood.

Maybe just a shot of fungal cream to the 'taint and a new line for my mission statement/morning routine.

It's not Funny?

Are you losing your sensitivity when you... 1) chant "Bring out your dead" (in the preop holding area) as they did on the Monty Python movie; 2) prescribe face pillow therapy to the pain-in-the-ass patient; 3) order "clown to bedside stat" for the depressed patient that generates 10 calls for you on a busy night (a real order from another resident at another institution—he got in trouble for that one)?

Is it funny to say that a person "took a dirt nap" when he dies?

Is it clever to be able to recite the pneumonic PBTBKLO (pine box to bedside, keep lid open) when a patient is going down the tubes?

Is it clever and funny to name the venous cannula that we use to put patients on cardiopulmonary bypass the "GK 46" (GK standing for Granny Killer) because of its stiff nature and potential for destruction of an old lady's atrium? Is it funny to name the cannula something that sounds like the name AK 47?

I must confess that somehow, in a sick way, it is.

Have I lost my sensitivity?

No.

Is this perhaps the most tragic and at the same time the most hilarious job in the world?

It is the best job in the world.

**Second Year of Cardiothoracic Surgery Fellowship......The Veteran's Hospital-Cardiothoracic Surgery**

Hours:          Every night home call; 110 hours per week
To work:        6 AM, Monday through Saturday; 6 AM Sunday
Home:           Average 8 PM during week; 2 PM Saturday;
                Noon Sunday
Note:           One week vacation per 4 month rotation

                Gross Pay Rate ............................$7.55
                Net Pay Rate................................$5.71

# 20

# Third Year of Cardiothoracic Surgery Fellowship

Total Years:    18 (2000-2001....................36 years old
Gross Salary/Debt:   $41,880 gross per year; $31,704 net per year;
                $60,000 debt
Hours:          Varied with rotation

**Third Year of Cardiothoracic Surgery Fellowship......The Big City University Hospital–Cardiothoracic Surgery**

Hours:          Every third night in-house call; 110 hours per week
To work:        6 AM, Monday through Saturday; 6 AM Sunday
Home:           Average 8 PM during week; 2 PM Saturday;
                Noon Sunday
Note:           Every third weekend off with pager turned off.
                One week vacation per 4 month rotation

                Gross Pay Rate ...........................$7.55
                Net Pay Rate ...............................$5.71

**Third Year of Cardiothoracic Surgery Fellowship......The W. T. G. Morton Hospital–Cardiothoracic Surgery**

Hours:          Every third night in-house call; 110 hours per week
To work:        6 AM, Monday through Saturday; 6 AM Sunday

Home:        Average 8 PM during week; 2 PM Saturday;
                     Noon Sunday
Note:         Every third weekend off with pager turned off.
                     One week vacation per 4 month rotation

                     Gross Pay Rate ............................$7.55
                     Net Pay Rate ...............................$5.71

## Third Year of Cardiothoracic Surgery Fellowship......The Grady's Urban MASH Unit–Cardiothoracic Surgery

Hours:        Every third night in-house call; 110 hours per week
To work:     6 AM, Monday through Saturday; 6 AM Sunday
Home:        Average 8 PM during week; 2 PM Saturday;
                     Noon Sunday
Note:         Every third weekend off with pager turned off.
                     One week vacation per 4 month rotation

                     Gross Pay Rate ............................$7.55
                     Net Pay Rate ...............................$5.71

This is the end of the line for the cardiothoracic surgery fellow. At The Grady's Urban MASH Unit you can be the doctor you always wanted to be. This is the place where you are very much on your own, mainly because nobody else wants to be there with you. You can be as busy or as laid back as you wish.

One of my present attendings (Meaty Flashknife) was much more aggressive and very interested in surgery of the aorta (the aorta is the large artery arising from the heart). He was seeing a patient in The Grady's ER who had an abnormal chest x-ray. The patient's friend (Mr. Tasty Case) came forward and stated that he had been coughing recently and wondered if he could "get a chest x-ray too." Dr. Flashknife granted his wish and was shocked to see that the guy had a huge mass that most likely represented a giant aneurysm (enlarged area of thin walled artery) of the aorta (what might otherwise be referred to as a "tasty case").

Dr. Flashknife, with a newfound sense of humanity recommended an immediate CAT scan.....

"You really need to get this looked at right now, buddy."

"I know, doc, but I'm hungry," responded Mr. Tasty Case.

"You really, really need to get this study done now, Mr. Tasty

Case" (before I rotate off of this service).

"I don't know doc, I'm really hungry. I want to go to McDonald's."

Let's compare..........hamburger.....huge aneurysm of your aorta ......hamburger.

"I tell you what, i'll buy you two Big Macs if you will get a CAT scan."

Pause.......Hmmmmmmmmm.....hamburger.....no, two Big Macs... AND huge aneurysm of my aorta about to explode.....Hmmmmmmm

"It's a deal, doc."

The story is as true as the 2 hour 18 minute skin to skin 4 vessel emergency CABG that I did with Meaty late last night. Mr. Tasty Case went on to have his CAT scan and a successful staged repair of his giant thoracic aortic aneurysm.

# 21

# Some Positive Recommendations from a Guy that Has Paid His Dues

The profession of surgery is an honorable one and my job is a privilege. America is training the best surgeons in the world. We have a system of training that works. I think that the time that I put in at the country's hardest program gives me the right to make a few suggestions.

**1) Academic Health Centers (AHCs) should not be held accountable for research, the training of residents, and indigent care and at the same time have to compete with private hospitals.**

There should be some measure of protection of the multiple noble missions of the AHC. Financial pressure from reduced federal (Medicare, Medicaid) reimbursement and loss of patient bases from the growth of HMOs threaten the very existence of AHCs (that are worth preserving). It used to be easy for AHCs to wear all three hats (clinical, research, teaching, with a huge load of indigent care thrown in) when reimbursement was okay. Now it is getting much harder to make ends meet and AHCs are having to be very creative to stay alive.

It seems to me that quality in clinical care (e.g., having the world's best surgeons) is what sets AHCs apart from the rest, and this must come first. If you lose those guys to private hospitals, much of the appeal of the AHC is lost; with or without the administrative hype of a precisely crafted mission statement.

Many AHCs around the country are losing some of their best surgeons. This is mainly because they are not paying their best clinicians a salary that is comparable to what they would receive in private practice. We are killing the goose that lays the golden eggs. Money talks. Academic surgeons ought to make close to (if not more than) private surgeons do, because they contribute more to the profession. AHCs ought to be protected, and academic surgeons ought to be an elite group of highly paid, world class practitioners. Once quality is established, AHCs can protect themselves by aggressively expanding their marketshare in the community, even if that means forming some sort of limited alliance with "The Beast" (HMOs). This partnership would increase the marketshare of the AHC, while giving the HMO association with the name of the AHC and at the same time exposing the HMO to something that they seemed to forget about—quality patient care. In the face of continued federal (Medicare, Medicaid) cutbacks, AHCs must aggressively seek additional funding in the form of charitable private endowments and fostering a strong and productive research environment that is able to win big government grants. This funding will support the second and third missions of the AHC, teaching and research.

Quality must come first. The big money presently goes to the guys in private practice. The money is going to the guys that the stars in the AHCs are training. What's that all about? Are we planning to keep the stars in the AHCs by appealing to their sense of altruism? News flash, as great as it looked on paper, communism did not work.

## 2) Surgery residency should be shorter and/or more focused on the eventual specialty.

I have credibility in stating this because I have done a good job and worked hard for 18 years after high school to become a heart surgeon. That is too long. Still, the price that you pay is small when compared to the excellence that is instilled upon you over this time of intense training. Greatness comes with a price in any field.

I hope that some day we will find a way to shorten the training period by perhaps focusing more on the resident's eventual specialty. For instance: 3 years general surgery/7 years cardiothoracic surgery instead of 7 years general surgery/3 years cardiothoracic surgery. Dr. Sternalpunch says that "Heart surgery is not hard to do, it is hard to get to do." He is damned sure right on that one.

### 3)  Residents should be paid more.

Much of the busywork that residents are asked to do in the name of "training" is nothing more than a short term financial solution made by a financially strapped institution that is trying to cope with the current environment of large scale reimbursement cutbacks. Residents do not have a choice because they do not have the ability to collectively bargain and have too much to lose.

The hospital gets around $70,000 per resident per year from the federal government (so we will be guaranteed enough doctors in the future). That is a great bonus for a hospital because they can turn around and pay their resident $30,000 per year to do all of the crap work that they would have to pay a non-migrant worker $150,000 per year to do.

Hospitals' desire to get residents on board is evidenced by the following statistics: There are approximately 17,000 medical students graduating from U.S. medical schools annually. There are 24,000 first year residency spots in the U.S. Why? Because it is so profitable for a hospital to have residents. These extra 7,000 spots were created by hospitals looking for the federal bonuses given to them by hiring lettuce pickers (residents).

$70,000 from the government minus $30,000 for the lettuce pickers' salary......$40,000 winner. Add $150,000 that you would have to pay a human being to do the same work.......$190,000 winner.

Looks like they could at least give me a parking spot closer to the hospital.

Sure, it is a great privilege to be able to save lives, but you don't have to pay me the salary of a Wendy's Restaurant employee. Some of the salaries paid to surgery interns who work 120 hours per week are illegal and would lose a labor grievance lawsuit if anyone had the time or the nerve to file it while they were still poor and under the control of the offender. If you can't find the funding, take it out of the 20 million dollar salaries of the HMO bosses that have popped up; or the legions of hospital administrators that go home at 5 PM and never save anybody.

Suppose I stopped going to school after four years of college and signed on as a professional care denier for an HMO. Suppose that I was promoted for my exceptional efforts at getting mothers and their newborn babies out of the hospital within 24 hours. Suppose that I was able to rise at a moderate rate through the ranks of the company and had a conservative investment portfolio. I calculated that I would be worth approximately $500,000 in the eleven years after college that it has taken me to finish my general surgery training and compile a $65,000 debt. I am not even going to try to figure out how much is lost if that difference is invested over the course of a lifetime.

Somehow it is wrong for the physician to talk about money. We are trained to put the patient's interest first in front of our own. That is appropriate and makes me proud of my profession. I recall being at a party for a friend in Bayview City in 1996. I had barely made it there due to some disaster in the hospital and was very tired and very much "post-call." I still remember the words of a young (younger than me) attorney proclaiming that "a profession ceases to be a profession once it allows its finances to be controlled by another group." I was too tired to respond effectively, but I remember thinking how pathetic that that sounded.

I submit that a profession such as medicine is a profession because it places the welfare of human beings above all else. It is our very nature as physicians, and not businessmen, that has lead us to the point where we are getting squeezed the way we are. We should continue to place excellence in patient care as our first priority. Aligning ourselves with such correct principles will ensure that we will remain a profession and stand strong against the test of time. We also have a right to fight for just compensation for such efforts.

I recently read an editorial written by a physician who has been a leader in surgical education in this country. The editorial quotes some remarkable statistics from a March issue of USA Today.

Administrative positions in health care have grown 20 times more rapidly than opportunities for physicians.

Insurance administrative costs have increased 25-fold in less than 30 years.

Bureaucratic costs now account for 25% of total hospital expenses.

Why not focus financial support on the only ones that provide direct medical care rather than this newly arrived "host of saprophytes that parasitize the one service that only physicians can provide?" 2 Hospitals should stop ripping off the guys that are doing the lion's share of the work (that makes a hospital a hospital). I have seen a hospital work without a bunch of administrators, I have never seen a hospital work without a bunch of doctors. Hospitals should take care of their own.

## 4) Residents should be able to defer their student loans until they are in practice.

I am 34 years old, $80,000 in debt, trying to support a wife and two children on $2500 per month, and here come the bill collectors asking for $500 per month to pay back my student loans.

Excuse me for being at the top of my class for twenty years and saving thousands of lives (including bankers). Would it be too much to ask you to wait a few more years until I am done with my training so that I won't have to ask my parents for tires to be able to safely get to work?

Legislation should be introduced that allows such protection for residents in training.

## 5) Residents ought to have one day per week when their beepers are completely off.

This is supposed to be a national policy. Some places honor it.

Robert Marion writes in his book "Learning to Play God" that "This system is grossly unfair not only to interns and residents but also, and more important, to their patients, who should be cared for by physicians whose sense of judgment have not been impaired by chronic, unrelenting exhaustion. There is no reason why this practice should continue."

I submit that there are multiple reasons for this system. A small reason is that the old guys in charge had to do it too, and it worked. Who could blame them? A giant reason for the persistence of the present system is the financial convenience for hospital administration to put highly trained, smart, motivated (by a need to survive, and escape the system) on the job at less than minimum wage. It makes the survival of the AHC just a little bit easier in the present environment of Medicare and Medicaid cutbacks. I am glad to be doing my part.

Lack of sleep does adversely affect performance. Hotshot, old school, fat surgeons that have done studies supposedly proving the contrary are so biased by their own position that is it funny.

Why do I hear all of this crap about the airline pilot that plowed into Little Rock having been up for over 12 hours and it is somehow okay for me to be watching all of this on CNN in between my fourth and fifth case of the day after having been up the entire night before? I guess what I am doing is not as demanding, it is only heart surgery.

Why is this?.....Because that is just "how it is."

I am not asking to skip my fifth case. I love to operate. I choose to do that fifth case. I choose to save lives. I also think that some consideration should be given to the amount of hours that surgery residents work. I believe that they should have to pull the 36 or 40-hour shifts. I have explained the reasons for this previously. I also think that the policy of each resident having a 24-hour period each week when the pager is off should be strictly enforced. The institution where I presently train respects this.

Use some common sense. There are lots of ways to do anything. The present system works. It is not the only way. Don't just pass the buck because you paid your dues. Doctors should take care of their own. No one else is looking out for them.

6) **Residents should not be vulnerable to lawsuits as long as they are acting within the institution's training process.**

Residents are often named in lawsuits simply because their name is on the chart and they represent a deep pocket due to their institutional insurance policy. When a lawsuit is settled out of court, the resident's name and indeed his future is compromised by placement on the National Practitioner's Data Bank. This is an injustice.

I spent 11 years in the land of "Jackpot Justice" and have recently had the final assault on my name dropped by some reasonable judge in that state that I wish I had time to go kiss.

And by the way, with respect to some attorneys' comments that lawsuits "aren't personal, just business."....It is personal, and they ought to be more responsible. Ethics do matter. I am not in the business of creating feeding frenzies against honest, hard working doctors for the financial gain of some second-rate attorney capitalizing on a family's grief. It is personal. That's what motivates me to be a good doctor.

7) **I was well trained by the "old system," and we must preserve its fundamental ideal that you do not clock out on a patient.**

In addition to this not being "ER," this "ain't no reform book." None of the above recommendations should be instituted if they compromise the transmission of the excellent education that I received at Bayview. I have come full circle, and I believe in extremism in the defense of excellence in patient care. Do not go into cardiothoracic surgery if you want rest, money, or both. Be a stockbroker.

I consider the treatment that I received on the Thirsten and Duncan Teabag Endowed Trauma Service to be nothing short of harassment. The screaming session over an HIV positive patient seems even worse as I sit here and look at my son playing on the floor. I could have taken this event to a higher level, but I am first a husband and a father. I just wanted to finish. My treatment (teabagging) on the Trauma Service was an isolated phenomenon and was not indicative of my overall experience at Bayview. I am proud to say that I was well trained by Superman, El Toro, and The Brain and many others (including the ever-present and powerful force of The Father, The Son, and The Holy Ghost).

**8) Doctors ought to get involved in their community and/or run for public office if they want to be a player in their fate.**

**9) Doctors should never lose focus of their role.**

The Hippocratic Oath makes it quite simple.

The physician must continue to keep the plight of the patient above all else. Strength comes from adhering to doing what is right. Every adversarial (or saprophytic) group that operates with the intention of skimming off of the resources that only physicians can provide will falter in the face of correct principles that existed long before they came into being and will remain present after they are gone.

**10) Final note to the reader:**

ER doctors are lesser-trained, nice, tan people with jewelry and a million non-medical hobbies (in addition to their medicine hobby). Half way doesn't work. I like heart surgery because I am of the biased opinion that they represent one of the last bastions of courage left in a country two generations removed from hardship. Operations don't take place in the elevator, people rarely do operations anywhere but in the OR, nobody wipes your forehead during operations, everybody in the hospital is not having sex with everyone else's girlfriend; and surgeons work the hardest. You can watch ER as long as you realize this. This ain't ER.

# 22

# A Successful but Ongoing Struggle to Maintain My Ideals

It has taken about seven years to put this book together. The main problem has been a lack of free time, and a general lack of brain rest. I was able to find the time to do this book by simply wanting to get my story out. It has been quite therapeutic.

I am now in my second year of fellowship in cardiothoracic surgery at The Big City University. I have evolved as I have written this book. Much that was written during the early years of my general surgery residency came from a less idealistic person, but the story that he told was perhaps more accurate and honest. Just as the first line of this book states, you cannot remember pain. I left the early thoughts in this book unchanged, though they might be a little raw.

I have come around full circle as I have pulled away from the experiences of my general surgery residency. I continue to believe that there are many extra-curricular abuses that went on and continue to go on in certain areas, but the overall package was and is strong. I was given great training and that will carry me through the rest of my career. I am forever indebted to the support of Superman. Time has proven that I was better trained than the most of the residents at other places around the country. I have a strong sense of responsibility to my patients. As I said earlier, it starts in your intern year with a fear of the attending-induced consequences of doing less than perfect work. As time and experience progress, you acquire a sense of pride as you see the results of a job well done. You see the positive impact that good work has on the patient's life. Certainly much is learned well before you come to the residency program. It also has very much to do with the values that were taught to you in your household.

I therefore must state that this book is not primarily about reforming the present system of training of our general surgery residents. I am more afraid that they will change it, or dumb it down. Certainly there are things that could be changed to make the latter quest a whole lot easier. I have made some specific recommendations along those lines in the preceding chapter.

Something that I never anticipated is the change that would come within me as this long quest came to pass. My priorities have changed. I am no longer just Patrick. Now I am a husband. Now I am dad, and my kids really don't care how good I am at sewing a vein graft to the back of the beating heart of an otherwise dying patient. They just know that I was not at their little league game.

Call it burnout; call it whatever you like. Sometimes I feel like I am just giving out of juice; more interested in discussing the latest episode of Nickelodeon's Cat/Dog than gearing up for someone's heart operation. It scares me that this is all happening before I even get out of the gate. I continue to have hope on the assumption that this fatigue and frustration-fueled state of mind; the cynicism, the anger, the desire to be alone; is all part of a reversible state that will fade away as I begin to receive some of the things that I have unapologetically come to think that I deserve—money, sleep, time with my family, and an occasional tee time that does not fall through at the last minute.

I think that it was hard for the generation of surgical residents that came before us. The residencies were even more difficult than they are today. There are new forces pressing on the residents these days that are unique to our generation: 1) Managed care and federal reimbursement cutbacks have had multi-level effects on the surgery resident. The patients that are allowed to stay in the hospital are much sicker and much more complex to manage. The hospitals are on a much tighter budget and are all too willing to replace "real workers" that can charge for overtime (and have rights) with minimum-wage residents who have everything to lose by complaining about it (including me, the author of this book). 2) Lawsuits continue to menace the trainee, who represents a great target given his institutional malpractice insurance policy, and the continued willingness of the legal system to allow their name to get smudged for the great sin of being on the chart of somebody that died. 3) The decision to pursue a career in academic surgery or medicine now means taking a much greater pay cut than it used to due to the cutbacks mentioned in problem number one. It used to be easier for academicians to make enough money to set aside some time to teach and do research. Those days are gone. "The Servers," "The Hiders," and less and less of "The Middle Guys" hold the torch up. I am inclined to follow the academic guys, just because they are right. There are other reasons, I'm too God damned tired to think of them.

Things (the end of the road "perks") are not going to get any better for the young, smart, energetic, and idealistic medical student that wants to save the world. I am certain of that. Less perks, same or worse training conditions: loss of quality applicants. It is the responsibility of the next generation's teachers to make the process more rewarding, and conducive to learning (namely by paying them a decent salary and occasionally letting them sleep), within the confines that I have previously outlined.

Someday I hope that that will happen. I plan to do my part during my career. This book is first and foremost a story of my struggle at self-preservation. It is about the quest to preserve the dreams of the young man that spoke so idealistically about his future and his desire to do some good in the world. The process carries danger with it. Sensitivity slips away, arrogance sneaks up on you, anger can eat you up, and greed is an endless path. It is easy for you to let these forces get to you. You have to aggressively preserve yourself. If you lose yourself, the family and ultimately patient care will follow. I have worked very hard to avoid being a formed "product" of this difficult process.

Perhaps the one thing that makes me most proud at the conclusion of this process is the preservation of my vulnerability. I have stayed sensitive, and I have weathered some pain because of it. It is the acts of kindness and compassion that mean the most as I look back. The rest is bravado, and mostly bullshit. It has not been easy to stay intact, and I have had a lot of help along the way.

My rock has been my relationship with my wife. I have found a soul mate in Alison, and she gives me the confidence and hope to maintain the struggle to preserve the things that I know are right. Alison's support can be seen in a card that she gave me on my arrival home after losing a patient that I was very close to...

*Dear Patrick,*

*I know you don't think that I understand what you have to go through every day at the hospital. I'm not there with you so I can't truly empathize, but I do understand what a sacrifice it is for you to give up everything during your residency and probably your life. Unfortunately I can't make it any easier for you though I do support you 100% in all that you do. It takes a unique person to be able to handle all of the stress and challenges that you are put through each day; most of all the death of one of your patients!*

*I am truly sorry that Mr. Pilgrim died on your service, in front of you yesterday. I know how sensitive you are, and how seriously you want every patient to recover. I am certain that seeing death daily changes one as a person and makes them realize how precious life truly is.*

*I could not be prouder of anyone. You are my hero and my inspiration. Because of you, I strive every day to be a better person (not that I am always successful!).*

*Never forget how much I love and admire you. You are my strength!*

> *Love Always,*
> *Alison*

You are my hero too, Alison. It has been a very long and rewarding struggle. I would not change one hard mile of it. And have I kept the faith?

Because of you....Yes.